Carnegie Learning Analytic Geometry

Student Skills Practice

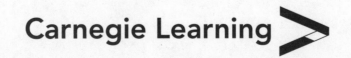
Carnegie Learning

Carnegie Learning >

437 Grant St., Suite 918
Pittsburgh, PA 15219
Phone 412.690.2442
Customer Service Phone 877.401.2527
Fax 412.690.2444

www.carnegielearning.com

Acknowledgments

We would like to thank those listed here who helped prepare the *Carnegie Learning Math Series*.

Carnegie Learning Authoring Team
- Sandy Bartle, Senior Academic Officer
- David Dengler, Sr. Director, Curriculum Development
- Joshua Fisher, Math Editor
- John Fitsioris, Curriculum Developer
- Beth Karambelkar, Curriculum Developer
- David "Augie" Rivera, Math Editor
- Lezlee Ross, Curriculum Developer

Contributing Authors
- Jaclyn Snyder
- Dr. Mary Lou Metz

Vendors
- Cenveo® Publisher Services
- Mathematical Expressions
- Bookmasters, Inc.
- Hess Print Solutions
- Bradford & Bigelow
- Mind Over Media
- Lapiz
- eInstruction

Special Thanks
- Carnegie Learning Managers of School Partnership for content and design review.
- CL Software Development Team for research and content review.
- William S. Hadley for his mentoring leadership and pedagogical pioneering in mathematics education.
- Amy Jones Lewis for content review.

ISBN: 978-1-60972-241-8
Student Skills Practice, Analytic Geometry

Printed in the United States of America
1-07/2013 B&B

Name _____ Date _____

Let's Get This Started!
Points, Lines, Planes, Rays, and Line Segments

Vocabulary

Write the term that best completes each statement.

1. A geometric figure created without using tools is a(n) _____.

2. _____ are two or more lines that are not in the same plane.

3. A(n) _____ is a location in space.

4. The points where a line segment begins and ends are the _____.

5. A(n) _____ is a straight continuous arrangement of an infinite number of points.

6. Two or more line segments of equal measure are _____.

7. You _____ a geometric figure when you use only a compass and straightedge.

8. Points that are all located on the same line are _____.

9. A(n) _____ is a portion of a line that includes two points and all of the collinear points between the two points.

10. A flat surface is a(n) _____.

11. A(n) _____ is a portion of a line that begins with a single point and extends infinitely in one direction.

12. Two or more lines located in the same plane are _____.

13. When you _____ a geometric figure, you use tools such as a ruler, straightedge, compass, or protractor.

Problem Set

Identify the point(s), line(s), and plane(s) in each figure.

1.

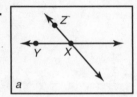

Points: *A*, *B*, and *C*
Lines: $\overleftrightarrow{AB}$ and $\overrightarrow{BC}$
Plane: *m*

2.

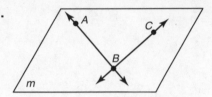

Points: X, Y, Z
Lines: $\overleftrightarrow{ZX}$, $\overrightarrow{YX}$
Plane: a

3.

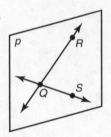

Points: Q, R, S
Lines: $\overrightarrow{RQ}$, $\overleftrightarrow{QS}$
Plane: p

4.

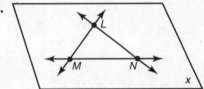

Points: L, M, N
Lines: $\overleftrightarrow{LN}$, $\overleftrightarrow{ML}$, $\overleftrightarrow{MN}$

Name _____ Date _____

Draw a figure for each description. Label all points mentioned in the description.

5. Points *R*, *S*, and *T* are collinear such that point *T* is located halfway between points *S* and *R*.

6. Points *A*, *D*, and *X* are collinear such that point *A* is located halfway between points *D* and *X*.

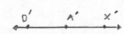

7. Points *A*, *B*, and *C* are collinear such that point *B* is between points *A* and *C* and the distance between points *A* and *B* is twice the distance between points *B* and *C*.

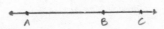

8. Points *F*, *G*, and *H* are collinear such that point *F* is between points *G* and *H* and the distance between points *F* and *G* is one third the distance between points *G* and *H*.

Identify all examples of coplanar lines in each figure.

9.

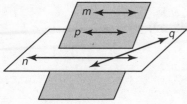

Lines *m* and *p* are coplanar.

Lines *n* and *q* are coplanar.

10.

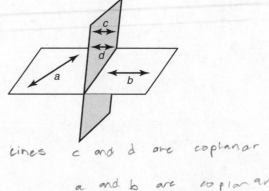

Lines *c* and *d* are coplanar

a and *b* are coplanar

11.

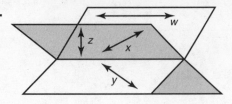

z , x = coplanar

w , y = coplanar

12.

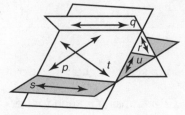

p , t = coplanar

s , u = coplanar

q , r = coplanar

Identify all skew lines in each figure.

13.

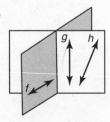

Lines *f* and *g* are skew.

Lines *f* and *h* are skew.

14.

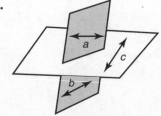

c , a = skew

c , b = skew

15.

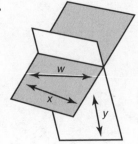

y , w = skew

y , x = skew

16.

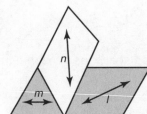

n , L = skew

n , m = skew

Name _____ Date _____

Draw and label an example of each geometric figure.

17. $\overleftrightarrow{XY}$

18. $\overline{CD}$

19. $\overline{PR}$

20. $\overrightarrow{FG}$

21. $\overleftrightarrow{HM}$

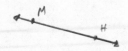

22. $\overrightarrow{KJ}$

Use symbols to write the name of each geometric figure.

23. R •————————————• T

$\overline{RT}$

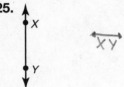

$\overline{RT}$

24.

$\overrightarrow{BA}$

25.

$\overleftrightarrow{XY}$

26.

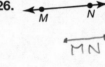

$\overleftrightarrow{MN}$

27.

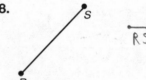

$\overrightarrow{CD}$

28.

$\overrightarrow{RS}$

Use a ruler to measure each segment to the nearest centimeter. Then use symbols to express the measure of each segment.

29. A ————————————— B

$AB = 4$ centimeters or $m\,\overline{AB} = 4$ centimeters

30. A ————————————————— B

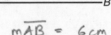

$m\overline{AB} = 6\,cm$

31. A————————————— B

$m\,\overline{AB} = 3.5\,cm$

32. A ———————————————— B

$m\,\overline{AB} = 5.2\,cm$

Name _____ Date _____

Attack of the Clones
Translating and Constructing Line Segments

Vocabulary

Choose the term from the box that best completes each statement.

Distance Formula	transformation	pre-image
rigid motion	translation	arc
copying (duplicating) a line segment	image	

1. A(n) _____rigid motion_____ is a transformation of points in space.

2. The new figure created from a translation is called the _____image_____.

3. A(n) _____arc_____ is a part of a circle and can be thought of as the curve between two points on a circle.

4. A(n) _____copying a line segment_____ is the mapping, or movement, of all the points of a figure in a plane according to a common operation.

5. The _____distance formula_____ can be used to calculate the distance between two points on a coordinate place.

6. In a translation, the original figure is called the _____pre-image_____.

7. A(n) _____translation_____ is a rigid motion that "slides" each point of a figure the same distance and direction.

8. A basic geometric construction called _____transformation_____ can be used to translate a line segment when measurement is not possible.

Problem Set

Calculate the distance between each given pair of points. Round your answer to the nearest tenth, if necessary.

1. (3, 1) and (6, 5)

$x_1 = 3, y_1 = 1, x_2 = 6, y_2 = 5$

$d = \sqrt{(x_2 - x_1)^2 + (y_2 - y_1)^2}$

$d = \sqrt{(6-3)^2 + (5-1)^2}$

$d = \sqrt{3^2 + 4^2}$

$d = \sqrt{9 + 16}$

$d = \sqrt{25}$

$d = 5$

2. (2, 8) and (4, 3)

$d = \sqrt{(2-4)^2 + (8-3)^2}$

$\phantom{d = \sqrt{(}} -2 5$

$d = \sqrt{4 + 25}$

$d = \sqrt{29}$ or

5.385164807

3. (−6, 4) and (5, −1)

$d = \sqrt{(-6-5)^2 + (4+1)^2}$

$\phantom{d = \sqrt{(}} -11 5$

$d = \sqrt{121 + 25}$

$d = \sqrt{146}$ or

12.08304597

4. (9, −2) and (2, −9)

$7^2 7^2$

$d = \sqrt{49 + 49}$

$d = \sqrt{98}$ or $7\sqrt{2}$

5. (0, −6) and (8, 0)

$(0-8)^2 \quad (-6-0)^2$

$d = \sqrt{64 + 36}$

$d = \sqrt{100}$

$d = 10$

6. (−5, −8) and (−2, −9)

$(-5+2)^2 \quad (-8+9)^2$

$d = \sqrt{9 + 1}$

$d = \sqrt{10}$

Name _____ Date _____

Calculate the distance between each given pair of points on the coordinate plane. Round your answer to the nearest tenth, if necessary.

7.

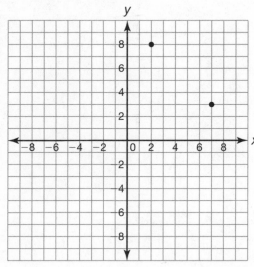

$x_1 = 2, y_1 = 8, x_2 = 7, y_2 = 3$

$d = \sqrt{(x_2 - x_1)^2 + (y_2 - y_1)^2}$

$d = \sqrt{(7 - 2)^2 + (3 - 8)^2}$

$d = \sqrt{5^2 + (-5)^2}$

$d = \sqrt{25 + 25}$

$d = \sqrt{50}$

$d \approx 7.1$

8.

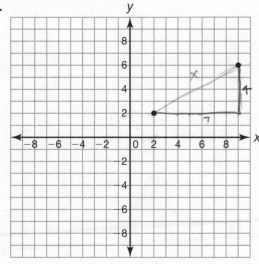

$7^2 + 4^2 = x^2$

$49 + 16 = \sqrt{x^2}$

$\sqrt{65} = x$

$8.06 = x$

9.

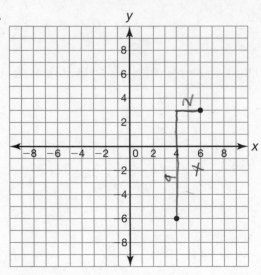

$$9^2 + 2^2 = x^2$$
$$81 + 4 = x^2$$
$$\sqrt{85} = x$$
$$9.21 = x$$

10.

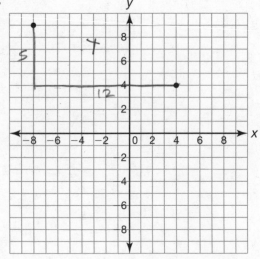

$$144 + 25 = x^2$$
$$\sqrt{169} = x$$
$$13 = x$$

Name _____ Date _____

11.

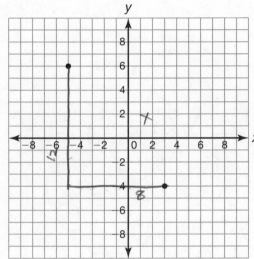

$$194 + 64 = x$$
$$\sqrt{208} = x$$
$$4\sqrt{13} = x$$

12.

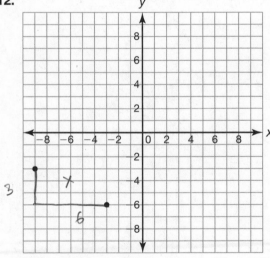

$$36 + 9 \quad \sqrt{45} = x$$
$$3\sqrt{5} = x$$

Translate each given line segment on the coordinate plane as described.

13. Translate $\overline{AB}$ 8 units to the left.

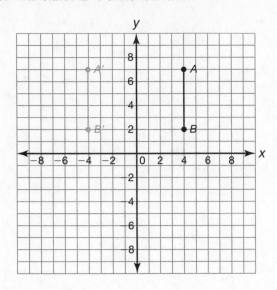

14. Translate $\overline{CD}$ 9 units down.

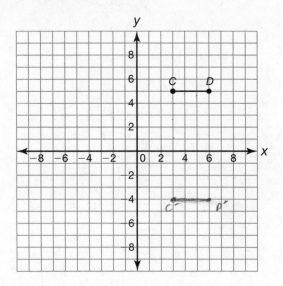

15. Translate $\overline{EF}$ 7 units to the right.

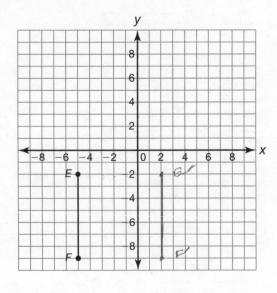

16. Translate $\overline{GH}$ 12 units up.

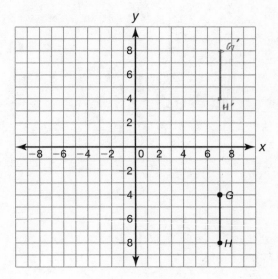

Name _____ Date _____

17. Translate $\overline{JK}$ 12 units down and 7 units to the left.

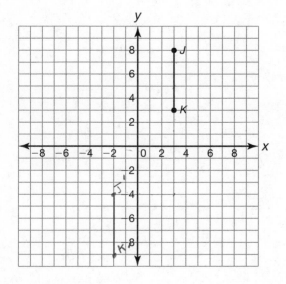

18. Translate $\overline{MN}$ 5 units down and 10 units to the right.

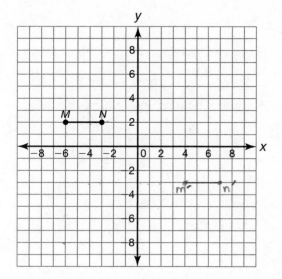

Construct each line segment described.

19. Duplicate $\overline{AB}$.

A•————————•B

A'•————————|B'

20. Duplicate $\overline{CD}$.

C•————————•D

←———C'•————D'•———→

21. Duplicate $\overline{EF}$.

E•————————————•F

←—•E'————————F'•—→

22. Duplicate $\overline{GH}$.

G•————————————•H

←—G'————————————H'—→

23. Construct a line segment twice the length of $\overline{JK}$.

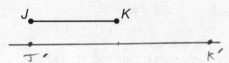

24. Construct a line segment twice the length of $\overline{MN}$.

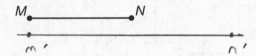

Name _____ Date _____

Stuck in the Middle
Midpoints and Bisectors

Vocabulary

Match each definition to the corresponding term.

C **1.** midpoint

a. a line, line segment, or ray that divides a line segment into two line segments of equal measure

D **2.** Midpoint Formula

b. a basic geometric construction used to locate the midpoint of a line segment

B **3.** segment bisector

c. a point exactly halfway between the endpoints of a line segment

A **4.** bisecting a line segment

d. $\left(\dfrac{x_1 + x_2}{2}, \dfrac{y_1 + y_2}{2}\right)$

Problem Set

Determine the midpoint of a line segment with each set of given endpoints.

1. (8, 0) and (4, 6)

$x_1 = 8, y_1 = 0$
$x_2 = 4, y_2 = 6$

$\left(\dfrac{x_1 + x_2}{2}, \dfrac{y_1 + y_2}{2}\right) = \left(\dfrac{8 + 4}{2}, \dfrac{0 + 6}{2}\right)$

$= \left(\dfrac{12}{2}, \dfrac{6}{2}\right)$

$= (6, 3)$

2. (3, 8) and (9, 10)

$(6, 9)$

3. $(-7, 2)$ and $(3, 6)$

$(2, 4)$

4. $(6, -3)$ and $(-4, 5)$

$(1, 1)$

5. $(-10, -1)$ and $(0, 4)$

$(-5, 1.5)$

6. $(-2, 7)$ and $(-8, -9)$

$(-5, -1)$

Determine the midpoint of the given line segment on each coordinate plane using the Midpoint Formula.

7.

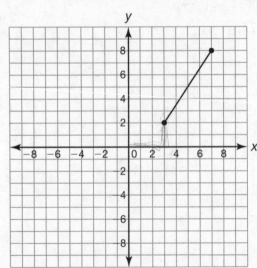

$x_1 = 3, y_1 = 2$
$x_2 = 7, y_2 = 8$

$$\left(\frac{x_1 + x_2}{2}, \frac{y_1 + y_2}{2}\right) = \left(\frac{3 + 7}{2}, \frac{2 + 8}{2}\right)$$

$$= \left(\frac{10}{2}, \frac{10}{2}\right)$$

$$= (5, 5)$$

Name _____ Date _____

8.

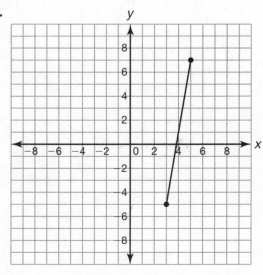

(5, 7) (3, -5)

(1 , 1)

9.

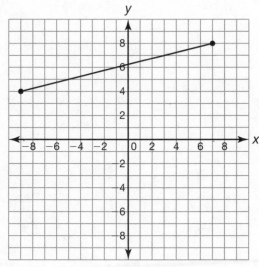

(-9, 4)   (7, 8)

(-1, 6)

10.

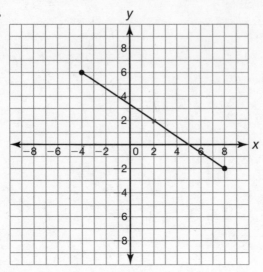

$(8, -2)$ $(-4, 6)$

$(2, 2)$

11.

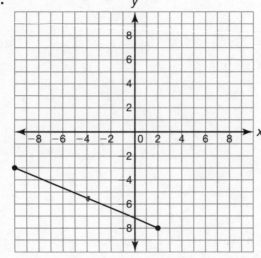

$(2, -8)$ $(-10, -3)$

$(-4, -5.5)$

Name _____ Date _____

12.

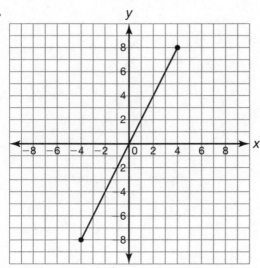

(0, 0)

Locate the midpoint of each line segment using construction tools and label it point *M*.

13.

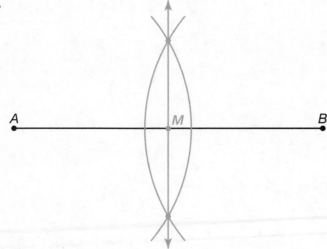

14.

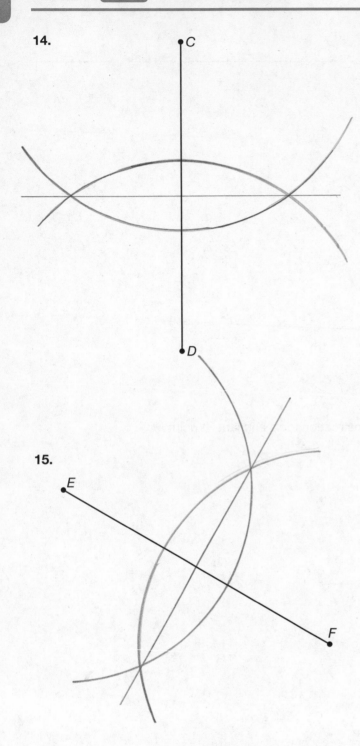

15.

Name _____ Date _____

16.

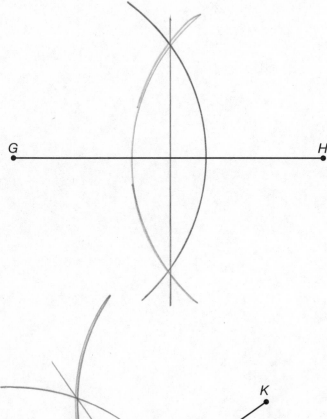

17.

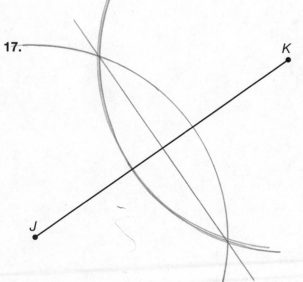

18.

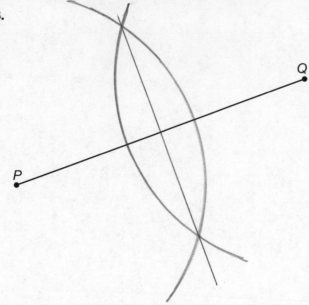

Name _____ Date _____

What's Your Angle?
Translating and Constructing Angles and Angle Bisectors

Vocabulary

Define each term in your own words.

1. angle

2 rays that intersect at the end point

2. angle bisector

half a angle

Describe how to perform each construction in your own words.

3. copying or duplicating an angle

4. bisecting an angle

Problem Set

Translate each given angle on the coordinate plane as described.

1. Translate ∠ABC 9 units to the left.

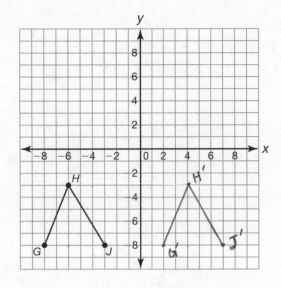

2. Translate ∠DEF 12 units down.

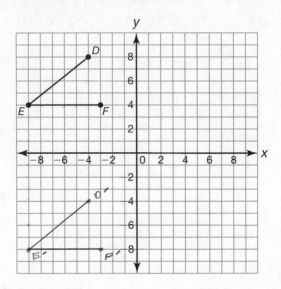

3. Translate ∠GHJ 10 units to the right.

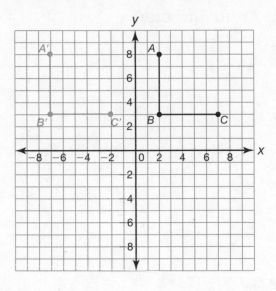

4. Translate ∠KLM 13 units up.

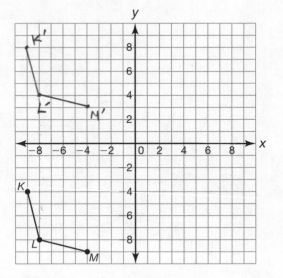

Name _____ Date _____

5. Translate ∠NPQ 8 units to the left and 11 units down.

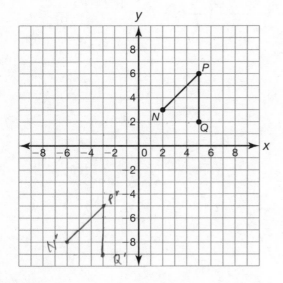

6. Translate ∠RST 15 units to the left and 9 units up.

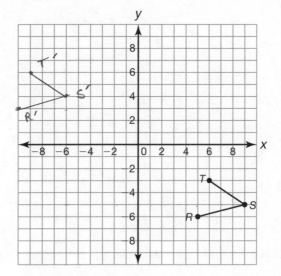

Construct each angle as described.

7. Copy ∠B.

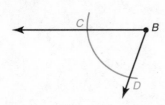

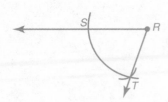

∠CBD ≅ ∠SRT

8. Copy ∠D.

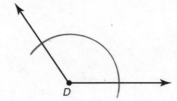

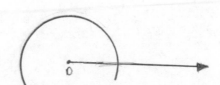

9. Copy ∠P.

10. Copy ∠Z.

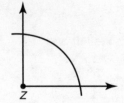

11. Construct an angle that is twice the measure of ∠K.

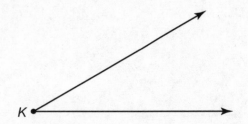

Name _____ Date _____

12. Construct an angle that is twice the measure of ∠M.

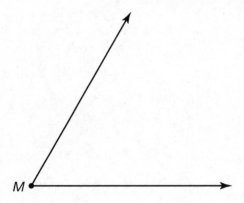

Construct the angle bisector of each given angle.

13.

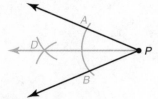

$\overline{PD}$ is the angle bisector of ∠P.

14.

15.

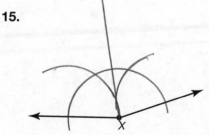

16.

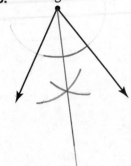

17. Construct an angle that is one-fourth the measure of ∠F.

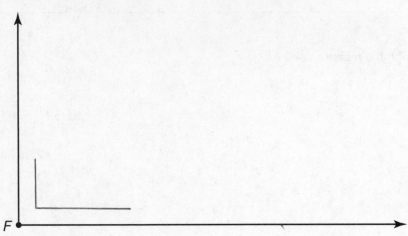

18. Construct an angle that is one-fourth the measure of ∠X.

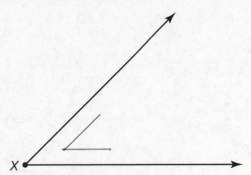

Name _____ Date _____

If You Build It . . .
Constructing Perpendicular Lines, Parallel Lines, and Polygons

Problem Set

Construct a line perpendicular to each given line and through the given point.

1. Construct a line that is perpendicular to $\overleftrightarrow{CD}$ and passes through point T.

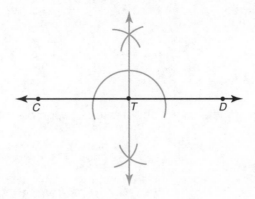

2. Construct a line that is perpendicular to $\overleftrightarrow{AB}$ and passes through point X.

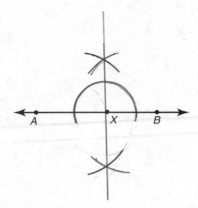

3. Construct a line that is perpendicular to $\overleftrightarrow{RS}$ and passes through point *W*.

4. Construct a line that is perpendicular to $\overleftrightarrow{YZ}$ and passes through point *G*.

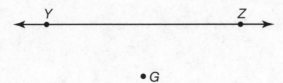

Name _____ Date _____

5. Construct a line that is perpendicular to $\overleftrightarrow{MN}$ and passes through point *J*.

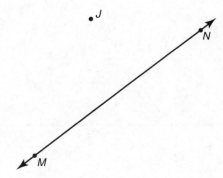

6. Construct a line that is perpendicular to $\overleftrightarrow{PQ}$ and passes through point *R*.

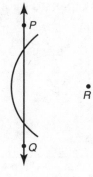

Construct a line parallel to each given line and through the given point.

7. Construct a line that is parallel to $\overleftrightarrow{AB}$ and passes through point *C*.

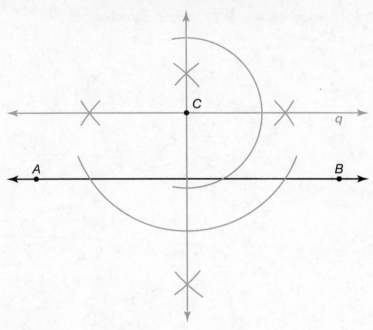

Line *q* is parallel to $\overleftrightarrow{AB}$.

8. Construct a line that is parallel to $\overleftrightarrow{DE}$ and passes through point *F*.

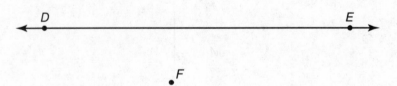

Name _____ Date _____

9. Construct a line that is parallel to $\overleftrightarrow{GH}$ and passes through point *J*.

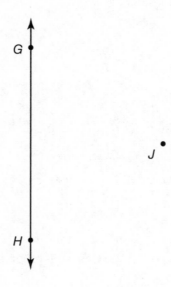

10. Construct a line that is parallel to $\overleftrightarrow{KL}$ and passes through point *M*.

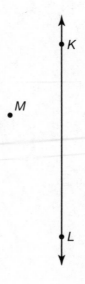

11. Construct a line that is parallel to $\overleftrightarrow{NP}$ and passes through point Q.

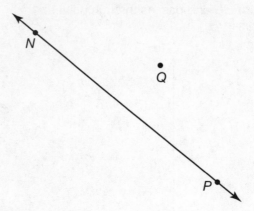

12. Construct a line that is parallel to $\overleftrightarrow{RT}$ and passes through point W.

Name _____ Date _____

Construct each geometric figure.

13. Construct an equilateral triangle. The length of one side is given.

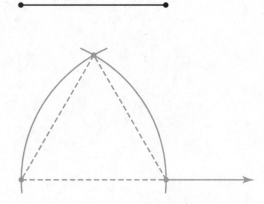

14. Construct an equilateral triangle. The length of one side is given.

15. Construct an isosceles triangle that is not an equilateral triangle such that each leg is longer than the base. The length of the base is given.

16. Construct an isosceles triangle that is not an equilateral triangle such that each leg is shorter than the base. The length of the base is given.

Name _____ Date _____

17. Construct a square. The perimeter of the square is given.

●————————————————————●

18. Construct a square. The perimeter of the square is given.

●————————————————————●

19. Construct a rectangle that is not a square. The perimeter of the rectangle is given.

20. Construct a rectangle that is not a square. The perimeter of the rectangle is given.

Name _____ Date _____

What's the Point?
Points of Concurrency

Vocabulary

Describe similarities and differences between each pair of terms.

1. concurrent and point of concurrency

2. incenter and orthocenter

3. centroid and circumcenter

4. altitude and median

Problem Set

Draw the incenter of each triangle.

1.
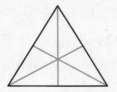

2.
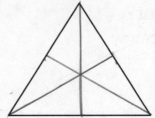

3.
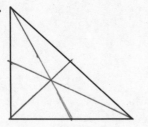

4.
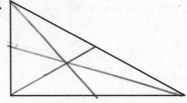

5.
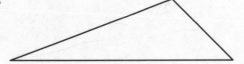

6.

7.
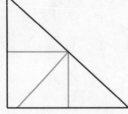

8.
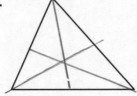

Draw the circumcenter of each triangle.

9.
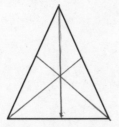

10.
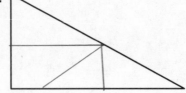

Name _____ Date _____

11.

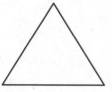

12.

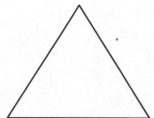

13.

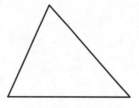

14.

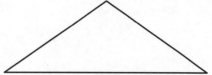

15.

16.

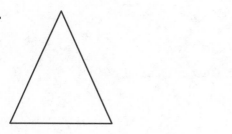

Draw the centroid of each triangle.

17.

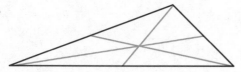

18.

19.

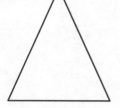

20.

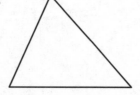

21.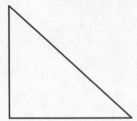

22.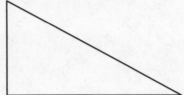

23.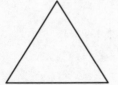

24.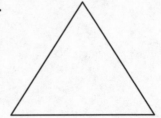

Draw the orthocenter of each triangle.

25.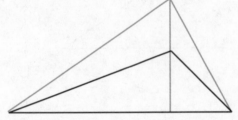

26.

27.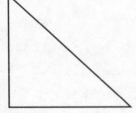

28.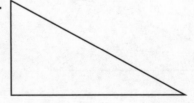

29.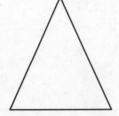

30.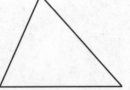

Name _____ Date _____

31.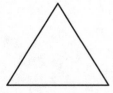

32.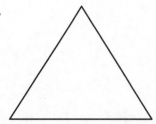

Answer each question about points of concurrency. Draw an example to illustrate your answer.

33. For which type of triangle are the incenter, circumcenter, centroid, and orthocenter the same point?

equilateral triangles

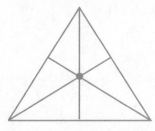

34. For which type of triangle are the orthocenter and circumcenter outside of the triangle?

35. For which type of triangle are the circumcenter and orthocenter on the triangle?

36. For which type of triangle are the incenter, circumcenter, centroid, and orthocenter all inside the triangle?

37. For what type(s) of triangle(s) do the centroid, circumcenter, and orthocenter all lie on a straight line?

38. For what type of triangle is the orthocenter a vertex of the triangle?

Name _____ Date _____

Given the coordinates of the vertices of a triangle, classify the triangle using algebra.

39. $A(-5, 5)$, $B(5, 5)$, $C(0, -5)$

segment AB

$d = \sqrt{[5 - (-5)]^2 + (5 - 5)^2}$

$d = \sqrt{10^2 + 0^2}$

$d = \sqrt{100}$

$d = 10$

segment AC

$d = \sqrt{[0 - (-5)]^2 + (-5 - 5)^2}$

$d = \sqrt{5^2 + (-10)^2}$

$d = \sqrt{125}$

$d \approx 11.18$

segment BC

$d = \sqrt{(0 - 5)^2 + (-5 - 5)^2}$

$d = \sqrt{(-5)^2 + (-10)^2}$

$d = \sqrt{125}$

$d \approx 11.18$

The lengths of two of the segments are equal, so the triangle is isosceles.

40. $R(-3, -1)$, $S(1, 2)$, $T(4, -2)$

41. $F(-2, 5)$, $G(1, 6)$, $H(5, -4)$

42. $M(5, -1), N(3, -5), P(-1, -3)$

43. $K(-2, 1), L(4, -3), M(-1, 5)$

Name _____ Date _____

44. $E(-5, 7)$, $F(3, 4)$, $G(-8, -1)$

Name _____ Date _____

A Little Dash of Logic
Foundations for Proof

2

Vocabulary

Define each term in your own words.

1. induction

2. deduction

3. counterexample

4. conditional statement

5. propositional form

6. propositional variables

7. hypothesis

8. conclusion

9. truth value

10. truth table

Problem Set

Identify the specific information, the general information, and the conclusion for each problem situation.

1. You read an article in the paper that says a high-fat diet increases a person's risk of heart disease. You know your father has a lot of fat in his diet, so you worry that he is at higher risk of heart disease.

Specific information: Your father has a lot of fat in his diet.

General information: High-fat diets increase the risk of heart disease.

Conclusion: Your father is at higher risk of heart disease.

2. You hear from your teacher that spending too much time in the sun without sunblock increases the risk of skin cancer. Your friend Susan spends as much time as she can outside working on her tan without sunscreen, so you tell her that she is increasing her risk of skin cancer when she is older.

3. Janice tells you that she has been to the mall three times in the past week, and every time there were a lot of people there. "It's always crowded at the mall," she says.

4. John returns from a trip out West and reports that it was over 100 degrees every day. "It's always hot out West," he says.

5. Mario watched 3 parades this summer. Each parade had a fire truck lead the parade. He concluded "A fire truck always leads a parade."

Name _____ Date _____

6. Ava read an article that said eating too much sugar can lead to tooth decay and cavities. Ava noticed that her little brother Phillip eats a lot of sugar. She concludes that Phillip's teeth will decay and develop cavities.

Determine whether inductive reasoning or deductive reasoning is used in each situation. Then determine whether the conclusion is correct and explain your reasoning.

7. Jason sees a line of 10 school buses and notices that each is yellow. He concludes that all school buses must be yellow.

It is inductive reasoning because he has observed specific examples of a phenomenon—the color of school buses—and come up with a general rule based on those specific examples.

The conclusion is not necessarily true. It may be the case, for example, that all or most of the school buses in this school district are yellow, while another school district may have orange school buses.

8. Caitlyn has been told that every taxi in New York City is yellow. When she sees a red car in New York City, she concludes that it cannot be a taxi.

9. Miriam has been told that lightning never strikes twice in the same place. During a lightning storm, she sees a tree struck by lightning and goes to stand next to it, convinced that it is the safest place to be.

10. Jose is shown the first six numbers of a series of numbers: 7, 11, 15, 19, 23, 27. He concludes that the general rule for the series of numbers is $a_n = 4n + 3$.

11. Isabella sees 5 red fire trucks. She concludes that all fire trucks are red.

12. Carlos is told that all garter snakes are not venomous. He sees a garter snake in his backyard and concludes that it is not venomous.

In each situation, identify whether each person is using inductive or deductive reasoning. Then compare and contrast the two types of reasoning.

13. When Madison babysat for the Johnsons for the first time, she was there 2 hours and was paid $30. The next time she was there for 5 hours and was paid $75. She decided that the Johnsons were paying her $15 per hour. The third time she went, she stayed for 4 hours. She tells her friend Jennifer that she makes $15 per hour babysitting. So, Jennifer predicted that Madison made $60 for her 4-hour babysitting job.

Madison used inductive reasoning to conclude that the Johnsons were paying her at a rate of $15 per hour. From that general rule, Jennifer used deductive reasoning to conclude that 4 hours of babysitting should result in a payment of $60. The inductive reasoning looks at evidence and creates a general rule from the evidence. By contrast, the deductive reasoning starts with a general rule and makes a prediction or deduction about what will happen in a particular instance.

Name _____ Date _____

14. When Holly was young, the only birds she ever saw were black crows. So, she told her little brother Walter that all birds are black. When Walter saw a bluebird for the first time, he was sure it had to be something other than a bird.

15. Tamika is flipping a coin and recording the results. She records the following results: heads, tails, heads, tails, heads, tails, heads. She tells her friend Javon that the coin alternates between heads and tails for each toss. Javon tells her that the next time the coin is flipped, it will definitely be tails.

16. John likes to watch the long coal trains moving past his house. Over the weeks of watching he notices that every train going east is filled with coal, but the trains heading west are all empty. He tells his friend Richard that all trains heading east have coal and all trains heading west are empty. When Richard hears a train coming from the west, he concludes that it will certainly be filled with coal.

17. Vance earned $60 mowing 5 lawns last weekend for the Greenvalley Homeowners Association. Vance concluded that he earned $12 for each lawn. Vance told Sherwin that he planned to mow 7 lawns for Greenvalley next weekend. Sherwin concluded that Vance would earn $84 mowing the 7 lawns.

18. As a child, the only frogs Emily ever saw were green. Emily told Juan that all frogs are green. When Juan visited a zoo and saw a blue poison dart frog he concluded that it must be something other than a frog.

Write each statement in propositional form.

19. The measure of an angle is 90°. So, the angle is a right angle.

If the measure of an angle is 90°, then the angle is a right angle.

20. Three points are all located on the same line. So, the points are collinear points.

21. Two lines are not on the same plane. So, the lines are skew.

22. Two angles are supplementary angles if the sum of their angle measures is equal to 180°.

Name _____ Date _____

23. Two angles share a common vertex and a common side. So, the angles are adjacent angles.

24. A ray divides an angle into two congruent angles. So, the ray is an angle bisector.

Identify the hypothesis and the conclusion of each conditional statement.

25. If two lines intersect at right angles, then the lines are perpendicular.

The hypothesis is "Two lines intersect at right angles."
The conclusion is "The lines are perpendicular."

26. If the sum of two angles is 180°, then the angles are supplementary.

27. If the sum of two adjacent angles is 180°, then the angles form a linear pair.

28. If the measure of an angle is 180°, then the angle is a straight angle.

29. If two lines are located in the same plane, then the lines are coplanar lines.

30. If the sum of two angle measures is equal to 90°, then the angles are complementary angles.

Answer each question about the given conditional statement.

31. Conditional statement: If the measure of angle *ABC* is 45° and the measure of angle *XYZ* is 45°, then ∠*ABC* = ∠*XYZ*.

What does it mean if the hypothesis is false and the conclusion is true, and then what is the truth value of the conditional statement?

If the hypothesis is false and the conclusion is true, then the measure of angle *ABC* is not 45 degrees and the measure of angle *XYZ* is not 45 degrees, and angles *ABC* and *XYZ* are congruent. The truth value of the conditional statement is true, because the angles could have measures that are equal, but different than 45 degrees.

32. Conditional statement: If the measure of angle *XYZ* is less than 90°, then angle *XYZ* is acute.

What does it mean if the hypothesis is true and the conclusion is false, and then what is the truth value of the conditional statement?

33. Conditional statement: If ∠1 and ∠2 are two nonadjacent angles formed by two intersecting lines, then they are vertical angles.

What does it mean if the hypothesis is true and the conclusion is true, and then what is the truth value of the conditional statement?

34. Conditional statement: If the measure of ∠*LMN* is 180°, then ∠*LMN* is a straight angle.

What does it mean if the hypothesis is false and the conclusion is false, and then what is the truth value of the conditional statement?

Name _____ Date _____

For each conditional statement, draw a diagram and then write the hypothesis as the "Given" and the conclusion as the "Prove."

35. If $\overrightarrow{RT}$ bisects $\angle PRS$, then $\angle PRT$ and $\angle SRT$ are adjacent angles.

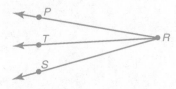

Given: $\overrightarrow{RT}$ bisects $\angle PRS$

Prove: $\angle PRT$ and $\angle SRT$ are adjacent angles

36. If $\angle QRS$ and $\angle SRT$ are complementary angles, then $m\angle QRS + m\angle SRT = 90°$.

Given:

Prove:

37. If $\overleftrightarrow{AB} \perp \overline{KJ}$ and $\overleftrightarrow{AB}$ bisects $\overline{KJ}$, then $\overleftrightarrow{AB}$ is the perpendicular bisector of $\overline{KJ}$.

Given:

Prove:

38. If $\overrightarrow{PG}$ bisects $\angle FPH$, then $\angle FPG \cong \angle GPH$.

Given:

Prove:

Name _____ Date _____

And Now From a New Angle
Special Angles and Postulates

2

Vocabulary

Draw a figure to illustrate each term.

1. supplementary angles

2. complementary angles

3. adjacent angles

4. linear pair

5. vertical angles

Define each term in your own words.

6. postulate

7. theorem

8. Euclidean geometry

State each postulate.

9. Linear Pair Postulate

10. Segment Addition Postulate

11. Angle Addition Postulate

Problem Set

Use a protractor to draw an angle that is supplementary to each given angle. Draw the angle so it shares a common side with the given angle. Label the measure of each angle.

1.

135° / 45°

2.

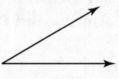

3.

4.

Use a protractor to draw an angle that is supplementary to each given angle. Draw the angle so it does not share a common side with the given angle. Label the measure of each angle.

5.

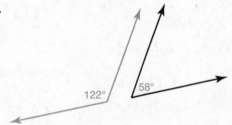

122° 58°

6.

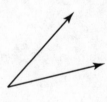

7.

8.

Name _____ Date _____

Use a protractor to draw an angle that is complementary to each given angle. Draw the angle so it shares a common side with the given angle. Label the measure of each angle.

9.

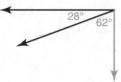

10.

11.

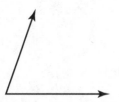

12.

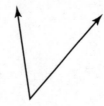

Use a protractor to draw an angle that is complementary to each given angle. Draw the angle so it does not share a common side with the given angle. Label the measure of each angle.

13.

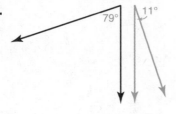

14.

15.

16.

Solve for *x*.

17.

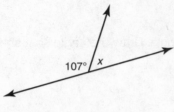

$x = 180° - 107° = 73°$

18.

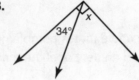

90
−34

56

19.

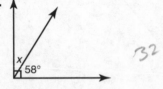

32

20.

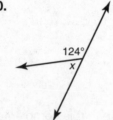

21.

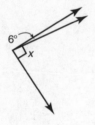

22.

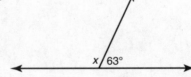

Name _____ Date _____

Use the given information to determine the measures of the angles in each pair.

23. The measure of the complement of an angle is three times the measure of the angle.
What is the measure of each angle?

$x + 3x = 90$

$\quad 4x = 90$

$\quad\quad x = 22.5$

The measure of the angle is 22.5° and the measure of the complement is 67.5°.

24. The measure of the supplement of an angle is one fourth the measure of the angle.
What is the measure of each angle?

25. The measure of the supplement of an angle is twice the measure of the angle.
What is the measure of each angle?

26. The measure of the complement of an angle is one fifth the measure of the angle.
What is the measure of each angle?

For each diagram, determine whether angles 1 and 2 are adjacent angles.

27.

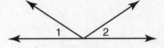

The angles are not adjacent.

28.

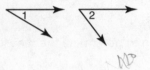

No

29.

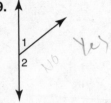

No Yes

30.

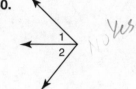

No Yes

For each diagram, determine whether angles 1 and 2 form a linear pair.

31.

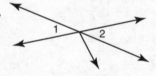

The angles do not form a linear pair.

32.

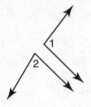

X

33.

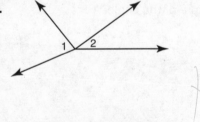

34.

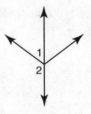

yes

Name _____ Date _____

Name each pair of vertical angles.

35.

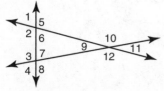

∠1 and ∠6, ∠2 and ∠5, ∠3 and ∠8,
∠4 and ∠7, ∠9 and ∠11, ∠10 and ∠12

36.

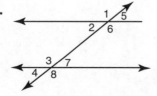

37.

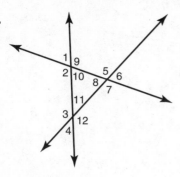

38.

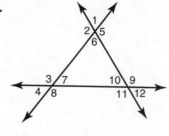

Write the postulate that confirms each statement.

39. Angles *GFH* and *KFH* are
supplementary angles.

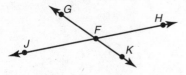

Linear Pair Postulate

40. $m\overline{RS} + m\overline{ST} = m\overline{RT}$

41. $m\angle WXZ + m\angle ZXY = m\angle WXY$

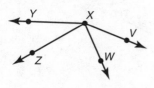

42. $m\angle 1 + m\angle 2 = 180°$

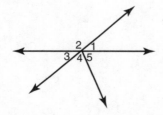

43. $BC + CD = BD$

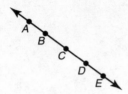

44. $m\angle DBE + m\angle EBF = m\angle DBF$

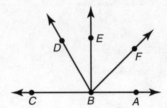

Complete each statement. The write the postulate you used.

45. $m\overline{LM} + m\overline{MN} = m\overline{LN}$

Segment Addition Postulate

46. $m\overline{AB} + m\quad = m\overline{AC}$

47. $m\angle YVZ + m\angle \quad = 180°$

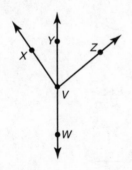

48. $m\angle \quad + m\angle \quad = m\angle MJK$

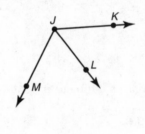

49. $m\quad + m\overline{GI} = m$

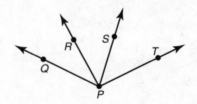

50. $m\angle \quad + m\angle RPS = m\angle RPT$

Name _____ Date _____

Forms of Proof
Paragraph Proof, Two-Column Proof, Construction Proof, and Flow Chart Proof

Vocabulary

Match each definition to its corresponding term.

1. If a is a real number, then $a = a$.

    a. Addition Property of Equality

2. If a, b, and c are real numbers, $a = b$, and $b = c$, then $a = c$.

    b. paragraph proof

3. If a, b, and c are real numbers and $a = b$, then $a + c = b + c$.

    c. construction proof

4. a proof in which the steps and corresponding reasons are written in complete sentences

    d. Subtraction Property of Equality

5. If a and b are real numbers and $a = b$, then a can be substituted for b.

    e. Transitive Property

6. a proof in which the steps are written in the left column and the corresponding reasons in the right column

    f. flow chart proof

7. a proof in which the steps and corresponding reasons are written in boxes

    g. Substitution Property

8. If a, b, and c are real numbers and $a = b$, then $a - c = b - c$.

    h. two-column proof

9. a proof that results from creating an object with specific properties using only a compass and straightedge

    i. Reflexive Property

Problem Set

Identify the property demonstrated in each example.

1. $m\angle ABC = m\angle XYZ$
$m\angle ABC - m\angle RST = m\angle XYZ - m\angle RST$
Subtraction Property of Equality

2. $m\overline{QT} = m\overline{TU}$
$m\overline{QT} + m\overline{WX} = m\overline{TU} + m\overline{WX}$

3. $\angle JKL \cong \angle JKL$

4. $GH = MN$ and $MN = OP$,
so $GH = OP$

5. $m\overline{XY} = 4$ cm and $m\overline{BC} = 4$ cm,
so $m\overline{XY} = m\overline{BC}$

6. $\overline{PR} \cong \overline{PR}$

7. $GH = JK$
$GH - RS = JK - RS$

8. $m\angle 1 = 134°$ and $m\angle 2 = 134°$,
so $m\angle 1 = m\angle 2$

9. $m\angle ABC = m\angle DEF$
$m\angle ABC + m\angle QRS = m\angle DEF + m\angle QRS$

10. $GH = GH$

11. $ED = 3$ in. and $PQ = 3$ in., so
$ED = PQ$

12. $\angle EFG \cong \angle LMN$ and $\angle LMN \cong SPT$,
so $\angle EFG \cong \angle SPT$

Write a statement that fits each given description.

13. Write a segment statement using the Reflexive Property.
Sample Answer: $\overline{XY} \cong \overline{XY}$

14. Write angle statements using the Addition Property of Equality.

Name _____ Date _____

15. Write angle statements using the Substitution Property.

16. Write segment statements using the Transitive Property.

17. Write segment statements using the Subtraction Property of Equality.

18. Write an angle statement using the Reflexive Property.

Rewrite each conditional statement by separating the hypothesis and conclusion. The hypothesis becomes the "Given" information and the conclusion becomes the "Prove" information.

19. Conditional statement: If $\angle 2 \cong \angle 1$, then $\angle 2 \cong \angle 3$.

Given: $\angle 2 \cong \angle 1$

Prove: $\angle 2 \cong \angle 3$

20. Conditional statement: $\overline{RT} \cong \overline{LM}$, if $\overline{RT} \cong \overline{AB}$

Given:

Prove:

21. Conditional statement: If $m\angle ABC = m\angle LMN$ then $m\angle ABC = m\angle XYZ$.

Given:

Prove:

22. Conditional statement: $AB + RS = CD + RS$, if $AB = CD$

Given:

Prove:

Use the indicated form of proof to prove each statement.

23. Prove the statement using a two-column proof.

Given: $m\overline{AX} = m\overline{CX}$

Given: $m\overline{BX} = m\overline{DX}$

Prove: $m\overline{AB} = m\overline{CD}$

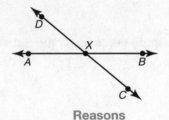

Statements	Reasons
1. $m\overline{AX} = m\overline{CX}$	1. Given
2. $m\overline{BX} = m\overline{DX}$	2. Given
3. $m\overline{AX} + m\overline{BX} = m\overline{CX} + m\overline{BX}$	3. Addition Property of Equality
4. $m\overline{AX} + m\overline{BX} = m\overline{CX} + m\overline{DX}$	4. Substitution Property
5. $m\overline{AX} + m\overline{BX} = m\overline{AB}$	5. Segment Addition Property
6. $m\overline{CX} + m\overline{DX} = m\overline{CD}$	6. Segment Addition Postulate
7. $m\overline{AB} = m\overline{CD}$	7. Substitution Property

24. Prove the statement using a construction proof.

Given: $\overline{KM} \cong \overline{LN}$

Prove: $\overline{KL} \cong \overline{MN}$

K L   M N

Name _____ Date _____

25. Prove the statement using a simple paragraph proof.

Given: $\angle VZW \cong \angle XZY$

Prove: $\angle VZX \cong \angle WZY$

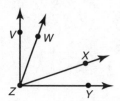

26. Prove the statement using a flow chart proof.

Given: $\angle ABC$ and $\angle XYZ$ are straight angles.

Prove: $\angle ABC \cong \angle XYZ$

27. Prove the statement using a simple paragraph proof.

Given: $\angle A$ is supplementary to $\angle B$

Given: $\angle C$ is supplementary to $\angle D$

Given: $\angle A \cong \angle D$

Prove: $\angle B \cong \angle C$

28. Prove the statement using a two-column proof.

Given: $\overleftrightarrow{AB} \perp \overleftrightarrow{DE}$

Prove: $\angle ABD \cong \angle CBD$

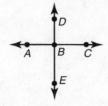

Name _____ Date _____

Write each given proof as the indicated proof.

29. Write the flow chart proof as a two-column proof.

Given: $\angle PQT \cong \angle RQS$

Prove: $\angle PQS \cong \angle RQT$

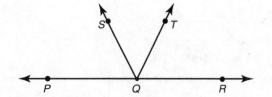

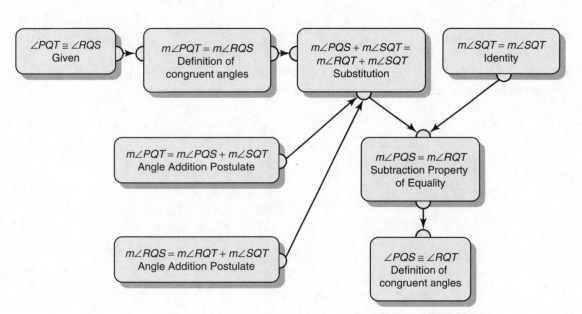

Statements	Reasons
1. $\angle PQT \cong \angle RQS$	1. Given
2. $m\angle PQT = m\angle RQS$	2. Definition of congruent angles
3. $m\angle PQT = m\angle PQS + m\angle SQT$	3. Angle Addition Postulate
4. $m\angle RQS = m\angle RQT + m\angle SQT$	4. Angle Addition Postulate
5. $m\angle PQS + m\angle SQT = m\angle RQT + m\angle SQT$	5. Substitution
6. $m\angle SQT = m\angle SQT$	6. Identity
7. $m\angle PQS = m\angle RQT$	7. Subtraction Property of Equality
8. $\angle PQS \cong m\angle RQT$	8. Definition of congruent angles

30. Write the flow chart proof of the Right Angle Congruence Theorem as a two-column proof.

Given: Angles *ACD* and *BCD* are right angles.

Prove: ∠*ACD* ≅ ∠*BCD*

2

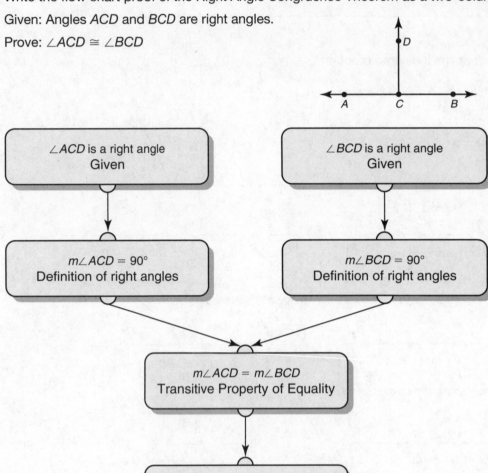

Name _____ Date _____

31. Write the two-column proof of the Congruent Supplement Theorem as a paragraph proof.

Given: ∠1 is supplementary to ∠2,
∠3 is supplementary to ∠4,
and ∠2 ≅ ∠4

Prove: ∠1 ≅ ∠3

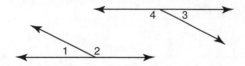

Statements	Reasons
1. ∠1 is supplementary to ∠2	**1.** Given
2. ∠3 is supplementary to ∠4	**2.** Given
3. ∠2 ≅ ∠4	**3.** Given
4. $m\angle 2 = m\angle 4$	**4.** Definition of congruent angles
5. $m\angle 1 + m\angle 2 = 180°$	**5.** Definition of supplementary angles
6. $m\angle 3 + m\angle 4 = 180°$	**6.** Definition of supplementary angles
7. $m\angle 1 + m\angle 2 = m\angle 3 + m\angle 4$	**7.** Substitution Property
8. $m\angle 1 + m\angle 2 = m\angle 3 + m\angle 2$	**8.** Substitution Property
9. $m\angle 1 = m\angle 3$	**9.** Subtraction Property of Equality
10. ∠1 ≅ ∠3	**10.** Definition of congruent angles

32. Write the two-column proof of the Congruent Complement Theorem as a paragraph proof.

Given: Angles *ABD* and *DBC* are
complementary, angles *WXZ* and *ZXY* are
complementary, and ∠*DBC* ≅ ∠*ZXY*

Prove: ∠*ABD* ≅ ∠*WXZ*

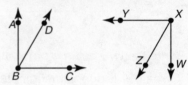

Statements	Reasons
1. ∠*ABD* is complementary to ∠*DBC*	**1.** Given
2. ∠*WXZ* is complementary to ∠*ZXY*	**2.** Given
3. ∠*DBC* ≅ ∠*ZXY*	**3.** Given
4. $m\angle ABD + m\angle DBC = 180°$	**4.** Definition of complementary angles
5. $m\angle WXZ + m\angle ZXY = 180°$	**5.** Definition of complementary angles
6. $m\angle DBC = m\angle ZXY$	**6.** Definition of congruent angles
7. $m\angle ABD + m\angle DBC$ $= m\angle WXZ + m\angle ZXY$	**7.** Substitution Property
8. $m\angle ABD + m\angle DBC$ $= m\angle WXZ + m\angle DBC$	**8.** Substitution Property
9. $m\angle ABD = m\angle WXZ$	**9.** Subtraction Property of Equality
10. ∠*ABD* ≅ ∠*WXZ*	**10.** Definition of congruent angles

Name _____ Date _____

33. Write the paragraph proof as a flow chart proof.

Given: $m\angle QXR = m\angle SXR$

Prove: $m\angle PXR = m\angle TXR$

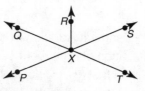

By the Angle Addition Postulate, $m\angle TXR = m\angle TXS + m\angle SXR$. It is given that $m\angle QXR = m\angle SXR$, so by substitution, $m\angle TXR = m\angle TXS + m\angle QXR$. Angles PXQ and TXS are vertical angles by the definition of vertical angles. Vertical angles are congruent by the Vertical Angle Theorem, so $\angle PXQ \cong \angle TXS$, and by the definition of congruent angles, $m\angle PXQ = m\angle TXS$. Using substitution, you can write $m\angle TXR = m\angle PXQ + m\angle QXR$. By the Angle Addition Postulate, $m\angle PXR = m\angle PXQ + m\angle QXR$. So, you can use substitution to write $m\angle PXR = m\angle TXR$.

34. Write the paragraph proof as a flow chart proof.

Given: $\overline{GH} \cong \overline{HJ}$ and $\overline{FH} \cong \overline{HK}$

Prove: $\overline{GK} \cong \overline{FJ}$

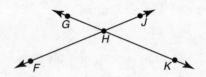

By the Segment Addition Postulate, $GK = GH + HK$. You are given that $\overline{GH} = \overline{HJ}$, so $GH = HJ$ by the definition of congruent segments, and you can use substitution to write $GK = HJ + HK$. You are also given that $\overline{FH} \cong \overline{HK}$, so $FH = HK$ by the definition of congruent segments, and you can use substitution to write $GK = HJ + FH$. By the Segment Addition Postulate, $FJ = FH + HJ$. So, you can use substitution to write $GK = FJ$. By the definition of congruent segments, $\overline{GK} \cong \overline{FJ}$.

Name _____ Date _____

What's Your Proof?
Angle Postulates and Theorems

Vocabulary

Define each theorem in your own words.

1. Alternate Interior Angle Theorem

2. Alternate Exterior Angle Theorem

3. Same-Side Interior Angle Theorem

SSS   A S A

AA   S A S

SAS   A A S

        HL

4. Same-Side Exterior Angle Theorem

5. Corresponding Angle Postulate

Problem Set

Write congruence statements for the pairs of corresponding angles in each figure.

1.

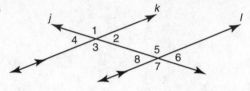

$\angle 1 \cong \angle 5, \angle 2 \cong \angle 6,$
$\angle 3 \cong \angle 7, \angle 4 \cong \angle 8$

2.

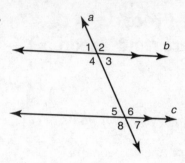

3.

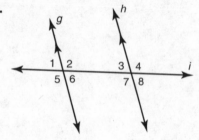

4.

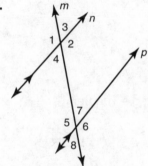

Name _____ Date _____

Make a conjecture to explain why each statement is true.

5. $\angle 3 \cong \angle 6$

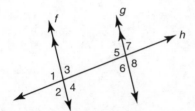

Alternate interior angles
are congruent.

6. $m\angle 1 + m\angle 4 = 180°$

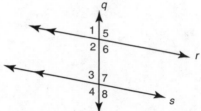

7. $\angle 1 \cong \angle 5$

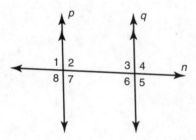

8. $\angle 4 \cong \angle 6$

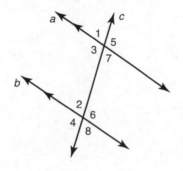

9. $m\angle 4 + m\angle 5 = 180°$

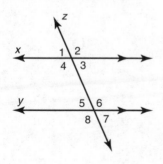

10. $\angle 5 \cong \angle 8$

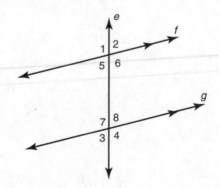

11. ∠6 ≅ ∠8

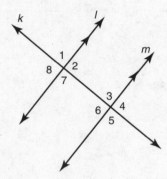

12. ∠6 ≅ ∠7

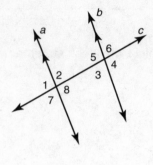

Draw and label a diagram to illustrate each theorem.

13. Same-Side Interior Angle Theorem

∠1 and ∠3 are supplementary or ∠2 and ∠4 are supplementary

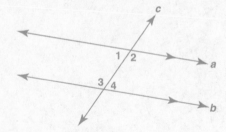

14. Alternate Exterior Angle Theorem

Name _____ Date _____

15. Alternate Interior Angle Theorem

16. Same-Side Exterior Angle Theorem

Use the diagram to write the "Given" and "Prove" statements for each theorem.

17. If two parallel lines are cut by a transversal, then the
exterior angles on the same side of the transversal
are supplementary.

Given: $r \parallel c$, n is a transversal

Prove: ∠1 and ∠7 are supplementary or ∠2 and ∠8
are supplementary

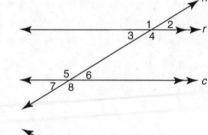

18. If two parallel lines are cut by a transversal,
then the alternate exterior angles are congruent.

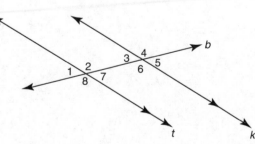

19. If two parallel lines are cut by a transversal,
then the alternate interior angles are congruent.

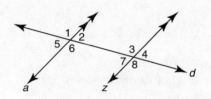

20. If two parallel lines are cut by a transversal,
then the interior angles on the same side
of the transversal are supplementary.

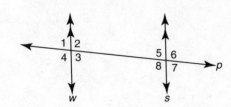

Prove each statement using the indicated type of proof.

21. Use a paragraph proof to prove the
Alternate Interior Angles Theorem. In
your proof, use the following
information and refer to the diagram.

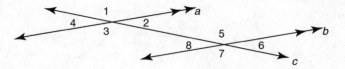

Given: $a \parallel b$, c is a transversal

Prove: $\angle 2 \cong \angle 8$

You are given that lines a and b are parallel and line c is a transversal, as shown
in the diagram. Angles 2 and 6 are corresponding angles by definition, and
corresponding angles are congruent by the Corresponding Angles Postulate.
So, $\angle 2 \cong \angle 6$. Angles 6 and 8 are vertical angles by definition, and vertical angles
are congruent by the Vertical Angles Congruence Theorem. So, $\angle 6 \cong \angle 8$.
Since $\angle 2 \cong \angle 6$ and $\angle 2 \cong \angle 8$, by the Transitive Property, $\angle 2 \cong \angle 8$.

22. Use a two-column proof to prove the Alternate
Exterior Angles Theorem. In your proof, use the
following information and refer to the diagram.

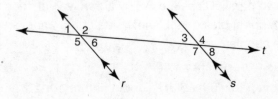

Given: $r \parallel s$, t is a transversal

Prove: $\angle 4 \cong \angle 5$

Name _____ Date _____

23. Use a flow chart proof to prove the Same-Side Interior Angles Theorem. In your proof, use the following information and refer to the diagram.

Given: $x \parallel y$, z is a transversal

Prove: $\angle 6$ and $\angle 7$ are supplementary

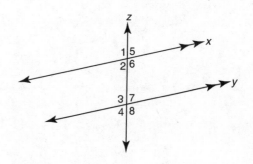

24. Use a two-column proof to prove the Same-Side Exterior Angles Theorem. In your proof, use the following information and refer to the diagram.

Given: $f \parallel g$, h is a transversal

Prove: $\angle 1$ and $\angle 4$ are supplementary

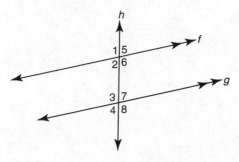

Write the theorem that is illustrated by each statement and diagram.

25. ∠4 and ∠7 are supplementary

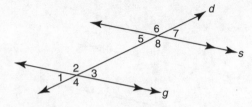

Same-Side Exterior Angles Theorem

26. ∠2 ≅ ∠6

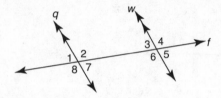

27. ∠1 ≅ ∠8

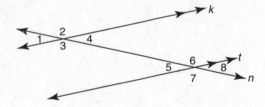

28. ∠2 and ∠5 are supplementary

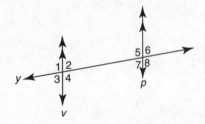

Name _____ Date _____

A Reversed Condition
Parallel Line Converse Theorems

2

Vocabulary

Answer the following question.

1. What is the converse of a statement?

Problem Set

Write the converse of each postulate or theorem.

1. Alternate Interior Angle Theorem:

   If a transversal intersects two parallel lines, then the alternate interior angles formed are congruent.

   If alternate interior angles formed by two lines and a transversal are congruent, then the two lines are parallel.

2. Alternate Exterior Angle Theorem:

   If a transversal intersects two parallel lines, then the alternate exterior angles formed are congruent.

3. Same-Side Interior Angle Theorem:

If a transversal intersects two parallel lines, then the interior angles on the same side of the transversal formed are supplementary.

4. Same-Side Exterior Angle Theorem:

If a transversal intersects two parallel lines, then the exterior angles on the same side of the transversal formed are supplementary.

Write the converse of each statement.

5. If a triangle has three congruent sides, then the triangle is an equilateral triangle.

Converse: If a triangle is an equilateral triangle, then the triangle has three congruent sides.

6. If a figure has four sides, then it is a quadrilateral.

7. If a figure is a rectangle, then it has four sides.

8. If two angles are vertical angles, then they are congruent.

Name _____ Date _____

9. If two angles in a triangle are congruent, then the triangle is isosceles.

10. If two intersecting lines form a right angle, then the lines are perpendicular.

Draw and label a diagram to illustrate each theorem.

11. Same-Side Interior Angle Converse Theorem

Given: ∠1 and ∠3 are supplementary or ∠2 and ∠4 are supplementary

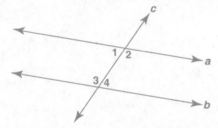

Conclusion: Lines *a* and *b* are parallel.

12. Alternate Exterior Angle Converse Theorem

2

13. Alternate Interior Angle Converse Theorem

14. Same-Side Exterior Angle Converse Theorem

Use the diagram to write the "Given" and "Prove" statements for each theorem.

15. If two lines, cut by a transversal, form same-side exterior angles that are supplementary, then the lines are parallel.

Given: *s* is a transversal; ∠1 and ∠8 are supplementary or ∠2 and ∠7 are supplementary

Prove: *w* ∥ *k*

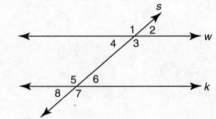

Name _____ Date _____

16. If two lines, cut by a transversal, form alternate exterior
angles that are congruent, then the lines are parallel.

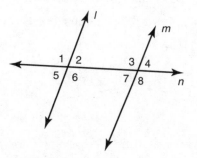

17. If two lines, cut by a transversal, form alternate interior
angles that are congruent, then the lines are parallel.

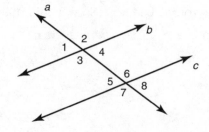

18. If two lines, cut by a transversal, form same-side interior
angles that are supplementary, then the lines are parallel.

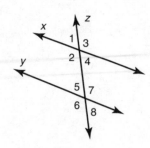

Prove each statement using the indicated type of proof.

19. Use a paragraph proof to prove the Alternate Exterior Angles Converse Theorem.
In your proof, use the following information and refer to the diagram.

Given: ∠4 ≅ ∠5, *j* is a transversal

Prove: *p* ∥ *x*

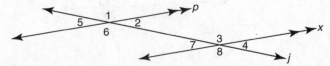

You are given that ∠4 ≅ ∠5 and line *j* is a transversal, as shown in the diagram. Angles 5 and 2 are vertical angles by definition, and vertical angles are congruent by the Vertical Angles Congruence Theorem. So, ∠5 ≅ ∠2. Since ∠4 ≅ ∠5 and ∠5 ≅ ∠2, by the Transitive Property, ∠4 ≅ ∠2. Angles 4 and 2 are corresponding angles by definition, and they are also congruent, so by the Corresponding Angles Converse Postulate, *p* ∥ *x*.

20. Use a two-column proof to prove the Alternate Interior Angles Converse Theorem.
In your proof, use the following information and refer to the diagram.

Given: ∠2 ≅ ∠7, *k* is a transversal

Prove: *m* ∥ *n*

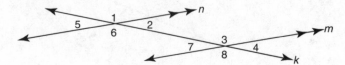

Name _____ Date _____

21. Use a two-column proof to prove the Same-Side Exterior Angles Converse Theorem.
In your proof, use the following information and refer to the diagram.

Given: ∠1 and ∠4 are supplementary, *u* is a transversal

Prove: *t* ∥ *v*

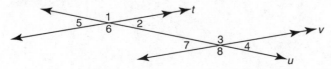

2

22. Use a flow chart to prove the Same-Side Interior Angles Converse Theorem. In your proof, use the following information and refer to the diagram.

Given: $\angle 6$ and $\angle 7$ are supplementary, e is a transversal

Prove: $f \parallel g$

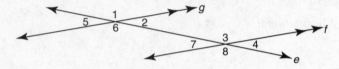

Name _____ Date _____

Inside Out
Triangle Sum, Exterior Angle, and Exterior Angle Inequality Theorems

3

Vocabulary

Write the term that best completes each statement.

1. The _____ states that the measure of an exterior angle of a triangle is greater than the measure of either of the remote interior angles of the triangle.

2. The _____ states that the sum of the measures of the interior angles of a triangle is 180°.

3. The _____ states that the measure of an exterior angle of a triangle is equal to the sum of the measures of the remote interior angles of the triangle.

4. The _____ are the two angles that are non-adjacent to the specified exterior angle.

Problem Set

Determine the measure of the missing angle in each triangle.

1.

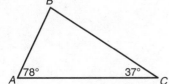

2.

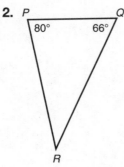

$m\angle B = 180° - (78° + 37°) = 65°$

3.

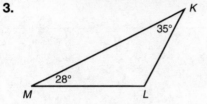

4.

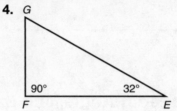

5.

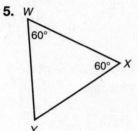

6.

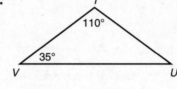

List the side lengths from shortest to longest for each diagram.

7.

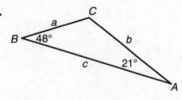

8.

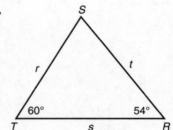

$m\angle C = 180° - (48° + 21°) = 111°$

The shortest side of a triangle is opposite the smallest angle. So, the side lengths from shortest to longest are *a*, *b*, *c*.

Name _____ Date _____

9.

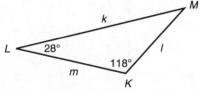

10.

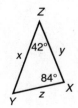

11.

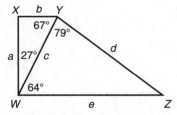

12.

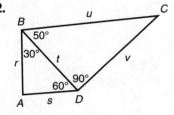

Identify the interior angles, the exterior angle, and the remote interior angles of each triangle.

13.

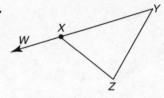

Interior angles: ∠XYZ, ∠YZX, ∠ZXY

Exterior angle: ∠WXZ

Remote interior angles: ∠XYZ, ∠YZX

14.

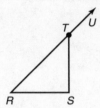

15.

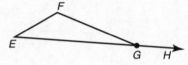

16.

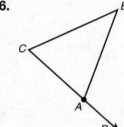

17.

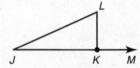

18.

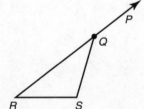

Name _____ Date _____

Solve for *x* in each diagram.

19.

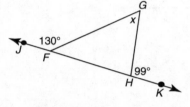

$m\angle GFH = 180° - 130° = 50°$

$m\angle GHK = m\angle GFH + m\angle FGH$
$\qquad 99° = 50° + x$
$\qquad 49° = x$

20.

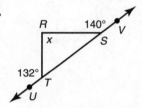

21.

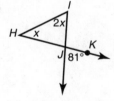

22.

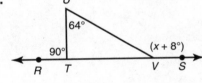

23.

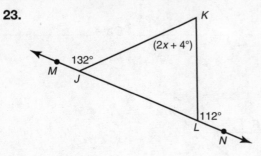

24.

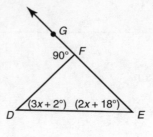

Use the given information for each triangle to write two inequalities that you would need to prove the Exterior Angle Inequality Theorem.

25.

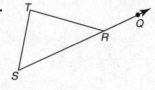

Given: Triangle *RST* with exterior ∠*TRQ*

Prove: $m\angle TRQ > m\angle S$ and
$m\angle TRQ > m\angle T$

26.

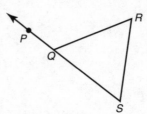

Given: Triangle *QRS* with exterior ∠*PQR*

Prove:

Name _____ Date _____

27.

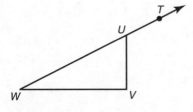

Given: Triangle *UVW* with exterior ∠*TUV*

Prove:

28.

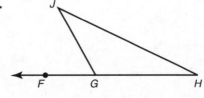

Given: Triangle *GHJ* with exterior ∠*FGJ*

Prove:

29.

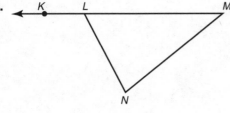

Given: Triangle *LMN* with exterior ∠*KLN*

Prove:

30.

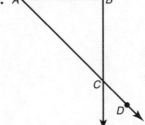

Given: Triangle *ABC* with exterior ∠*BCD*

Prove:

Name _____ Date _____

Trade Routes and Pasta, Anyone?
The Triangle Inequality Theorem

Vocabulary

Identify an example of each term in the diagram of triangle *ABC*.

1. Triangle Inequality Theorem

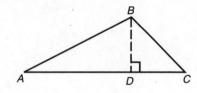

Problem Set

Without measuring the angles, list the angles of each triangle in order from least to greatest measure.

1.

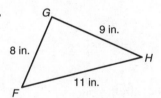

The smallest angle of a triangle is opposite the shortest side. So, the angles from least to greatest are ∠*H*, ∠*F*, ∠*G*.

2.

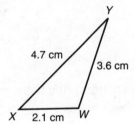

3.

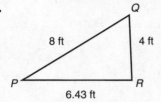

4.

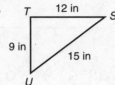

5.

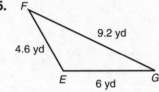

6.

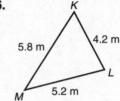

Determine whether it is possible to form a triangle using each set of segments with the given measurements. Explain your reasoning.

7. 3 inches, 2.9 inches, 5 inches

Yes. A triangle can be formed
because the sum of the two shortest
sides is greater than the longest side.
Sum of the Two Shortest Sides: 3 + 2.9 = 5.9
Longest Side: 5

8. 8 feet, 9 feet, 11 feet

9. 4 meters, 5.1 meters, 12.5 meters

10. 7.4 centimeters, 8.1 centimeters, 9.8 centimeters

Name _____ Date _____

11. 10 yards, 5 yards, 21 yards

12. 13.8 kilometers, 6.3 kilometers, 7.5 kilometers

13. 112 millimeters, 300 millimeters, 190 millimeters

14. 20.2 inches, 11 inches, 8.2 inches

15. 30 cm, 12 cm, 17 cm

16. 8 ft, 8 ft, 8 ft

Write an inequality that expresses the possible lengths of the unknown side of each triangle.

17. What could be the length of $\overline{AB}$?

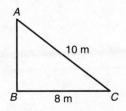

$AB < AC + BC$
$AB < 10\ \text{meters} + 8\ \text{meters}$
$AB < 18\ \text{meters}$

18. What could be the length of $\overline{DE}$?

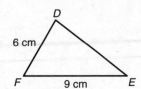

19. What could be the length of $\overline{HI}$?

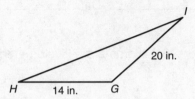

20. What could be the length of $\overline{JL}$?

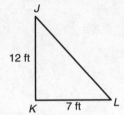

21. What could be the length of $\overline{MN}$?

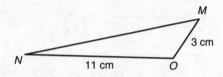

22. What could be the length of $\overline{QR}$?

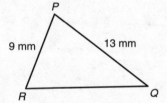

Name _____ Date _____

Stamps Around the World
Properties of a 45°–45°–90° Triangle

Vocabulary

Define the term in your own words.

1. 45°–45°–90° Triangle Theorem

Problem Set

Determine the length of the hypotenuse of each 45°–45°–90° triangle. Write your answer as a radical in simplest form.

1.

2 in. c

2 in.

$c = 2\sqrt{2}$

The length of the hypotenuse is $2\sqrt{2}$ inches.

2.

5 cm c

5 cm

$5\sqrt{2}$

3.

9 ft c

9 ft

$9\sqrt{2}$

4.

7 km c

7 km

$7\sqrt{2}$

Determine the lengths of the legs of each 45°–45°–90° triangle. Write your answer as a radical in simplest form.

5.

$a\sqrt{2} = 16$

$a = \dfrac{16}{\sqrt{2}}$

$a = \dfrac{16\sqrt{2}}{\sqrt{2}\sqrt{2}}$

$a = \dfrac{16\sqrt{2}}{2} = 8\sqrt{2}$

The length of each leg is $8\sqrt{2}$ centimeters.

6.

$6\sqrt{2}$

7.

6

8.

8

Use the given information to answer each question. Round your answer to the nearest tenth, if necessary.

9. Soren is flying a kite on the beach. The string forms a 45° angle with the ground. If he has let out 16 meters of line, how high above the ground is the kite?

$a\sqrt{2} = 16$

$a = \dfrac{16}{\sqrt{2}}$

$a = \dfrac{16\sqrt{2}}{\sqrt{2}\sqrt{2}}$

$a = \dfrac{16\sqrt{2}}{2} = 8\sqrt{2} \approx 11.3$

The kite is approximately 11.3 meters above the ground.

Name _____ Date _____

10. Meena is picking oranges from the tree in her yard. She rests a 12-foot ladder against the tree at a 45° angle. How far is the top of the ladder from the ground?

11. Emily is building a square bookshelf. She wants to add a diagonal support beam to the back to strengthen it. The diagonal divides the bookshelf into two 45°–45°–90° triangles. If each side of the bookshelf is 4 feet long, what must the length of the support beam be?

12. Prospect Park is a square with side lengths of 512 meters. One of the paths through the park runs diagonally from the northeast corner to the southwest corner, and it divides the park into two 45°–45°–90° triangles. How long is that path?

Determine the area of each triangle.

13.

$a\sqrt{2} = 16$ $A = \frac{1}{2}(8\sqrt{2})(8\sqrt{2})$

$a = \frac{16}{\sqrt{2}}$ $A = \frac{64(\sqrt{2})^2}{2}$

$a = \frac{16\sqrt{2}}{\sqrt{2}\sqrt{2}}$ $A = \frac{64(2)}{2}$

$a = \frac{16\sqrt{2}}{2}$ $A = 64$

$a = 8\sqrt{2}$

The area of the triangle is 64 square millimeters.

14.

$9\sqrt{2} \times 9\sqrt{2}$

162

15.

24.5

4.94

Name _____ Date _____

16.

Use the given information to answer each question.

17. Eli is making a mosaic using tiles shaped like 45°–45°–90° triangles. The length of the hypotenuse of each tile is 13 centimeters. What is the area of each tile?

$$a\sqrt{2} = 13 \qquad\qquad A = \frac{1}{2}\left(\frac{13\sqrt{2}}{2}\right)\left(\frac{13\sqrt{2}}{2}\right)$$

$$a = \frac{13}{\sqrt{2}} = \frac{13(\sqrt{2})}{\sqrt{2}(\sqrt{2})} \qquad A = \frac{169(\sqrt{2})^2}{8} = \frac{169(2)}{8}$$

$$a = \frac{13\sqrt{2}}{2} \qquad\qquad A = \frac{169}{4} = 42.25$$

The area of each tile is 42.25 square centimeters.

18. Baked pita chips are often in the shape of 45°–45°–90° triangles. Caitlyn determines that the longest side of a pita chip in one bag measures 3 centimeters. What is the area of the pita chip?

19. Annika is making a kite in the shape of a 45°–45°–90° triangle. The longest side of the kite is 28 inches. What is the area of the piece of fabric needed for the kite?

20. A tent has a mesh door that is shaped like a 45°–45°–90° triangle. The longest side of the door is 36 inches. What is the area of the mesh door?

Name _____ Date _____

Construct each isosceles triangle described using the given segment.

21. Construct right isosceles triangle *ABC* with segment *BC* as the hypotenuse by constructing 45° angles at *B* and *C*.

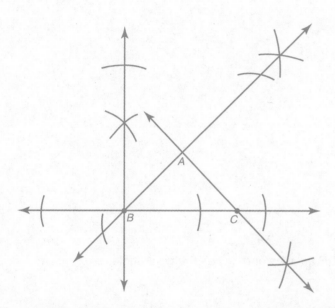

22. Construct right isosceles triangle *WXY* with segment *WX* as the hypotenuse by constructing 45° angles at *W* and *X*.

23. Construct right isosceles triangle *PQR* with $\overline{RQ}$ as a leg and $\angle R$ as the right angle.

24. Construct right isosceles triangle *DEF* with $\overline{DF}$ as a leg and $\angle D$ as the right angle.

Name _____ Date _____

More Stamps, Really?
Properties of a 30°–60°–90° Triangle

Vocabulary

Write the term that best completes each statement.

1. The _____ states that the length of the hypotenuse in a 30°–60°–90° triangle is two times the length of the shorter leg, and the length of the longer leg is $\sqrt{3}$ times the length of the shorter leg.

Problem Set

Determine the measure of the indicated interior angle.

1.

$m\angle ABC = 60°$

2.

$m\angle DFE =$

3.

$m\angle HAK =$

4.

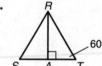

$m\angle TRA =$

Given the length of the short leg of a 30°–60°–90° triangle, determine the lengths of the long leg and the hypotenuse. Write your answers as radicals in simplest form.

5.

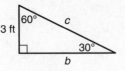

$a = 3$ feet

$b = 3\sqrt{3}$ feet

$c = 2(3) = 6$ feet

6.

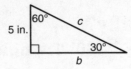

7.

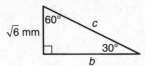

8.

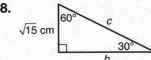

Given the length of the hypotenuse of a 30°–60°–90° triangle, determine the lengths of the two legs. Write your answers as radicals in simplest form.

9.

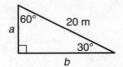

$c = 20$ meters

$a = \dfrac{20}{2} = 10$ meters

$b = 10\sqrt{3}$ meters

10.

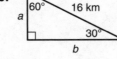

11.

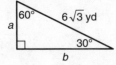

12.

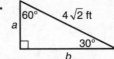

Name _____ Date _____

Given the length of the long side of a 30°–60°–90° triangle, determine the lengths of the short leg and the hypotenuse. Write your answers as radicals in simplest form.

13.

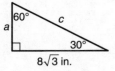

$b = 8\sqrt{3}$ inches

$a = \dfrac{8\sqrt{3}}{\sqrt{3}} = 8$ inches

$c = 2(8) = 16$ inches

14.

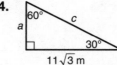

15.

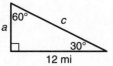

16.

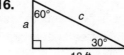

Determine the area of each 30°–60°–90° triangle. Round your answer to the nearest tenth, if necessary.

17.

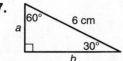

$a = \dfrac{6}{2} = 3$ centimeters

$b = 3\sqrt{3}$ centimeters

$A = \dfrac{1}{2} \cdot 3 \cdot 3\sqrt{3}$

$A = \dfrac{9\sqrt{3}}{2} \approx 7.8$ square centimeters

The area of the triangle is approximately 7.8 square centimeters.

18.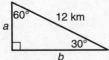

19. Universal Sporting Goods sells pennants in the shape of 30°–60°–90° triangles. The length of the longest side of each pennant is 16 inches.

20. A factory produces solid drafting triangles in the shape of 30°–60°–90° triangles. The length of the side opposite the right angle is 15 centimeters.

Name _____ Date _____

Construct each triangle described using the given segment.

21. Construct a 30°–60°–90° triangle by first constructing an equilateral triangle with $\overline{MN}$ as a side and then bisecting one of the sides.

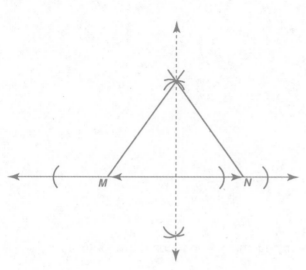

22. Construct a 30°–60°–90° triangle *RST* by first constructing an equilateral triangle with $\overline{RS}$ as a side and then bisecting the angle at *R*.

23. Construct a 30°–60°–90° triangle *EFG* with $\overline{EF}$ as the side opposite the 30° angle by first constructing an equilateral triangle.

24. Construct a 30°–60°–90° triangle *ABC* by first copying angle *A* and then drawing $\overline{AB}$ as the hypotenuse.

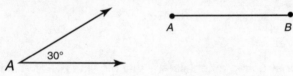

Name _____ Date _____

Big and Small
Dilating Triangles to Create Similar Triangles

Vocabulary

Define the term in your own words.

1. similar triangles

Problem Set

Rectangle $L'M'N'P'$ is a dilation of rectangle $LMNP$. The center of dilation is point Z. Use a metric ruler to determine the actual lengths of $\overline{ZL}$, $\overline{ZN}$, $\overline{ZM}$, $\overline{ZP}$, $\overline{ZL'}$, $\overline{ZN'}$, $\overline{ZM'}$, and $\overline{ZP'}$ to the nearest tenth of a centimeter. Then, express the ratios $\dfrac{ZL'}{ZL}$, $\dfrac{ZN'}{ZN}$, $\dfrac{ZM'}{ZM}$, and $\dfrac{ZP'}{ZP}$ as decimals.

1.

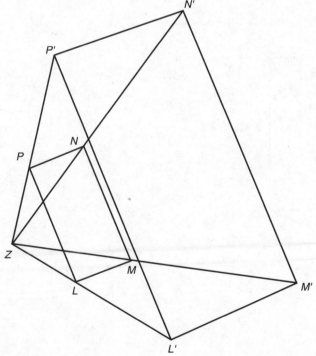

$ZL = 2$, $ZN = 3$, $ZM = 3$, $ZP = 2$, $ZL' = 5$, $ZN' = 7.5$, $ZM' = 7.5$, $ZP' = 5$

$\dfrac{ZL'}{ZL} = \dfrac{5}{2} = 2.5$, $\dfrac{ZN'}{ZN} = \dfrac{7.5}{3} = 2.5$, $\dfrac{ZM'}{ZM} = \dfrac{7.5}{3} = 2.5$, $\dfrac{ZP'}{ZP} = \dfrac{5}{2} = 2.5$

2.

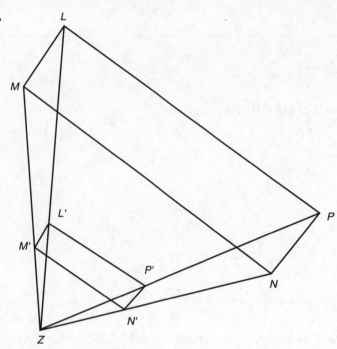

4

3.

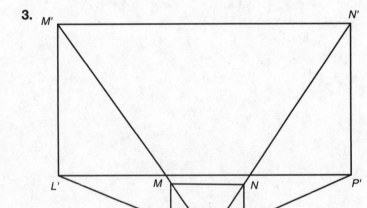

Name _____ Date _____

4.

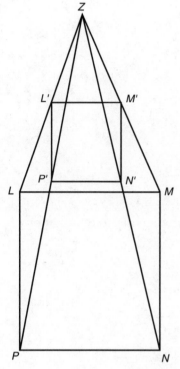

Given the image and pre-image, determine the scale factor.

5.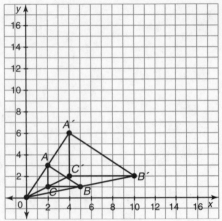

The scale factor is 2.

Each coordinate of the image is two times the corresponding coordinate of the pre-image.

△*ABC* has vertex coordinates *A*(2, 3), *B*(5, 1), and *C*(2, 1).

△*A'B'C'* has vertex coordinates *A'*(4, 6), *B'*(10, 2), and *C'*(4, 2).

6.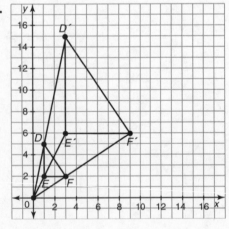

Name _____ Date _____

7.

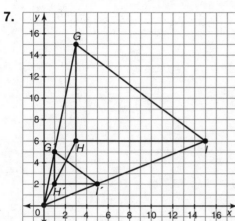

8.

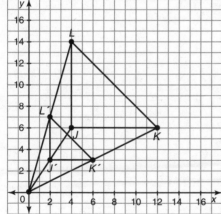

Given the pre-image, scale factor, and center of dilation, use a compass and straight edge to graph the image.

9. The scale factor is 3 and the center of dilation is the origin.

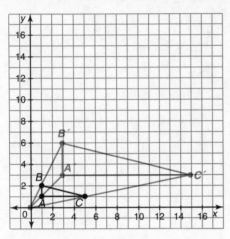

10. The scale factor is 4 and the center of dilation is the origin.

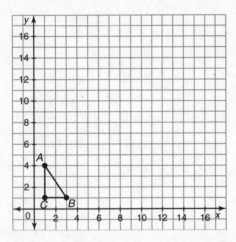

11. The scale factor is 2 and the center of dilation is the origin.

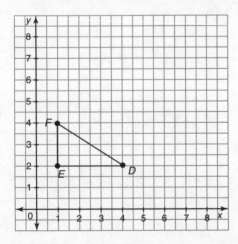

Name _____ Date _____

12. The scale factor is 5 and the center of dilation is the origin.

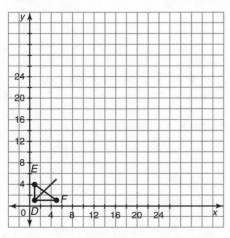

Use coordinate notation to determine the coordinates of the image.

13. △ABC has vertices A(1, 2), B(3, 6), and C(9, 7). What are the vertices of the image after a dilation with a scale factor of 4 using the origin as the center of dilation?

A(1, 2) → A′(4(1), 4(2)) = A′(4, 8)

B(3, 6) → B′(4(3), 4(6)) = B′(12, 24)

C(9, 7) → C′(4(9), 4(7)) = C′(36, 28)

14. △DEF has vertices D(8, 4), E(2, 6), and F(3, 1). What are the vertices of the image after a dilation with a scale factor of 5 using the origin as the center of dilation?

15. △GHI has vertices G(0, 5), H(4, 2), and I(3, 3). What are the vertices of the image after a dilation with a scale factor of 9 using the origin as the center of dilation?

16. △JKL has vertices J(6, 2), K(1, 3), and L(7, 0). What are the vertices of the image after a dilation with a scale factor of 12 using the origin as the center of dilation?

17. △ABC has vertices A(8, 4), B(14, 16), and C(6, 10). What are the vertices of the image after a dilation with a scale factor of $\frac{1}{2}$ using the origin as the center of dilation?

18. △DEF has vertices D(25, 25), E(15, 10), and F(20, 10). What are the vertices of the image after a dilation with a scale factor of $\frac{1}{5}$ using the origin as the center of dilation?

19. △GHI has vertices G(0, 20), H(16, 24), and I(12, 12). What are the vertices of the image after a dilation with a scale factor of $\frac{3}{4}$ using the origin as the center of dilation?

4

20. △JKL has vertices J(8, 2), K(6, 0), and L(4, 10). What are the vertices of the image after a dilation with a scale factor of $\frac{5}{2}$ using the origin as the center of dilation?

Name _____ Date _____

Similar Triangles or Not?
Similar Triangle Theorems

Vocabulary

Give an example of each term. Include a sketch with each example.

1. Angle-Angle Similarity Theorem

2. Side-Side-Side Similarity Theorem

3. Side-Angle-Side Similarity Theorem

4. included angle

5. included side

Name _____ Date _____

Problem Set

Explain how you know that the triangles are similar.

1.

The triangles are congruent by the Angle-Angle Similarity Theorem. Two corresponding angles are congruent.

2.

A A

3.

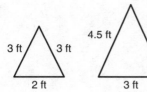

SSS

$$\frac{3}{4.5} = \frac{2}{3}$$

4.

 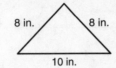   SSS

5.

 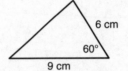   S AS

6.

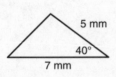 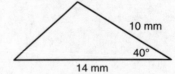   S AS

Name _____ Date _____

Determine what additional information you would need to prove that the triangles are similar using the given theorem.

7. What information would you need to use the Angle-Angle Similarity Theorem to prove that the triangles are similar?

To prove that the triangles are similar using the Angle-Angle Similarity Theorem, the first triangle should have a corresponding 60 degree angle and the second triangle should have a corresponding 35 degree angle.

8. What information would you need to use the Angle-Angle Similarity Theorem to prove that the triangles are similar?

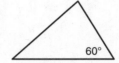

9. What information would you need to use the Side-Angle-Side Similarity Theorem to prove that the triangles are similar?

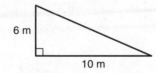

10. What information would you need to use the Side-Angle-Side Similarity Theorem to prove that the triangles are similar?

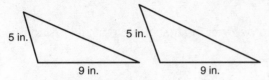

11. What information would you need to use the Side-Side-Side Similarity Theorem to prove that these triangles are similar?

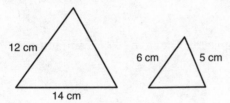

12. What information would you need to use the Side-Side-Side Similarity Theorem to prove that these triangles are similar?

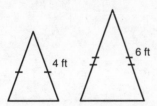

Name _____ Date _____

Determine whether each pair of triangles is similar. Explain your reasoning.

13.

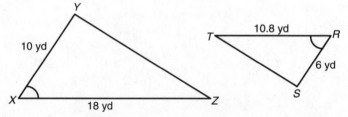

The triangles are similar by the Side-Angle-Side Similarity Theorem because the included angles in both triangles are congruent and the corresponding sides are proportional.

$\dfrac{XY}{RS} = \dfrac{10}{6} = \dfrac{5}{3}$

$\dfrac{XZ}{RT} = \dfrac{18}{10.8} = \dfrac{5}{3}$

4

14.

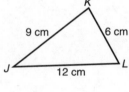
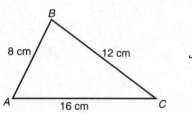

15.

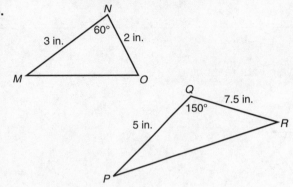

16.

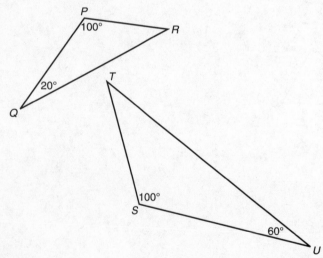

Name _____ Date _____

17.

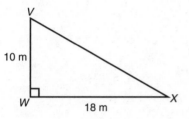

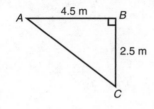

18.

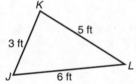

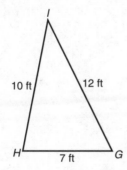

19.

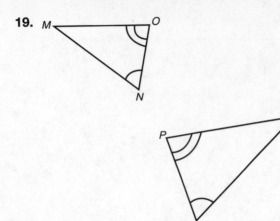

20.

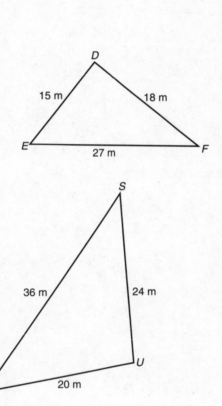

Name _____ Date _____

Keep It in Proportion
Theorems About Proportionality

Vocabulary

Match each definition to its corresponding term.

1. Angle Bisector/Proportional Side Theorem

    a. If a line parallel to one side of a triangle intersects the other two sides, then it divides the two sides proportionally.

2. Triangle Proportionality Theorem

    b. A bisector of an angle in a triangle divides the opposite side into two segments whose lengths are in the same ratio as the lengths of the sides adjacent to the angle.

3. Converse of the Triangle Proportionality Theorem

    c. If a line divides two sides of a triangle proportionally, then it is parallel to the third side.

4. Proportional Segments Theorem

    d. The midsegment of a triangle is parallel to the third side of the triangle and half the measure of the third side of the triangle

5. Triangle Midsegment Theorem

    e. If three parallel lines intersect two transversals, then they divide the transversals proportionally.

4

Problem Set

Calculate the length of the indicated segment in each figure.

1. $\overline{HJ}$ bisects $\angle H$. Calculate *HF*.

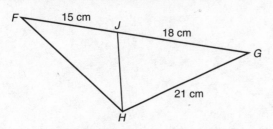

The length of segment *HF* is 17.5 centimeters.

$$\frac{GH}{HF} = \frac{GJ}{JF}$$

$$\frac{21}{HF} = \frac{18}{15}$$

$$18 \cdot HF = 315$$

$$HF = 17.5$$

2. $\overline{LN}$ bisects $\angle L$. Calculate *NM*.

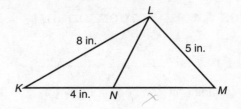

$$\frac{4}{8} \qquad \frac{x}{5}$$

$$\frac{8x}{8} = \frac{20}{8}$$

$$x = 2-5$$

3. $\overline{BD}$ bisects $\angle B$. Calculate *AD*.

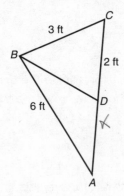

4. $\overline{SQ}$ bisects $\angle S$. Calculate *SP*.

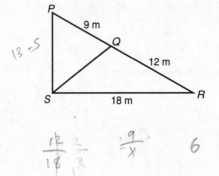

13-5

$$\frac{12}{18} = \qquad \frac{9}{x} \qquad 6$$

Name _____ Date _____

5. $\overline{YZ}$ bisects $\angle Y$. Calculate *YW*.

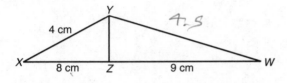

6. $\overline{VX}$ bisects $\angle V$. Calculate *XW*.

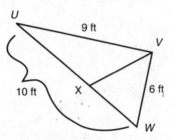

4

7. $\overline{GE}$ bisects $\angle G$. Calculate *FD*.

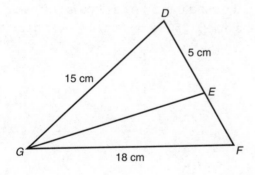

8. $\overline{ML}$ bisects $\angle M$. Calculate *NL*.

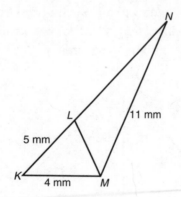

Use the given information to answer each question.

9. On the map shown, Willow Street bisects the angle formed by Maple Avenue and South Street. Mia's house is 5 miles from the school and 4 miles from the fruit market. Rick's house is 6 miles from the fruit market. How far is Rick's house from the school?

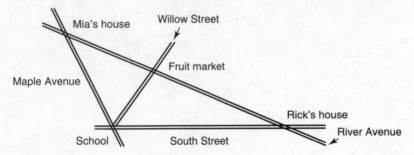

Rick's house is 7.5 miles from the school.

$$\frac{5}{4} = \frac{x}{6}$$

$$4x = 30$$

$$x = 7.5$$

4

10. Jimmy is hitting a golf ball towards the hole. The line from Jimmy to the hole bisects the angle formed by the lines from Jimmy to the oak tree and from Jimmy to the sand trap. The oak tree is 200 yards from Jimmy, the sand trap is 320 yards from Jimmy, and the hole is 250 yards from the sand trap. How far is the hole from the oak tree?

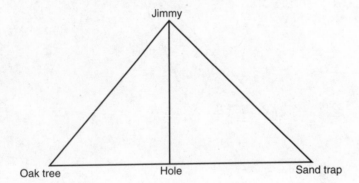

Name _____ Date _____

11. The road from Central City on the map shown bisects the angle formed by the roads from Central City to Minville and from Central City to Oceanview. Central City is 12 miles from Oceanview, Minville is 6 miles from the beach, and Oceanview is 8 miles from the beach. How far is Central City from Minville?

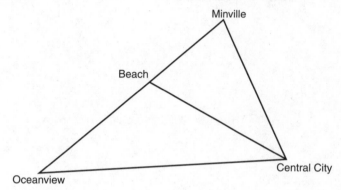

12. Luigi is racing a remote control car from the starting point to the winner's circle.That path bisects the angle formed by the lines from the starting point to the house and from the starting point to the retention pond. The house and the retention pond are each 500 feet from the starting point. The house is 720 feet from the retention pond. How far is the winner's circle from the retention pond?

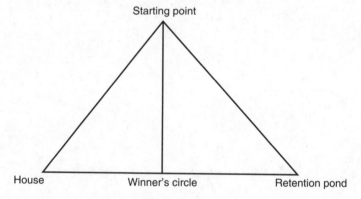

Use the diagram and given information to write a statement that can be justified using the Proportional Segments Theorem, Triangle Proportionality Theorem, or its Converse. State the theorem used.

13.

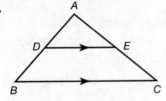

14.

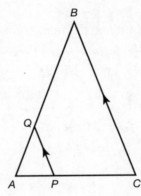

$\dfrac{AD}{DB} = \dfrac{AE}{EC}$, Triangle Proportionality Theorem

15.

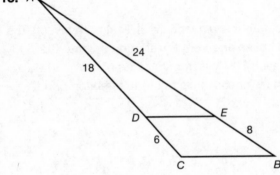

16.

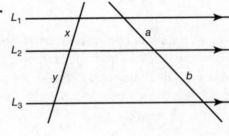

17.

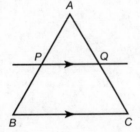

18.

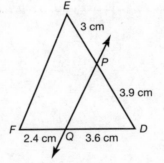

Name _____ Date _____

19.

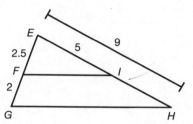

20.

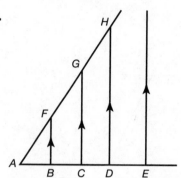

Use the Triangle Proportionality Theorem and the Proportional Segments Theorem to determine the missing value.

21.

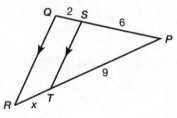

$$\frac{x}{9} = \frac{2}{6}$$

$$6x = 18$$

$$x = 3$$

22.

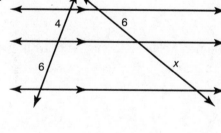

9

23.

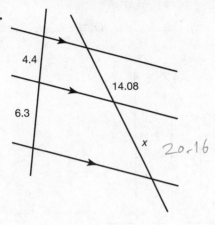

4.4

14.08

6.3

x 20.16

24.

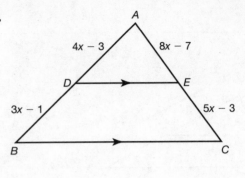

$4x - 3$

$8x - 7$

D

E

$3x - 1$

$5x - 3$

B

C

A

Use the diagram and given information to write two statements that can be justified using the Triangle Midsegment Theorem.

25.

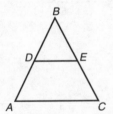

Given: *ABC* is a triangle

D is the midpoint of $\overline{AB}$

E is the midpoint of BC

$\overline{DE} \parallel \overline{AC}$, $DE = \frac{1}{2} AC$

26.

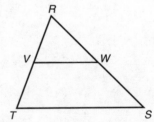

Given: *RST* is a triangle

V is the midpoint of $\overline{RT}$

W is the midpoint of $\overline{RS}$

Name _____ Date _____

27.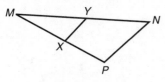

Given: *MNP* is a triangle

    X is the midpoint of $\overline{MP}$

    Y is the midpoint of $\overline{MN}$

28.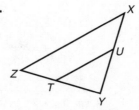

Given: *XYZ* is a triangle

    T is the midpoint of $\overline{YZ}$

    U is the midpoint of $\overline{XY}$

Given each diagram, compare the measures described. Simplify your answers, but do not evaluate any radicals.

29. The sides of triangle *LMN* have midpoints *O*(0, 0), *P*(−9, −3), and *Q*(0, −3). Compare the length of $\overline{OP}$ to the length of $\overline{LM}$.

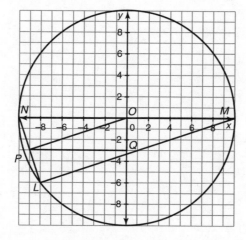

Segment *LM* is two times the length of segment *OP*.

$$OP = \sqrt{(-9 - 0)^2 + (-3 - 0)^2}$$

$$= \sqrt{(-9)^2 + (-3)^2} = \sqrt{81 + 9}$$

$$= \sqrt{90} = 3\sqrt{10}$$

$$LM = \sqrt{(10 - (-8)^2 + (0 - (-6))^2}$$

$$= \sqrt{18^2 + 6^2} = \sqrt{324 + 36}$$

$$= \sqrt{360} = 6\sqrt{10}$$

30. The sides of triangle *LMN* have midpoint *P*(0, 0), *Q*(−2, 2), and *R*(2, 2). Compare the length of $\overline{QP}$ to the length of $\overline{LN}$.

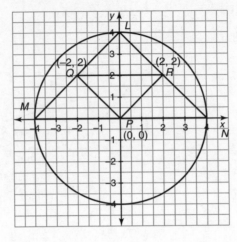

Name _____ Date _____

Geometric Mean
More Similar Triangles

Vocabulary

Write the term from the box that best completes each statement.

Right Triangle/Altitude Similarity Theorem	geometric mean
Right Triangle Altitude/Hypotenuse Theorem	Right Triangle Altitude/Leg Theorem

1. The _____ states that if an altitude is drawn to the hypotenuse of a right triangle, then the two triangles formed are similar to the original triangle and to each other.

2. The _____ states that if the altitude is drawn to the hypotenuse of a right triangle, each leg of the right triangle is the geometric mean of the measure of the hypotenuse and the measure of the segment of the hypotenuse adjacent to the leg.

3. The _____ of two positive numbers a and b is the positive number x such that $\frac{a}{x} = \frac{x}{b}$.

4. The _____ states that the measure of the altitude drawn from the vertex of the right angle of a right triangle to its hypotenuse is the geometric mean between the measures of the two segments of the hypotenuse.

Problem Set

Construct an altitude to the hypotenuse of each right triangle.

1.

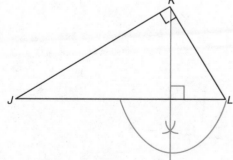

2.

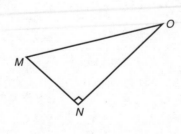

3.

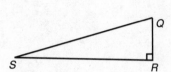

4.

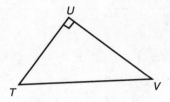

Use each similarity statement to write the corresponding sides of the triangles as proportions.

5. $\triangle CGJ \sim \triangle MKP$

$\dfrac{CG}{MK} = \dfrac{GJ}{KP} = \dfrac{CJ}{MP}$

6. $\triangle XZC \sim \triangle YMN$

7. $\triangle ADF \sim \triangle GLM$

8. $\triangle WNY \sim \triangle CQR$

Use the Right Triangle/Altitude Similarity Theorem to write three similarity statements involving the triangles in each diagram.

9.

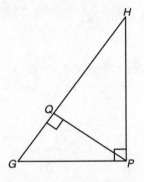

$\triangle HPG \sim \triangle PQG$, $\triangle HPG \sim \triangle HQP$,
$\triangle PQG \sim \triangle HQP$

10.

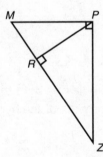

11.

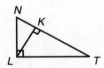

12.

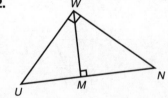

Name _____ Date _____

Solve for *x*.

13.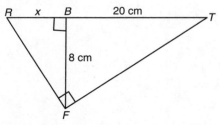

$$\frac{FB}{TB} = \frac{RB}{FB}$$

$$\frac{8}{20} = \frac{x}{8}$$

$20x = 64$

$x = 3.2$ cm

14.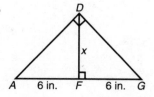

15.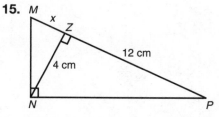

16.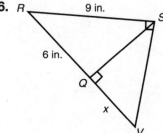

17.

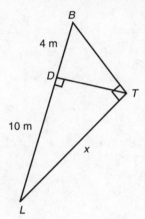

18.

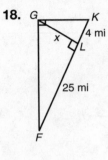

Solve for *x*, *y*, and *z*.

19.

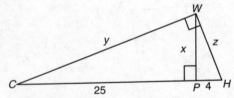

$$\frac{CP}{WP} = \frac{WP}{PH}$$

$$\frac{25}{x} = \frac{x}{4}$$

$$x^2 = 100$$

$$x = 10$$

$$x^2 + 25^2 = y^2$$

$$100 + 625 = y^2$$

$$725 = y^2$$

$$5\sqrt{29} = y$$

$$4^2 + x^2 = z^2$$

$$16 + 100 = z^2$$

$$116 = z^2$$

$$2\sqrt{29} = z$$

Name _____ Date _____

20.

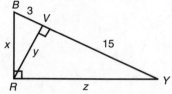

21.

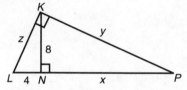

22.

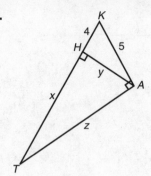

Use the given information to answer each question.

23. You are on a fishing trip with your friends. The diagram shows the location of the river, fishing hole, camp site, and bait store. The camp site is located 200 feet from the fishing hole. The bait store is located 110 feet from the fishing hole. How wide is the river?

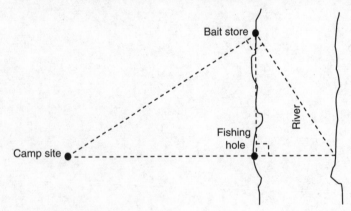

The river is 60.5 feet wide.

$$\frac{200}{110} = \frac{110}{x}$$

$$200x = 12,100$$

$$x = 60.5$$

Name _____ Date _____

24. You are standing at point *D* in the diagram looking across a bog at point *B*. Point *B* is 84 yards from point *A* and 189 yards from point *C*. How wide across is the bog?

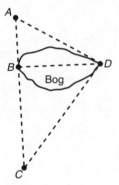

25. Marsha wants to walk from the parking lot through the forest to the clearing, as shown in the diagram. She knows that the forest ranger station is 154 feet from the flag pole and the flag pole is 350 feet from the clearing. How far is the parking lot from the clearing?

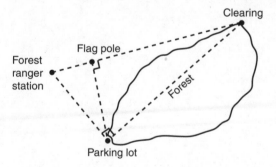

26. Andre is camping with his uncle at one edge of a ravine. The diagram shows the location of their tent. The tent is 1.2 miles from the fallen log and the fallen log is 0.75 miles from the observation tower. How wide is the ravine?

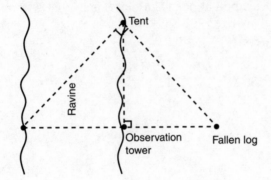

Name _____ Date _____

Proving the Pythagorean Theorem
Proving the Pythagorean Theorem and the Converse of the Pythagorean Theorem

Problem Set

Write the Given and Prove statements that should be used to prove the indicated theorem using each diagram.

1. Prove the Pythagorean Theorem.

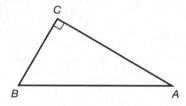

Given: $\triangle ABC$ with right angle C

Prove: $AC^2 + BC^2 = AB^2$

2. Prove the Converse of the Pythagorean Theorem.

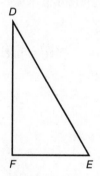

Given:

Prove:

3. Prove the Pythagorean Theorem.

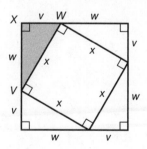

Given:

Prove:

4. Prove the Pythagorean Theorem.

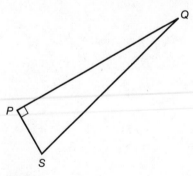

Given:

Prove:

5. Prove the Pythagorean Theorem.

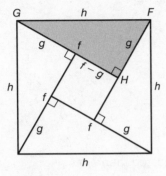

Given:

Prove:

6. Prove the Converse of
the Pythagorean Theorem.

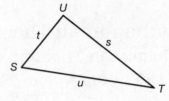

Given:

Prove:

Prove each theorem for the diagram that is given. Use the method indicated. In some cases, the proof has been started for you.

7. Prove the Pythagorean Theorem using similar triangles.

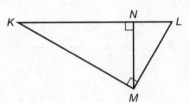

Draw an altitude to the hypotenuse at point *N*.

According to the Right Triangle/Similarity
Theorem, $\triangle KLM \sim \triangle LMN \sim \triangle MKN$.

According to the definition of similar triangles, the sides of similar
triangles are proportional.

$\dfrac{KL}{KM} = \dfrac{KM}{KN}$
$KM^2 = KL \times KN$

$\dfrac{KL}{ML} = \dfrac{ML}{NL}$
$ML^2 = KL \times NL$

$KM^2 + ML^2 = KL \times KN + KL \times NL$

$KM^2 + ML^2 = KL(KN + NL)$

$KM^2 + ML^2 = KL(KL)$

$KM^2 + ML^2 = KL^2$

Name _____ Date _____

8. Prove the Pythagorean Theorem using algebraic reasoning.

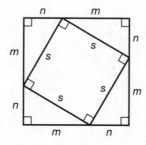

9. Prove the Converse of the Pythagorean Theorem using algebraic reasoning and the SSS Theorem.

Construct a right triangle that has legs the same lengths as the original triangle, q and r, opposite angles Q and R. Label the hypotenuse of this triangle t, opposite the right angle T.

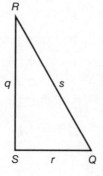

10. Prove the Pythagorean Theorem using similarity.

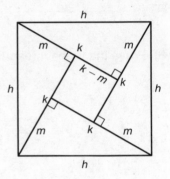

4

11. Prove the Converse of the Pythagorean Theorem using algebraic reasoning.

Construct a right triangle that shares side *h* with the original triangle and has one leg length *g*, as in the original triangle, and the other leg length *w*.

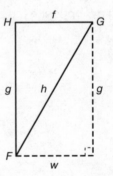

Name _____ Date _____

12. Prove the Pythagorean Theorem using similar triangles.

Given: $\triangle ABC$ with right angle C

Place side a along the diameter of a circle of radius c
so that B is at the center of the circle.

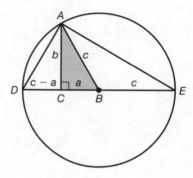

Name _____ Date _____

Indirect Measurement
Application of Similar Triangles

Vocabulary

Provide an example of the term.

1. indirect measurement

Problem Set

Explain how you know that each pair of triangles are similar.

1.

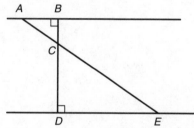

The angles where the vertices of the triangle intersect are vertical angles, so angles ∠ACB and ∠ECD are congruent. The angles formed by BD intersecting the two parallel lines are right angles, so they are also congruent. So by the Angle-Angle Similarity Theorem, the triangles formed are similar.

2.

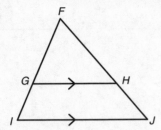

3.

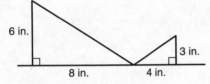

4.

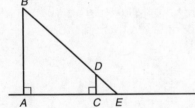

Name _____ Date _____

Use indirect measurement to calculate the missing distance.

5. Elly and Jeff are on opposite sides of a canyon that runs east to west, according to the graphic. They want to know how wide the canyon is. Each person stands 10 feet from the edge. Then, Elly walks 24 feet west, and Jeff walks 360 feet east.

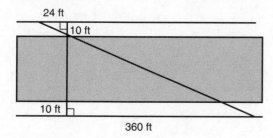

What is the width of the canyon?

The distance across the canyon is 140 feet.

$$\frac{10 + x}{10} = \frac{360}{24}$$

$10 + x = 150$

$x = 140$

6. Zoe and Ramon are hiking on a glacier. They become separated by a crevasse running east to west. Each person stands 9 feet from the edge. Then, Zoe walks 48 feet east, and Ramon walks 12 feet west.

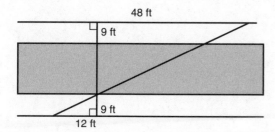

What is the width of the crevasse?

7. Minh wanted to measure the height of a statue. She lined herself up with the statue's shadow so that the tip of her shadow met the tip of the statue's shadow. She marked the spot where she was standing. Then, she measured the distance from where she was standing to the tip of the shadow, and from the statue to the tip of the shadow.

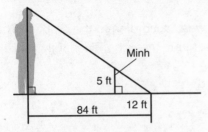

What is the height of the statue?

8. Dimitri wants to measure the height of a palm tree. He lines himself up with the palm tree's shadow so that the tip of his shadow meets the tip of the palm tree's shadow. Then, he asks a friend to measure the distance from where he was standing to the tip of his shadow and the distance from the palm tree to the tip of its shadow.

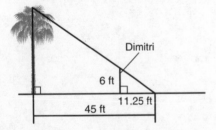

What is the height of the palm tree?

Name _____ Date _____

9. Andre is making a map of a state park. He finds a small bog, and he wants to measure the distance across the widest part. He first marks the points *A*, *C*, and *E*. Andre measures the distances shown on the image. Andre also marks point *B* along *AC* and point *D* along *AE*, such that *BD* is parallel to *CE*.

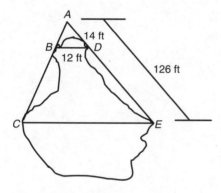

What is the width of the bog at the widest point?

4

10. Shira finds a tidal pool while walking on the beach. She wants to know the maximum width of the tidal pool. Using indirect measurement, she begins by marking the points *A*, *C*, and *E*. Shira measures the distances shown on the image. Next, Shira marks point *B* along *AC* and point *D* along *AE*, such that *BD* is parallel to *CE*.

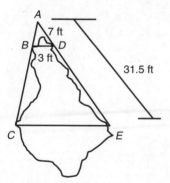

What is the distance across the tidal pool at its widest point?

11. Keisha is visiting a museum. She wants to know the height of one of the sculptures. She places a small mirror on the ground between herself and the sculpture, then she backs up until she can see the top of the sculpture in the mirror.

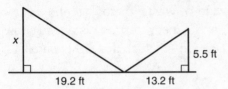

What is the height of the sculpture?

12. Micah wants to know the height of his school. He places a small mirror on the ground between himself and the school, then he backs up until he can see the highest point of the school in the mirror.

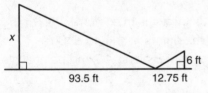

What is the height of Micah's school?

Name _____ Date _____

We Like to Move It!
Translating, Rotating, and Reflecting Geometric Figures

Problem Set

Transform each given geometric figure on the coordinate plane as described.

1. Translate trapezoid *ABCD* 11 units to the right.

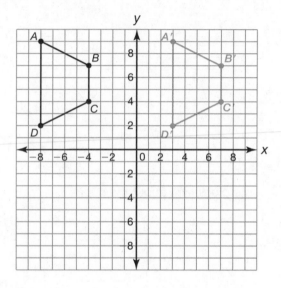

2. Translate triangle *EFG* 8 units up.

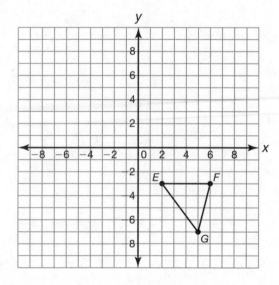

3. Rotate rectangle *HJKL* 90° counterclockwise about the origin.

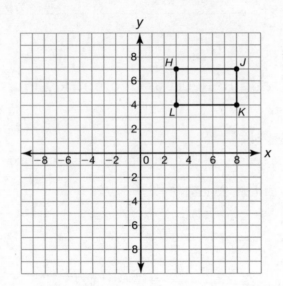

4. Rotate triangle *MNP* 180° counterclockwise about the origin.

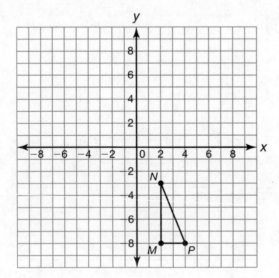

Name _____ Date _____

5. Rotate trapezoid *QRST* 90° counterclockwise about the origin.

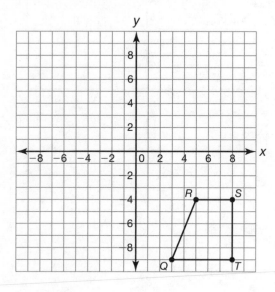

6. Rotate parallelogram *WXYZ* 180° counterclockwise about the origin.

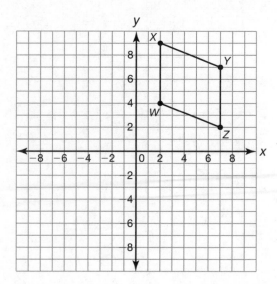

7. Reflect triangle *ABC* over the *y*-axis.

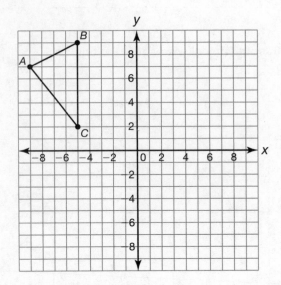

8. Reflect parallelogram *DEFG* over the *x*-axis.

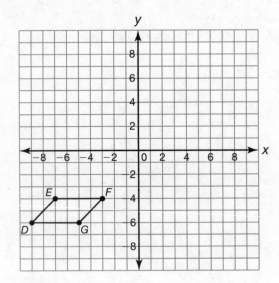

Name _____ Date _____

9. Reflect trapezoid *HJKL* over the *x*-axis.

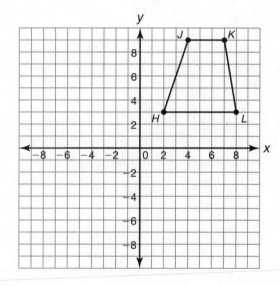

10. Reflect quadrilateral *MNPQ* over the *y*-axis.

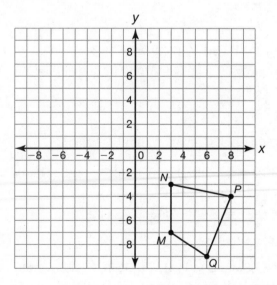

Determine the coordinates of each translated image without graphing.

11. The vertices of triangle *ABC* are *A* (5, 3), *B* (2, 8), and *C* (−4, 5). Translate the triangle 6 units to the left to form triangle *A′ B′ C′*.

    The vertices of triangle *A′ B′ C′* are *A′* (−1, 3), *B′* (−4, 8), and *C′* (−10, 5).

12. The vertices of rectangle *DEFG* are *D* (−7, 1), *E* (−7, 8), *F* (1, 8), and *G* (1, 1). Translate the rectangle 10 units down to form rectangle *D′ E′ F′ G′*.

13. The vertices of parallelogram *HJKL* are *H* (2, −6), *J* (3, −1), *K* (7, −1), and *L* (6, −6). Translate the parallelogram 7 units up to form parallelogram *H′ J′ K′ L′*.

14. The vertices of trapezoid *MNPQ* are *M* (−6, −5), *N* (0, −5), *P* (−1, 2), and *Q* (−4, 2). Translate the trapezoid 4 units to the right to form trapezoid *M′ N′ P′ Q′*.

15. The vertices of triangle *RST* are *R* (0, 3), *S* (2, 7), and *T* (3, −1). Translate the triangle 5 units to the left and 3 units up to form triangle *R′ S′ T′*.

16. The vertices of quadrilateral *WXYZ* are *W* (−10, 8), *X* (−2, −1), *Y* (0, 0), and *Z* (3, 7). Translate the quadrilateral 5 units to the right and 8 units down to form quadrilateral *W′ X′ Y′ Z′*.

Determine the coordinates of each rotated image without graphing.

17. The vertices of triangle *ABC* are *A* (5, 3), *B* (2, 8), and *C* (−4, 5). Rotate the triangle about the origin 90° counterclockwise to form triangle *A′ B′ C′*.

    The vertices of triangle *A′ B′ C′* are *A′* (−3, 5), *B′* (−8, 2), and *C′* (−5, −4).

18. The vertices of rectangle *DEFG* are *D* (−7, 1), *E* (−7, 8), *F* (1, 8), and *G* (1, 1). Rotate the rectangle about the origin 180° counterclockwise to form rectangle *D′ E′ F′ G′*.

Name _____ Date _____

19. The vertices of parallelogram *HJKL* are *H* (2, −6), *J* (3, −1), *K* (7, −1), and *L* (6, −6). Rotate the parallelogram about the origin 90° counterclockwise to form parallelogram *H′ J′ K′ L′*.

20. The vertices of trapezoid *MNPQ* are *M* (−6, −5), *N* (0, −5), *P* (−1, 2), and *Q* (−4, 2). Rotate the trapezoid about the origin 180° counterclockwise to form trapezoid *M′ N′ P′ Q′*.

21. The vertices of triangle *RST* are *R* (0, 3), *S* (2, 7), and *T* (3, −1). Rotate the triangle about the origin 90° counterclockwise to form triangle *R′ S′ T′*.

22. The vertices of quadrilateral *WXYZ* are *W* (−10, 8), *X* (−2, −1), *Y* (0, 0), and *Z* (3, 7). Rotate the quadrilateral about the origin 180° counterclockwise to form quadrilateral *W′ X′ Y′ Z′*.

Determine the coordinates of each reflected image without graphing.

23. The vertices of triangle *ABC* are *A* (5, 3), *B* (2, 8), and *C* (−4, 5). Reflect the triangle over the *x*-axis to form triangle *A′ B′ C′*.

The vertices of triangle *A′ B′ C′* are *A′* (5, −3), *B′* (2, −8), and *C′* (−4, −5).

24. The vertices of rectangle *DEFG* are *D* (−7, 1), *E* (−7, 8), *F* (1, 8), and *G* (1, 1). Reflect the rectangle over the *y*-axis to form rectangle *D′ E′ F′ G′*.

25. The vertices of parallelogram *HJKL* are *H* (2, −6), *J* (3, −1), *K* (7, −1), and *L* (6, −6). Reflect the parallelogram over the *x*-axis to form parallelogram *H′ J′ K′ L′*.

26. The vertices of trapezoid *MNPQ* are *M* (−6, −5), *N* (0, −5), P (−1, 2), and *Q* (−4, 2). Reflect the trapezoid over the *y*-axis to form trapezoid *M′ N′ P′ Q′*.

5

27. The vertices of triangle *RST* are *R* (0, 3), *S* (2, 7), and *T* (3, −1). Reflect the triangle over the *x*-axis to form triangle *R′ S′ T′*.

28. The vertices of quadrilateral *WXYZ* are *W* (−10, 8), *X* (−2, −1), *Y* (0, 0), and *Z* (3, 7). Reflect the quadrilateral over the *y*-axis to form quadrilateral *W′ X′ Y′ Z′*.

5

Name _____ Date _____

Hey, Haven't I Seen You Before?
Congruent Triangles

Problem Set

Identify the transformation used to create △XYZ on each coordinate plane. Identify the congruent angles and the congruent sides. Then, write a triangle congruence statement.

1.

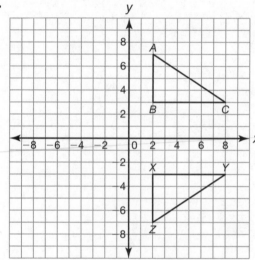

Triangle *BCA* was reflected over the *x*-axis to create triangle *XYZ*.

$BC \cong \overline{XY}$, $\overline{CA} \cong \overline{YZ}$, and $\overline{BA} \cong \overline{XZ}$; $\angle B \cong \angle X$, $\angle C \cong \angle Y$, and $\angle A \cong \angle Z$.

$\triangle BCA \cong \triangle XYZ$

2.

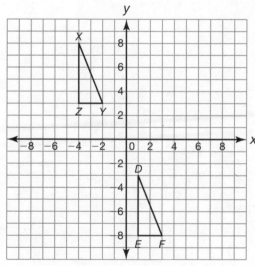

3.

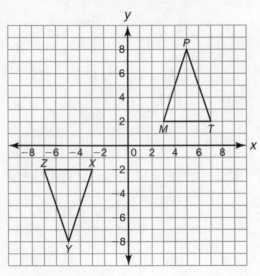

4.

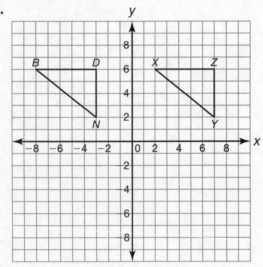

Name _____ Date _____

5.

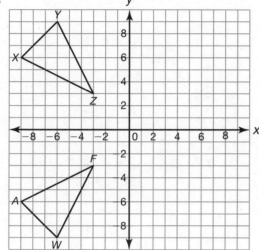

6.

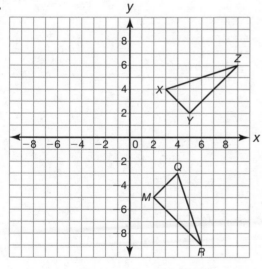

7.

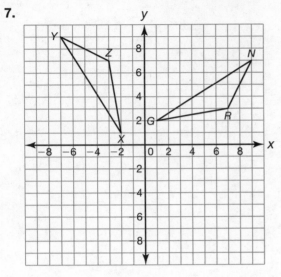

8.

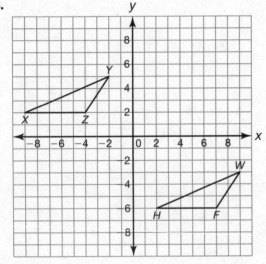

Name _____ Date _____

9.

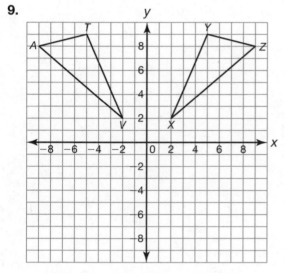

10.

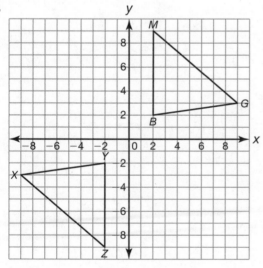

List the corresponding sides and angles, using congruence symbols, for each pair of triangles represented by the given congruence statement.

11. $\triangle JPM \cong \triangle TRW$

$\overline{JP} \cong \overline{TR}, \overline{PM} \cong \overline{RW}$, and $\overline{JM} \cong \overline{TW}$; $\angle J \cong \angle T, \angle P \cong \angle R$, and $\angle M \cong \angle W$.

12. $\triangle AEU \cong \triangle BCD$

13. $\triangle LUV \cong \triangle MTH$

14. $\triangle RWB \cong \triangle VCQ$

15. $\triangle TOM \cong \triangle BEN$

16. $\triangle JKL \cong \triangle RST$

17. $\triangle CAT \cong \triangle SUP$

18. $\triangle TOP \cong \triangle GUN$

Name _____ Date _____

It's All About the Sides
Side-Side-Side Congruence Theorem

Vocabulary

Define the term in your own words.

1. Side-Side-Side (SSS) Congruence Theorem

Problem Set

Determine whether each pair of given triangles are congruent by SSS. Use the Distance Formula and a protractor when necessary.

1.

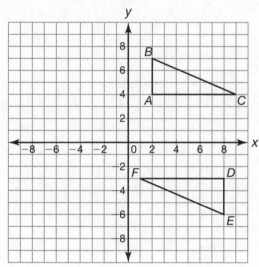

$AB = DE = 3$

$AC = DF = 7$

$d = \sqrt{(x_2 - x_1)^2 + (y_2 - y_1)^2}$

$BC = \sqrt{(9 - 2)^2 + (4 - 7)^2}$

$BC = \sqrt{7^2 + (-3)^2}$

$BC = \sqrt{49 + 9}$

$BC = \sqrt{58} \approx 7.62$

$d = \sqrt{(x_2 - x_1)^2 + (y_2 - y_1)^2}$

$EF = \sqrt{(1 - 8)^2 + (-3 - (-6))^2}$

$EF = \sqrt{(-7)^2 + 3^2}$

$EF = \sqrt{49 + 9}$

$EF = \sqrt{58} \approx 7.62$

$BC = EF$

The triangles are congruent by the SSS Congruence Theorem.

5

2.

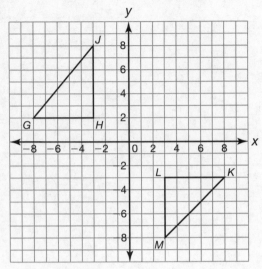

Name _____ Date _____

3.

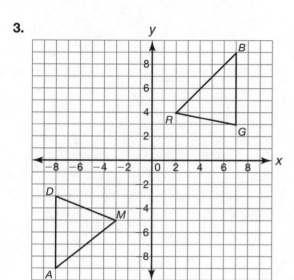

4.

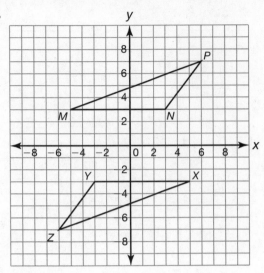

Name _____ Date _____

5.

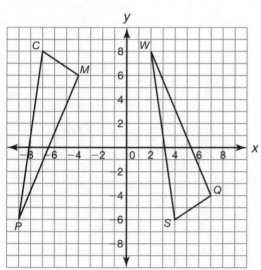

6.

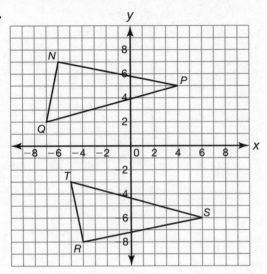

Name _____ Date _____

Perform the transformation described on each given triangle. Then, verify that the triangles are congruent by SSS. Use the Distance Formula and a protractor when necessary.

7. Reflect $\triangle ABC$ over the *y*-axis to form $\triangle XYZ$. Verify that $\triangle ABC \cong \triangle XYZ$ by SSS.

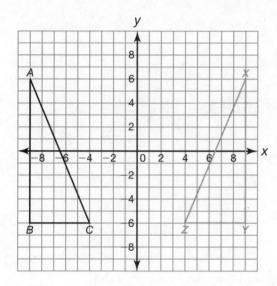

$AB = XY = 12$

$BC = YZ = 5$

$d = \sqrt{(x_2 - x_1)^2 + (y_2 - y_1)^2}$

$AC = \sqrt{(-4 - (-9))^2 + (-6 - 6)^2}$

$AC = \sqrt{5^2 + (-12)^2}$

$AC = \sqrt{25 + 144}$

$AC = \sqrt{169} = 13$

$d = \sqrt{(x_2 - x_1)^2 + (y_2 - y_1)^2}$

$XZ = \sqrt{(4 - 9)^2 + (-6 - 6)^2}$

$XZ = \sqrt{(-5)^2 + (-12)^2}$

$XZ = \sqrt{25 + 144}$

$XZ = \sqrt{169} = 13$

$AC = XZ$

The triangles are congruent by the SSS Congruence Theorem.

5

8. Rotate △*DEF* 180° clockwise about the origin to form △*QRS*. Verify that △*DEF* ≅ △*QRS* by SSS.

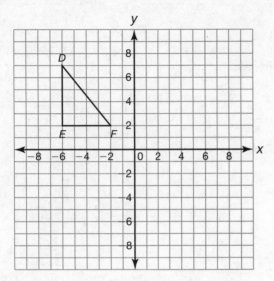

Name _____ Date _____

9. Reflect △*JKL* over the *x*-axis to form △*MNP*. Verify that △*JKL* ≅ △*MNP* by SSS.

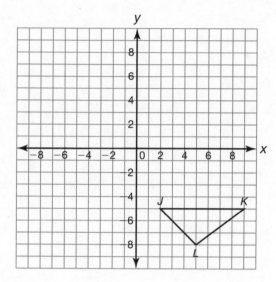

10. Translate △*HMZ* 10 units to the left and 1 unit down to form △*BNY*. Verify that △*HMZ* ≅ △*BNY* by SSS.

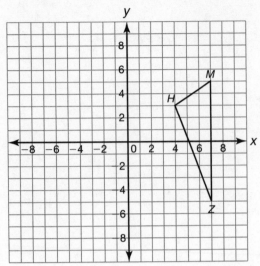

Name _____ Date _____

11. Rotate △*AFP* 90° counterclockwise about the origin to form △*DHW*. Verify that △*AFP* ≅ △*DHW* by SSS.

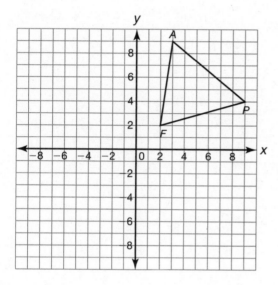

12. Translate △*ACE* 3 units to the right and 9 units up to form △*JKQ*. Verify that △*ACE* ≅ △*JKQ* by SSS.

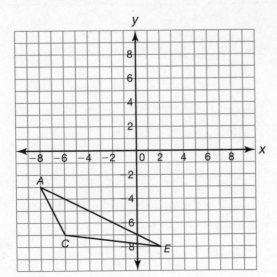

Name _____ Date _____

Make Sure the Angle Is Included
Side-Angle-Side Congruence Theorem

Vocabulary

Describe how to prove the given triangles are congruent. Use the *Side-Angle-Side Congruence Theorem* in your answer.

1.

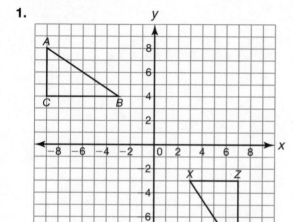

Problem Set

Determine whether each pair of given triangles are congruent by SAS. Use the Distance Formula and a protractor when necessary.

1. Determine whether $\triangle ABC$ is congruent to $\triangle DEF$ by SAS.

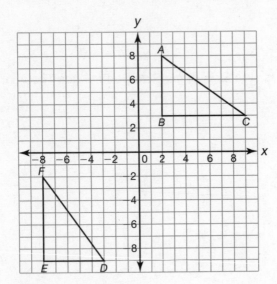

$AB = DE = 5$

$BC = EF = 7$

$m\angle B = m\angle E = 90°$

The triangles are congruent by the SAS Congruence Theorem.

2. Determine whether $\triangle CKY$ is congruent to $\triangle DLZ$ by SAS.

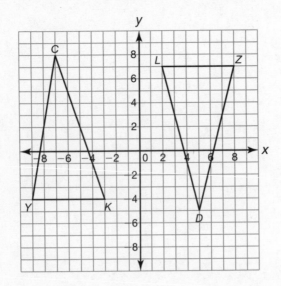

Name _____ Date _____

3. Determine whether △*FMR* is congruent to △*JQW* by SAS.

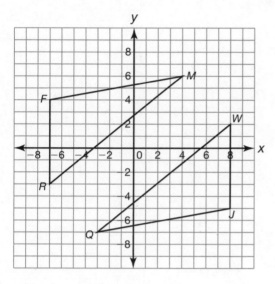

4. Determine whether △*QRS* is congruent to △*XYZ* by SAS.

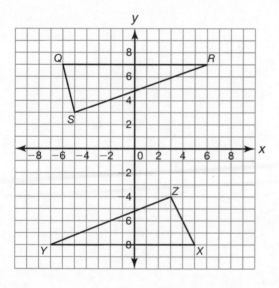

5. Determine whether △*JKL* is congruent to △*MNP* by SAS.

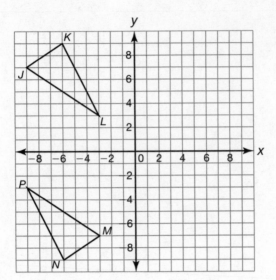

Name _____ Date _____

6. Determine whether △*ATV* is congruent to △*DNP* by SAS.

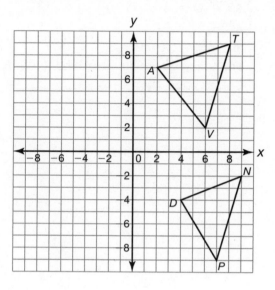

Perform the transformation described on each given triangle. Then, verify that the triangles are congruent by SAS. Use the Distance Formula and a protractor when necessary.

7. Reflect △ABC over the *y*-axis to form △XYZ. Verify that △ABC ≅ △XYZ by SAS.

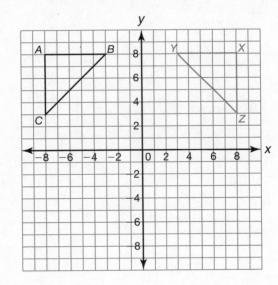

$AB = XY = 5$

$AC = XZ = 5$

$m\angle A = m\angle X = 90°$

The triangles are congruent by the SAS Congruence Theorem.

8. Translate △DEF 11 units to the left and 10 units down to form △QRS. Verify that △DEF ≅ △QRS by SAS.

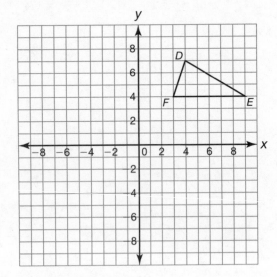

Name _____ Date _____

9. Rotate △*JKL* 180° counterclockwise about the origin to form △*MNP*. Verify that △*JKL* ≅ △*MNP* by SAS.

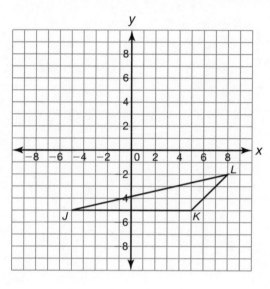

10. Reflect △*AFP* over the *y*-axis to form △*DHW*. Verify that △*AFP* ≅ △*DHW* by SAS.

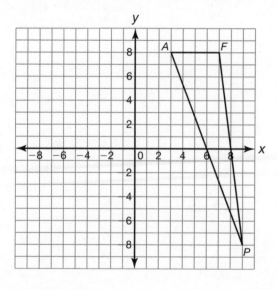

11. Translate $\triangle ACE$ 4 units to the right and 4 units down to form $\triangle JKQ$. Verify that $\triangle ACE \cong \triangle JKQ$ by SAS.

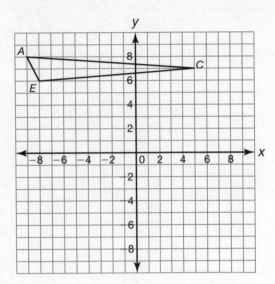

Name _____ Date _____

12. Rotate △*BMZ* 90° counterclockwise about the origin to form △*DRT.* Verify that △*BMZ* ≅ △*DRT* by SAS.

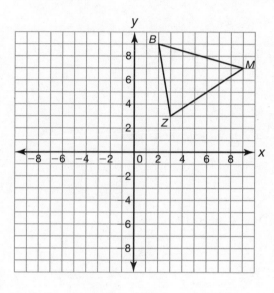

Determine the angle measure or side measure that is needed in order to prove that each set of triangles are congruent by SAS.

13. In $\triangle ART$, $AR = 12$, $RT = 8$, and $m\angle R = 70°$. In $\triangle BSW$, $BS = 12$, and $m\angle S = 70°$.

   SW = 8

14. In $\triangle CDE$, $CD = 7$, and $DE = 11$. In $\triangle FGH$, $FG = 7$, $GH = 11$, and $m\angle G = 45°$.

15. In $\triangle JKL$, $JK = 2$, $KL = 3$, and $m\angle K = 60°$. In $\triangle MNP$, $NP = 3$, and $m\angle N = 60°$.

16. In $\triangle QRS$, $QS = 6$, $RS = 4$, and $m\angle S = 20°$. In $\triangle TUV$, $TV = 6$, and $UV = 4$.

17.

18.

Name _____ Date _____

19.

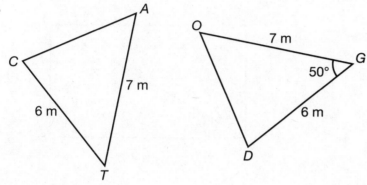

20.

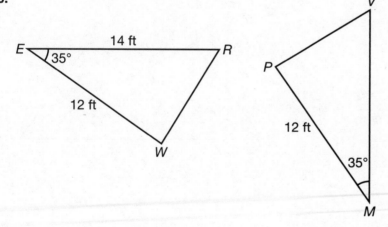

Determine whether there is enough information to prove that each pair of triangles are congruent by SSS or SAS. Write the congruence statements to justify your reasoning.

21. $\triangle MNP \overset{?}{\cong} \triangle PQM$

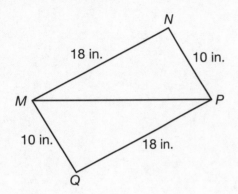

The triangles are congruent by SSS.

$\overline{MN} \cong \overline{PQ}$

$\overline{NP} \cong \overline{QM}$

$\overline{MP} \cong \overline{PM}$

22. $\triangle WXY \overset{?}{\cong} \triangle ZYX$

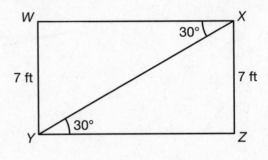

23. $\triangle BCE \overset{?}{\cong} \triangle DAF$

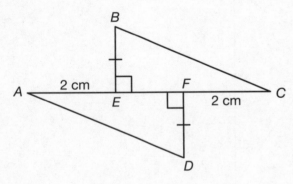

24. $\triangle HJM \overset{?}{\cong} \triangle MKH$

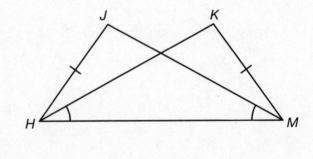

Name _____ Date _____

25. $\triangle PQR \overset{?}{\cong} \triangle STW$

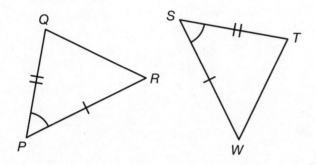

26. $\triangle MAT \overset{?}{\cong} \triangle MHT$

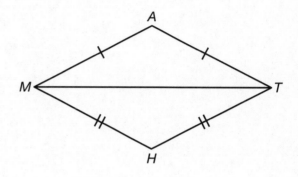

27. $\triangle BDW \overset{?}{\cong} \triangle BRN$

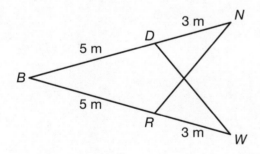

28. $\triangle ABC \overset{?}{\cong} \triangle EDC$

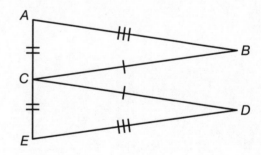

5

Name _____ Date _____

Angle to the Left of Me, Angle to the Right of Me
Angle-Side-Angle Congruence Theorem

Vocabulary

Describe how to prove the given triangles are congruent. Use the *Angle-Side-Angle Congruence Theorem* in your answer.

1.

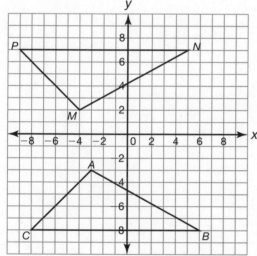

Problem Set

Determine whether each pair of given triangles are congruent by ASA. Use the Distance Formula and a protractor when necessary.

1. Determine whether △ABC is congruent to △DEF by ASA.

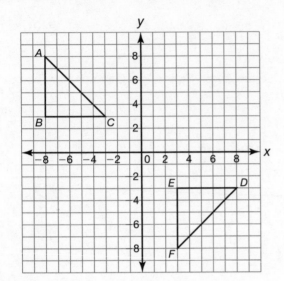

$m\angle B = m\angle E = 90°$

$m\angle C = m\angle F = 45°$

$BC = EF = 5$

The triangles are congruent by the ASA Congruence Theorem.

2. Determine whether △NPQ is congruent to △RST by ASA.

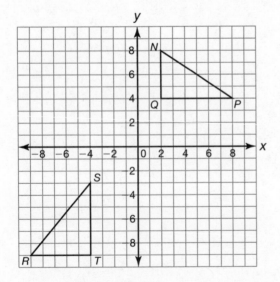

Name _____ Date _____

3. Determine whether △*AGP* is congruent to △*BHQ* by ASA.

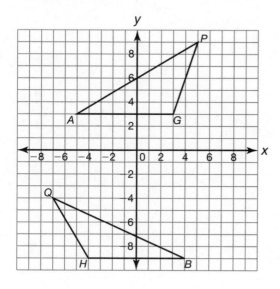

4. Determine whether △*CKY* is congruent to △*DLZ* by ASA.

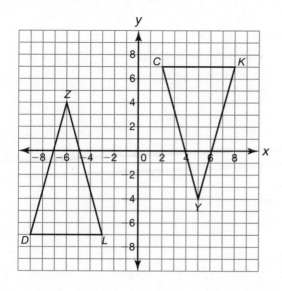

5. Determine whether △*FMR* is congruent to △*JQW* by ASA.

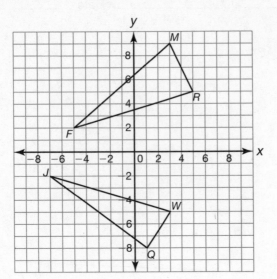

6. Determine whether △*GHJ* is congruent to △*KLM* by ASA.

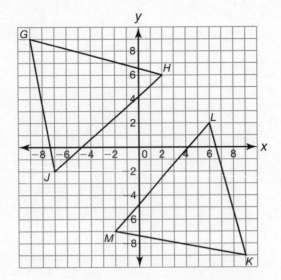

Name _____ Date _____

Perform the transformation described on each given triangle. Then, verify that the triangles are congruent by ASA. Use the Distance Formula and a protractor when necessary.

7. Reflect △ABC over the y-axis to form △XYZ. Verify that △ABC ≅ △XYZ by SAS.

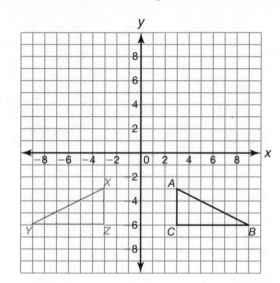

$m\angle C = m\angle Z = 90°$

$m\angle A = m\angle X = 63°$

$AC = XZ = 3$

The triangles are congruent by the ASA Congruence Theorem.

8. Rotate △DEF 90° clockwise about the origin to form △QRS. Verify that △DEF ≅ △QRS by SAS.

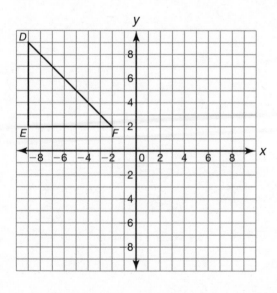

9. Translate △*HMZ* 6 units to the right and 10 units up to form △*BNY*. Verify that △*HMZ* ≅ △*BNY* by ASA.

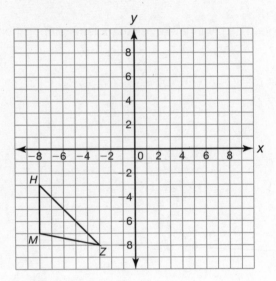

10. Reflect △*AFP* over the *y*-axis to form △*DHW*. Verify that △*AFP* ≅ △*DHW* by ASA.

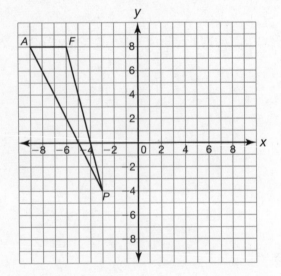

Name _____ Date _____

11. Rotate △*ACE* 180° counterclockwise about the origin to form △*JKQ*. Verify that △*ACE* ≅ △*JKQ* by SAS.

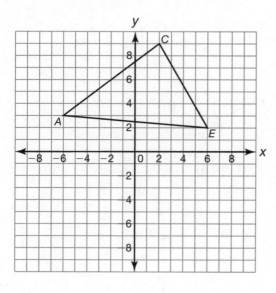

12. Reflect △*JKL* over the *x*-axis to form △*MNP*. Verify that △*JKL* ≅ △*MNP* by ASA.

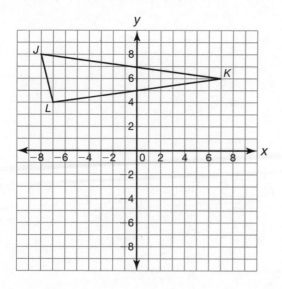

Determine the angle measure or side measure that is needed in order to prove that each set of triangles are congruent by ASA.

13. In $\triangle ADZ$, $m\angle A = 20°$, $AD = 9$, and $m\angle D = 70°$. In $\triangle BEN$, $BE = 9$, and $m\angle E = 70°$.

   $m\angle B = 20°$

14. In $\triangle CUP$, $m\angle U = 45°$, and $m\angle P = 55°$. In $\triangle HAT$, $AT = 14$, $m\angle A = 45°$, and $m\angle T = 55°$.

15. In $\triangle HOW$, $m\angle H = 10°$, $HW = 3$, and $m\angle W = 60°$. In $\triangle FAR$, $FR = 3$, and $m\angle F = 10°$.

16. In $\triangle DRY$, $m\angle D = 100°$, $DR = 25$, and $m\angle R = 30°$. In $\triangle WET$, $m\angle W = 100°$, and $m\angle E = 30°$.

17.

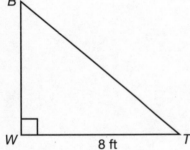

18.

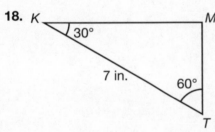
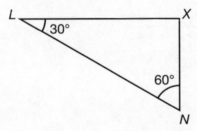

Name _____ Date _____

19.

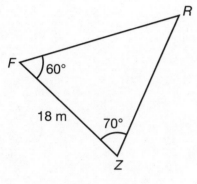

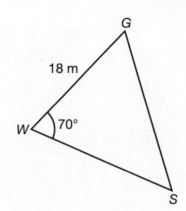

20.

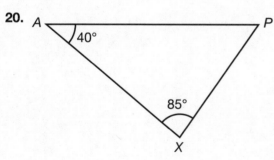

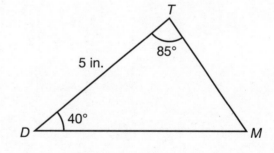

SSS
SAS
ASA
AAS
HL

5

Name _____ Date _____

Sides Not Included
Angle-Angle-Side Congruence Theorem

Vocabulary

Describe how to prove the given triangles are congruent. Use the *Angle-Angle-Side Congruence Theorem* in your answer.

1.

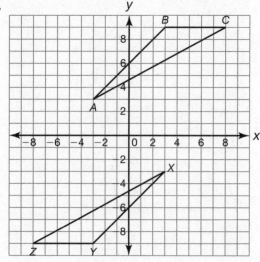

Problem Set

Determine whether each set of given triangles are congruent by AAS. Use the Distance Formula and a protractor when necessary.

1. Determine whether △*ABC* is congruent to △*DEF* by AAS.

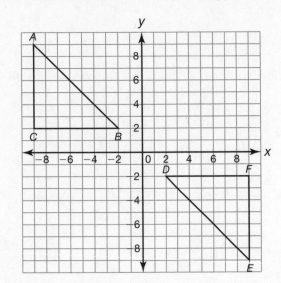

$m\angle A = m\angle D = 45°$

$m\angle B = m\angle E = 45°$

$BC = EF = 7$

The triangles are congruent by the AAS Congruence Theorem.

2. Determine whether △*GHJ* is congruent to △*KLM* by AAS.

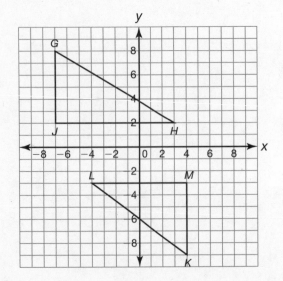

Name _____ Date _____

3. Determine whether △*AGP* is congruent to △*BHQ* by AAS.

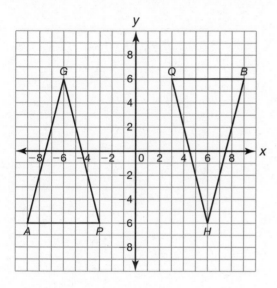

4. Determine whether △*CKY* is congruent to △*DLZ* by AAS.

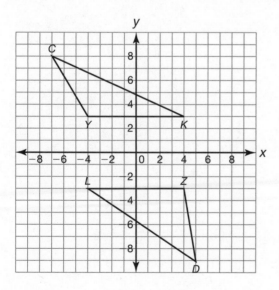

5. Determine whether △*FMR* is congruent to △*JQW* by AAS.

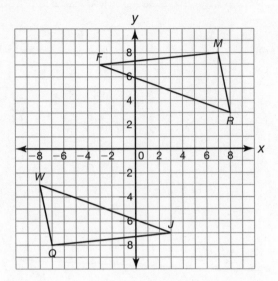

6. Determine whether △*NPQ* is congruent to △*RST* by AAS.

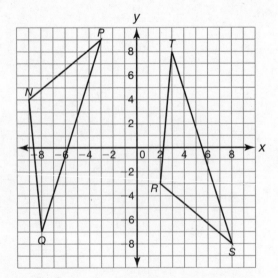

Name _____ Date _____

Perform the transformation described on each given triangle. Then, verify that the triangles are congruent by AAS. Use the Distance Formula and a protractor when necessary.

7. Reflect △*ABC* over the *y*-axis to form △*XYZ*. Verify that △*ABC* ≅ △*XYZ* by AAS.

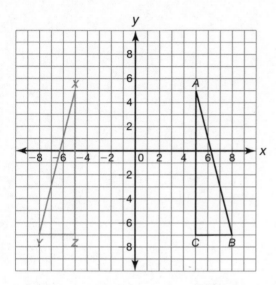

$m\angle B = m\angle Y = 76°$

$m\angle C = m\angle Z = 90°$

$AC = XZ = 12$

The triangles are congruent by the AAS Congruence Theorem.

8. Translate △*DEF* 11 units to the left and 11 units down to form △*QRS*. Verify that △*DEF* ≅ △*QRS* by AAS.

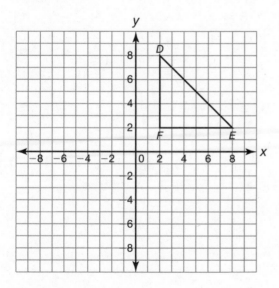

9. Rotate △JKL 180° counterclockwise about the origin to form △MNP. Verify that △JKL ≅ △MNP by AAS.

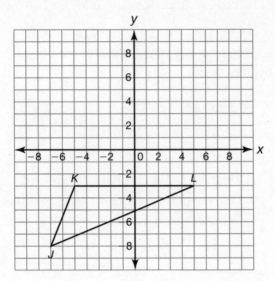

10. Translate △CUP 9 units to the left and 4 units up to form △JAR. Verify that △CUP ≅ △JAR by AAS.

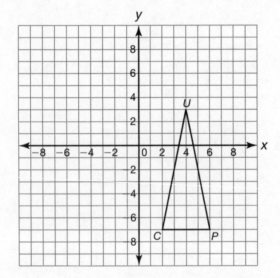

Name _____ Date _____

11. Reflect △*AFP* over the *x*-axis to form △*DHW*. Verify that △*AFP* ≅ △*DHW* by AAS.

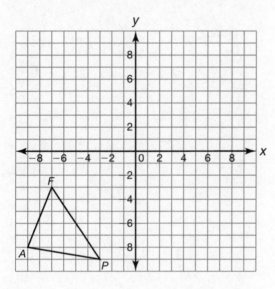

12. Rotate △ACE 270° counterclockwise about the origin to form △JKQ. Verify that △ACE ≅ △JKQ by AAS.

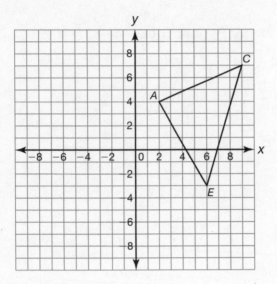

Determine the angle measure or side measure that is needed in order to prove that each set of triangles are congruent by AAS.

13. In △ANT, $m\angle A = 30°$, $m\angle N = 60°$, and $NT = 5$. In △BUG, $m\angle U = 60°$, and $UG = 5$.

   $m\angle B = 30°$

14. In △BCD, $m\angle B = 25°$, and $m\angle D = 105°$. In △RST, $RS = 12$, $m\angle R = 25°$, and $m\angle T = 105°$.

15. In △EMZ, $m\angle E = 40°$, $EZ = 7$, and $m\angle M = 70°$. In △DGP, $DP = 7$, and $m\angle D = 40°$.

16. In △BMX, $m\angle M = 90°$, $BM = 16$, and $m\angle X = 15°$. In △CNY, $m\angle N = 90°$, and $m\angle Y = 15°$.

Name _____ Date _____

17.

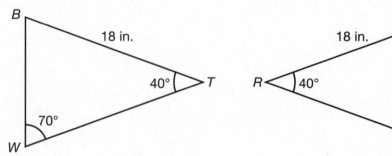

18.

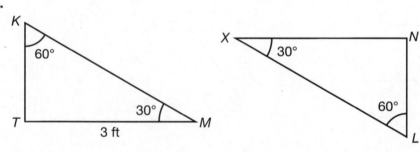

19.

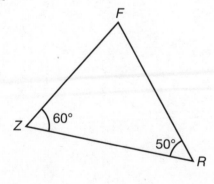

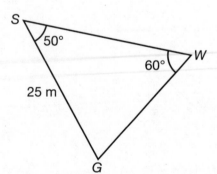

20.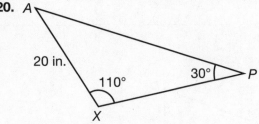

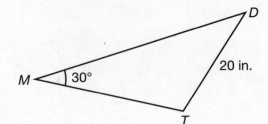

Determine whether there is enough information to prove that each pair of triangles are congruent by ASA or AAS. Write the congruence statements to justify your reasoning.

21. △ABD ≅ △CBD

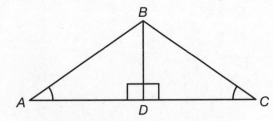

The triangles are congruent by AAS.

∠BAD ≅ ∠BCD

∠ADB ≅ ∠CDB

$\overline{BD} \cong \overline{BD}$

22. △EFG ≅ △HJK

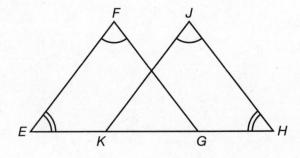

23. △MNQ ≅ △PQN

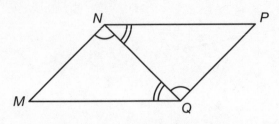

24. △RST ≅ △WZT

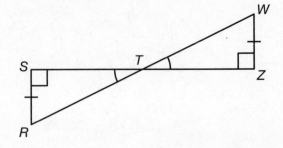

Name _____ Date _____

25. △BDM $\stackrel{?}{\cong}$ △MDH

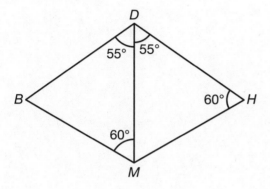

26. △FGH $\stackrel{?}{\cong}$ △JHG

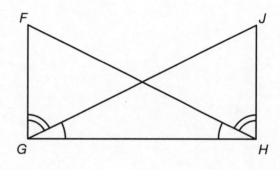

27. △DFG $\stackrel{?}{\cong}$ △JMT

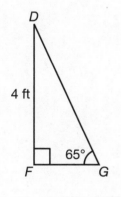
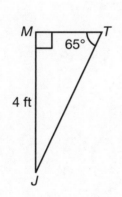

28. △RST $\stackrel{?}{\cong}$ △WXY

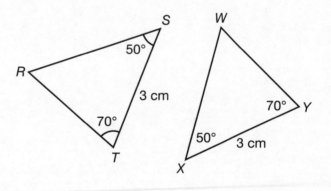

5

5

Name _____ Date _____

Any Other Theorems You Forgot to Mention?
Using Congruent Triangles

Problem Set

Construct a perpendicular bisector to each line segment. Connect points on the bisector on either side of the line segment to form the new line segment indicated.

1. $\overline{MN}$ bisected by $\overline{PR}$ at point Q

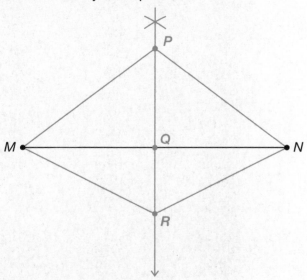

2. $\overline{HJ}$ bisected by $\overline{KM}$ at point L

3. $\overline{AB}$ bisected by $\overline{CE}$ at point D

4. $\overline{PQ}$ bisected by $\overline{RT}$ at point S

5. $\overline{FG}$ bisected by $\overline{HK}$ at point J

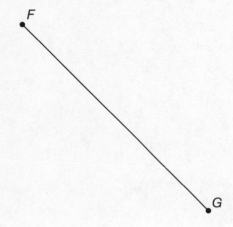

6. $\overline{ST}$ bisected by $\overline{UW}$ at point V

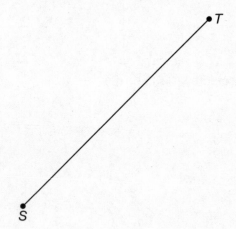

Name _____ Date _____

Use a triangle congruence theorem to complete each proof. Some of the statements and reasons are provided for you.

7. Given: $\overline{HK}$ is a perpendicular bisector of $\overline{FJ}$ at point J

   Prove: Point H is equidistant to points F and G

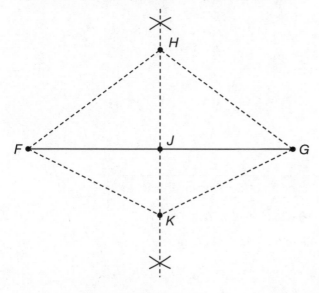

1. $\overline{FG} \perp \overline{HK}$, $\overline{HK}$ bisects $\overline{FG}$	1. Definition of perpendicular bisector
2. $\angle FJH$ and $\angle GJH$ are right angles.	2. Definition of perpendicular lines
3. $\angle FJH \cong \angle GJH$	3. All right angles are congruent.
4. $\overline{FJ} \cong \overline{GJ}$	4. Definition of bisect
5. $\overline{HJ} \cong \overline{HJ}$	5. Reflexive Property
6. $\triangle FJH \cong \triangle GJH$	6. SAS Congruence Theorem
7. $\overline{FH} \cong \overline{GH}$	7. Corresponding sides of congruent triangles are congruent
8. Point H is equidistant to points F and G	8. Definition of equidistant

8. Given: $\overline{PM}$ is a perpendicular bisector of $\overline{ST}$ at point N

Prove: Point M is equidistant to points S and T

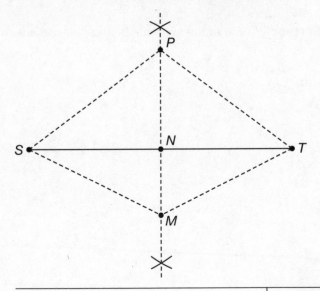

1.	**1.** Definition of perpendicular bisector
2.	**2.** Definition of perpendicular lines
3.	**3.** All right angles are congruent.
4.	**4.**
5.	**5.**
6.	**6.**
7.	**7.**
8. Point M is equidistant to points S and T	**8.** Definition of equidistant

Name _____ Date _____

9. Given: $\overline{CA}$ is a perpendicular bisector of $\overline{UW}$ at point B

Prove: Point C is equidistant to points U and W

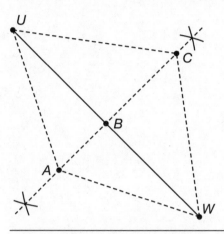

1. $\overline{UW} \perp \overline{CA}$, $\overline{CA}$ bisects $\overline{UW}$	1. Definition of perpendicular bisector
2.	2.
3.	3. All right angles are congruent.
4.	4. Definition of bisect
5.	5.
6.	6.
7.	7. Corresponding sides of congruent triangles are congruent
8.	8.

5

10. Given: $\overline{TK}$ is a perpendicular bisector of $\overline{LM}$ at point R

Prove: Point T is equidistant to points L and M

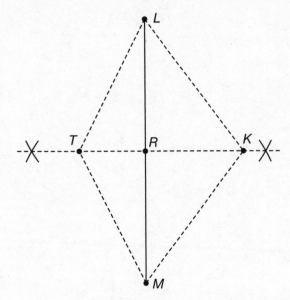

1.	1.
2.	2. Definition of perpendicular lines
3.	3. All right angles are congruent.
4.	4.
5. $\overline{TR} \cong \overline{TR}$	5. Reflexive Property
6.	6.
7.	7.
8.	8. Definition of equidistant

Name _____ Date _____

11. Given: $\overline{HT}$ is a perpendicular bisector of $\overline{UV}$ at point P

Prove: Point H is equidistant to points U and V

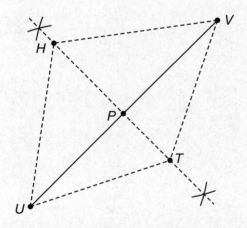

1.	**1.**
2. ∠UPH and ∠VPH are right angles.	**2.** Definition of perpendicular lines
3.	**3.**
4.	**4.** Definition of bisect
5.	**5.**
6.	**6.**
7.	**7.**
8.	**8.**

12. Given: $\overline{UW}$ is a perpendicular bisector of $\overline{CD}$ at point V

Prove: Point U is equidistant to points C and D

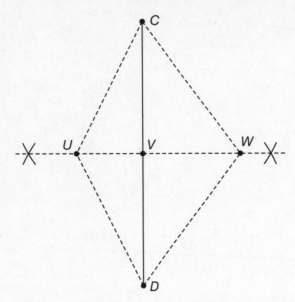

1.	**1.** Definition of perpendicular bisector
2.	**2.**
3. $\angle CVU \cong \angle DVU$	**3.** All right angles are congruent.
4.	**4.**
5.	**5.**
6.	**6.**
7.	**7.** Corresponding sides of congruent triangles are congruent
8.	**8.**

Name _____ Date _____

Complete each diagram to provide a counterexample that proves the indicated theorem does not work for congruent triangles. Explain your reasoning. A hint is provided in each case.

13. Angle-Angle-Angle (Hint: Use vertical angles.)

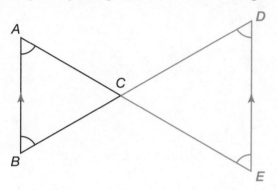

Extend $\overline{AC}$ and $\overline{BC}$, and connect points D and E so that $\overline{AB}$ is parallel to $\overline{DE}$. Since vertical angles are congruent, all three corresponding angles of the two triangles are congruent. The side lengths, however, are different, so $\triangle ABC$ is not congruent to $\triangle DEC$.

14. Side-Side-Angle (Hint: Draw a triangle that shares $\angle P$ with the given triangle.)

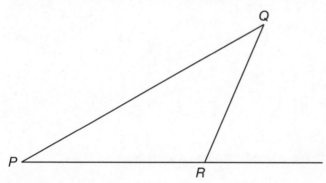

15. Angle-Angle-Angle (Hint: Draw a triangle that shares $\angle T$ with the given triangle.)

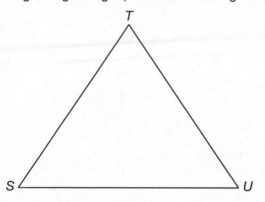

16. Side-Side-Angle (Hint: Draw a triangle that shares ∠L with the given triangle.)

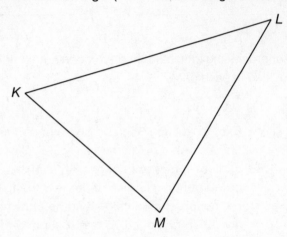

17. Angle-Angle-Angle (Hint: Draw a triangle that has an angle with the same measure as ∠E.)

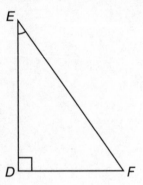

18. Side-Side-Angle (Hint: Draw a triangle that shares ∠U with the given triangle.)

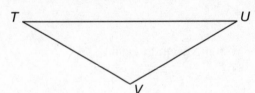

Name _____ Date _____

State the congruence theorem that proves the triangles in each diagram are congruent. If not enough information is given, name an example of information that could be given that you could use to prove congruency. Explain your reasoning.

19. Given: $\overline{VW} \cong \overline{XW}$

Prove: $\triangle VYW \cong \triangle XYW$

Not enough information is given.

If $\angle VWY \cong \angle XWY$ is given, then $\triangle VYW \cong \triangle XYW$ by the SAS Triangle Congruence Theorem.

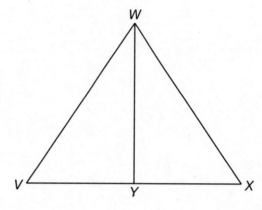

20. Given: $\overline{CE}$ is a perpendicular bisector of $\overline{FD}$

Prove: $\triangle FEC \cong \triangle DEC$

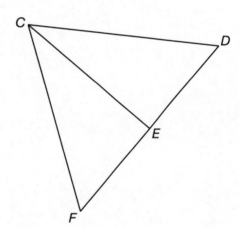

21. Given: $\angle WST \cong \angle VUT, \overline{ST} \cong \overline{UT}$

Prove: $\triangle WST \cong \triangle VUT$

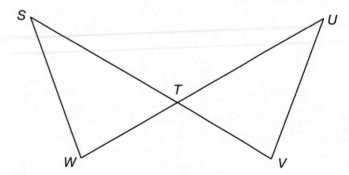

22. Given: △ABD is isosceles with $\overline{AB} \cong \overline{AD}$

Prove: △ABC ≅ △ADC

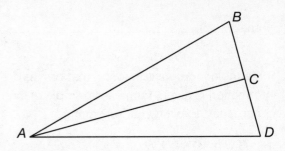

23. Given: $\overline{GH} \cong \overline{JK}, \overline{HJ} \cong \overline{KG}$

Prove: △GHK ≅ △JKH

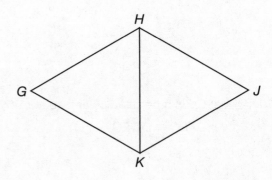

24. Given: $\overline{PT} \cong \overline{SR}$, ∠PQT ≅ ∠RQS

Prove: △TPQ ≅ △SRQ

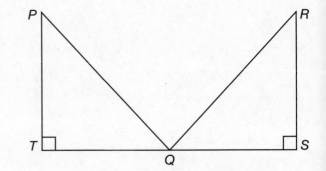

Name _____   Date _____

Time to Get Right
Right Triangle Congruence Theorems

Vocabulary

Choose the diagram that models each right triangle congruence theorem.

1. Hypotenuse-Leg (HL) Congruence Theorem

a.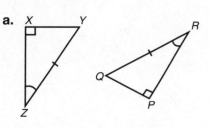

2. Leg-Leg (LL) Congruence Theorem

b.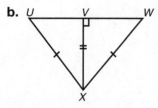

3. Hypotenuse-Angle (HA) Congruence Theorem

c.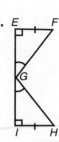

4. Leg-Angle (LA) Congruence Theorem

d.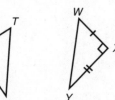

6

Problem Set

Mark the appropriate sides to make each congruence statement true by the Hypotenuse-Leg Congruence Theorem.

1. △DPR ≅ △QFM

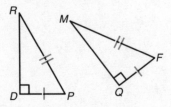

2. △ACI ≅ △GCE

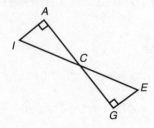

3. △QTR ≅ △SRT

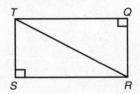

4. △ADG ≅ △HKN

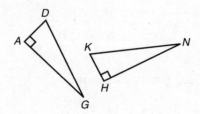

Mark the appropriate sides to make each congruence statement true by the Leg-Leg Congruence Theorem.

5. △BZN ≅ △TGC

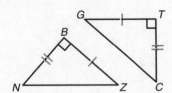

6. △MNO ≅ △QPO

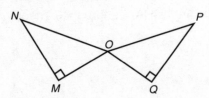

7. △PZT ≅ △PZX

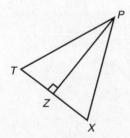

8. △EGI ≅ △ONQ

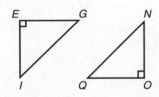

Name _____ Date _____

Mark the appropriate sides and angles to make each congruence statement true by the Hypotenuse-Angle Congruence Theorem.

9. △SVM ≅ △JFW

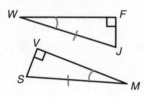

10. △MSN ≅ △QRT

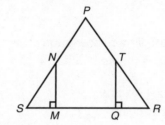

11. △IEG ≅ △IEK

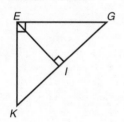

12. △DCB ≅ △ZYX

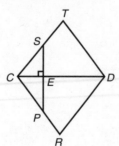

Mark the appropriate sides and angles to make each congruence statement true by the Leg-Angle Congruence Theorem.

13. △XTD ≅ △HPR

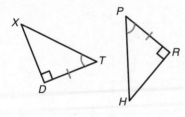

14. △SEC ≅ △PEC

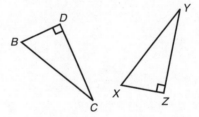

6

15. △PBJ ≅ △OTN

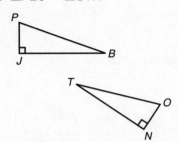

16. △AXT ≅ △YBU

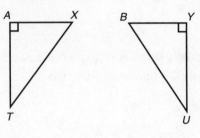

For each figure, determine if there is enough information to prove that the two triangles are congruent. If so, name the congruence theorem used.

17. Given: $\overline{GF}$ bisects ∠RGS, and ∠R and ∠S are right angles.

Is △FRG ≅ △FSG?

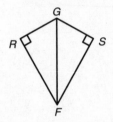

Yes. There is enough information to conclude that △FRG ≅ △FSG by HA.

18. Given: $\overline{DV} \perp \overline{TU}$

Is △DVT ≅ △DVU?

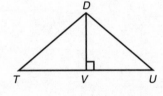

19. Given: $\overline{NM} \cong \overline{EM}$, $\overline{DM} \cong \overline{OM}$, and ∠NMD and ∠EMO are right angles.

Is △NMD ≅ △EMO?

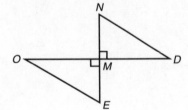

20. Given: $\overline{RP} \cong \overline{QS}$, and ∠R and ∠Q are right angles.

Is △SRP ≅ △PQS?

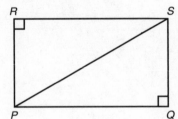

Name _____ Date _____

21. Given: $\overline{GO} \cong \overline{MI}$, and $\angle E$ and $\angle K$ are right angles.

Is $\triangle GEO \cong \triangle MKI$?

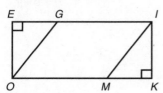

22. Given: $\overline{HM} \cong \overline{VM}$, and $\angle H$ and $\angle V$ are right angles.

Is $\triangle GHM \cong \triangle UVM$?

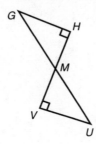

Use the given information to answer each question.

23. Two friends are meeting at the library. Maria leaves her house and walks north on Elm Street and then east on Main Street to reach the library. Paula leaves her house and walks south on Park Avenue and then west on Main Street to reach the library. Maria walks the same distance on Elm Street as Paula walks on Main Street, and she walks the same distance on Main Street as Paula walks on Park Avenue. Is there enough information to determine whether Maria's walking distance is the same as Paula's walking distance?

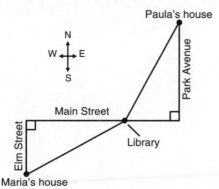

Yes. Maria's walking distance to the library is equal to Paula's walking distance. The triangles formed are right triangles. The corresponding legs of the triangles are congruent. So, by the Leg-Leg Congruence Theorem, the triangles are congruent. If the triangles are congruent, the hypotenuses are congruent.

6

24. An auto dealership displays one of their cars by driving it up a ramp onto a display platform. Later they will drive the car off the platform using a ramp on the opposite side. Both ramps form a right triangle with the ground and the platform. Is there enough information to determine whether the two ramps have the same length? Explain.

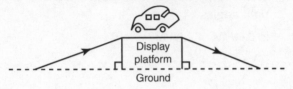

25. A radio station erected a new transmission antenna to provide its listeners with better reception. The antenna was built perpendicular to the ground, and to keep the antenna from swaying in the wind two guy wires were attached from it to the ground on opposite sides of the antenna. Is there enough information to determine if the guy wires have the same length? Explain.

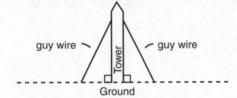

Name _____ Date _____

26. Two ladders resting on level ground are leaning against the side of a house. The bottom of each
ladder is exactly 2.5 feet directly out from the base of the house. The point at which each ladder rests
against the house is 10 feet directly above the base of the house. Is there enough information to
determine whether the two ladders have the same length? Explain.

Create a two-column proof to prove each statement.

27. Given: $\overline{WZ}$ bisects $\overline{VY}$, $\overline{WV} \perp \overline{VY}$, and $\overline{YZ} \perp \overline{VY}$
Prove: $\triangle WVX \cong \triangle ZYX$

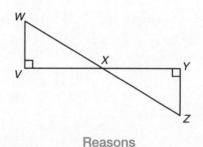

Statements	Reasons
1. $\overline{WV} \perp \overline{VY}$ and $\overline{YZ} \perp \overline{VY}$	1. Given
2. $\angle WVX$ and $\angle ZYX$ are right angles.	2. Definition of perpendicular angles
3. $\triangle WVX$ and $\triangle ZYX$ are right triangles.	3. Definition of right triangles
4. $\overline{WZ}$ bisects $\overline{VY}$.	4. Given
5. $\overline{VX} \cong \overline{YX}$	5. Definition of segment bisector
6. $\angle WXV \cong \angle ZXY$	6. Vertical Angle Theorem
7. $\triangle WVX \cong \triangle ZYX$	7. LA Congruence Theorem

6

28. Given: Point *D* is the midpoint of $\overline{EC}$,
   $\triangle ADB$ is an isosceles triangle with base
   $\overline{AB}$, and $\angle E$ and $\angle C$ are right angles.

   Prove: $\triangle AED \cong \triangle BCD$

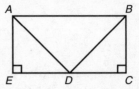

29. Given: $\overline{SU} \perp \overline{UP}, \overline{TP} \perp \overline{UP}$, and $\overline{UR} \cong \overline{PR}$

   Prove: $\triangle SUR \cong \triangle TPR$

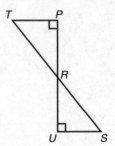

Name _____ Date _____

30. Given: Rectangle *MNWX* and ∠*NMW* ≅ ∠*XWM*

   Prove: △*MNW* ≅ △*WXM*

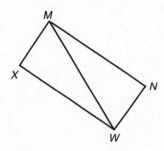

6

Name _____ Date _____

CPCTC
Corresponding Parts of Congruent Triangles are Congruent

Vocabulary

Provide an example to illustrate each term.

1. Corresponding parts of congruent triangles are congruent (CPCTC)

2. Isosceles Triangle Base Angle Theorem

3. Isosceles Triangle Base Angle Converse Theorem

Problem Set

Create a two-column proof to prove each statement.

1. Given: $\overline{RS}$ is the ⊥ bisector of $\overline{PQ}$.

Prove: ∠SPT ≅ ∠SQT

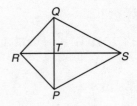

Statements	Reasons
1. $\overline{RS}$ is the ⊥ bisector of $\overline{PQ}$.	1. Given
2. $\overline{RS} \perp \overline{PQ}$	2. Definition of perpendicular bisector
3. ∠PTS and ∠QTS are right angles.	3. Definition of perpendicular lines
4. △PTS and △QTS are right triangles.	4. Definition of right triangles
5. $\overline{RS}$ bisects $\overline{PQ}$	5. Definition of perpendicular bisector
6. $\overline{PT} \cong \overline{QT}$	6. Definition of bisect
7. $\overline{TS} \cong \overline{TS}$	7. Reflexive Property of ≅
8. △PTS ≅ △QTS	8. Leg-Leg Congruence Theorem
9. ∠SPT ≅ ∠SQT	9. CPCTC

2. Given: $\overline{TZ} \cong \overline{WX}$, $\overline{TM} \cong \overline{WT}$, and $\overline{TZ} \parallel \overline{WX}$

Prove: $\overline{MZ} \cong \overline{TX}$

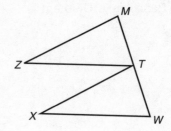

Name _____ Date _____

3. Given: $\overline{AG}$ and $\overline{EK}$ intersect at C,
   $\overline{AC} \cong \overline{EC}, \overline{CK} \cong \overline{CG}$

   Prove: $\angle K \cong \angle G$

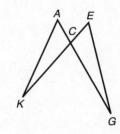

4. Given: $\angle JHK \cong \angle LHK$, $\angle JKH \cong \angle LKH$
   Prove: $\overline{JK} \cong \overline{LK}$

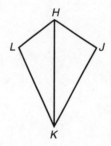

5. Given: △UGT ≅ △SGB

Prove: ∠TUS ≅ ∠BSU

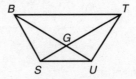

6. Given: ∠TPN ≅ ∠TNP, $\overline{TP} \cong \overline{QP}$

Prove: $\overline{TN} \cong \overline{QP}$

Name _____ Date _____

7. Given: $\overline{AC} \perp \overline{DB}, \overline{AC}$ bisects $\overline{DB}$

   Prove: $\overline{AD} \cong \overline{AB}$

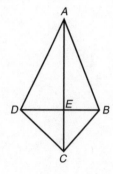

8. Given: $\angle KGH \cong \angle KHG, \overline{FG} \cong \overline{JH}, \overline{FK} \cong \overline{JK}$

   Prove: $\angle F \cong \angle J$

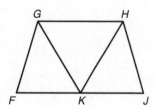

9. Given: $\overline{AT} \cong \overline{AQ}$, $\overline{AC}$ bisects $\angle TAQ$

Prove: $\overline{AC}$ bisects $\overline{TQ}$

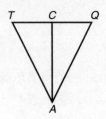

10. Given: $\overline{EL} \cong \overline{EI}$, $\angle LNJ \cong IGJ$, J is the midpoint of $\overline{LI}$

Prove: $\overline{NJ} \cong \overline{GJ}$

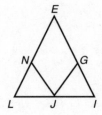

Name _____ Date _____

11. Given: $\angle E \cong \angle EUV$, $\angle F \cong \angle FVU$

Prove: $\overline{UF} \cong \overline{VE}$

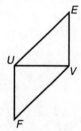

12. Given: $\overline{CT} \cong \overline{CP}$, $\overline{AT} \cong \overline{AP}$

Prove: $m\angle CTA = m\angle CPA$

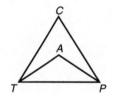

Use the given information to answer each question.

13. Samantha is hiking through the forest and she comes upon a canyon. She wants to know how wide the canyon is. She measures the distance between points A and B to be 35 feet. Then, she measures the distance between points B and C to be 35 feet. Finally, she measures the distance between points C and D to be 80 feet. How wide is the canyon? Explain.

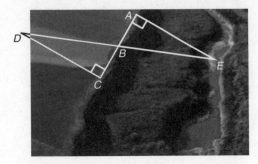

The canyon is 80 feet wide.

The triangles are congruent by the Leg-Angle Congruence Theorem. Corresponding parts of congruent triangles are congruent, so $\overline{CD} = \overline{AE}$.

14. Explain why $m\angle NMO = 20°$.

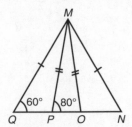

15. Calculate MR given that the perimeter of $\triangle HMR$ is 60 centimeters.

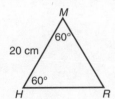

Name _____ Date _____

16. Greta has a summer home on Lake Winnie. Using the diagram, how wide is Lake Winnie?

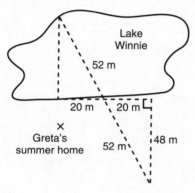

17. Jill is building a livestock pen in the shape of a triangle. She is using one side of a barn for one of the sides of her pen and has already placed posts in the ground at points *A*, *B*, and *C*, as shown in the diagram. If she places fence posts every 10 feet, how many more posts does she need? Note: There will be no other posts placed along the barn wall.

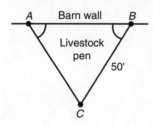

18. Given rectangle *ACDE*, calculate the measure of ∠*CDB*.

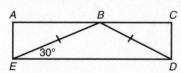

6

Name _____ Date _____

Congruence Theorems in Action
Isosceles Triangle Theorems

Vocabulary

Choose the term from the box that best completes each sentence.

Isosceles Triangle Altitude to Congruent Sides Theorem	Isosceles Triangle Base Theorem
	vertex angle
Isosceles Triangle Vertex Angle Theorem	Isosceles Triangle Angle Bisector to Congruent
Isosceles Triangle Perpendicular Bisector Theorem	Sides Theorem

1. A(n) _____ is the angle formed by the
   two congruent legs in an isosceles triangle.

2. In an isosceles triangle, the altitudes to the congruent sides are congruent,
   as stated in the _____.

3. In an isosceles triangle, the angle bisectors to the congruent sides are congruent, as stated in the
   _____.

4. The _____ states that the altitude
   from the vertex angle of an isosceles triangle is the perpendicular bisector of the base.

5. The _____ states that the altitude to
   the base of an isosceles triangle bisects the base.

6. The altitude to the base of an isosceles triangle bisects the vertex angle, as stated in the
   _____.

Problem Set

Write the theorem that justifies the truth of each statement.

1. In isosceles $\triangle MRG$, $\overline{RD} \cong \overline{GC}$.

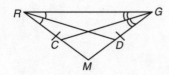

Isosceles Triangle Angle Bisector
to Congruent Sides Theorem

2. In isosceles $\triangle TGC$ with altitude $\overline{TP}$, $\overline{TP} \perp \overline{GC}$, and $\overline{GP} \cong \overline{CP}$.

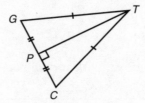

3. In isosceles $\triangle BRU$ with altitude $\overline{BD}$, $\overline{UD} \cong \overline{RD}$.

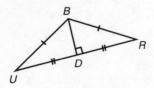

4. In isosceles $\triangle JFI$ with altitude $\overline{JH}$, $\angle HJF \cong \angle HJI$.

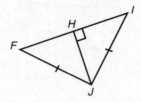

5. In isosceles $\triangle MNO$, $\overline{OA} \cong NB$.

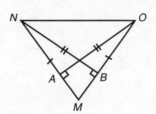

6. In isosceles $\triangle HJK$, $\overline{KN}$ bisects $\angle HKJ$, $\overline{JM}$ bisects $\angle HJK$, and $\overline{MJ} \cong \overline{NK}$.

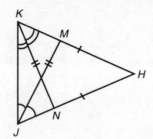

Name _____ Date _____

Determine the value of *x* in each isosceles triangle.

7.

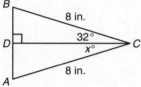

x = 32°

8.

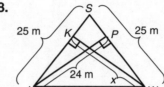

9.

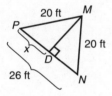

10.

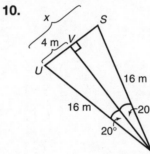

11.

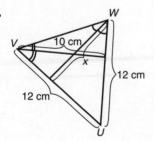

12.

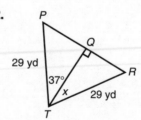

Complete each two-column proof.

13. Given: Isosceles $\triangle ABC$ with $\overline{AB} \cong \overline{CB}$, $\overline{BD} \perp \overline{AC}, \overline{DE} \perp \overline{AB}$, and $\overline{DF} \perp \overline{CB}$

Prove: $\overline{ED} \cong \overline{FD}$

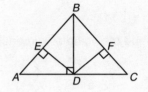

Statements	Reasons
1. $\overline{AB} \cong \overline{CB}$	1. Given
2. $\overline{BD} \perp \overline{AC}, \overline{DE} \perp \overline{AB}, \overline{DF} \perp \overline{CB}$	2. Given
3. $\angle AED$ and $\angle CFD$ are right angles.	3. Definition of perpendicular lines
4. $\triangle AED$ and $\triangle CFD$ are right triangles.	4. Definition of right triangle
5. $\angle A \cong \angle C$	5. Base Angle Theorem
6. $\overline{AD} \cong \overline{CD}$	6. Isosceles Triangle Base Theorem
7. $\triangle AED \cong \triangle CFD$	7. HA Congruence Theorem
8. $\overline{ED} \cong \overline{FD}$	8. CPCTC

Name _____ Date _____

14. Given: Isosceles $\triangle MNB$ with $\overline{MN} \cong \overline{MB}$,
$\overline{NO}$ bisects $\angle ANB$, $\overline{BA}$ bisects $\angle OBN$

Prove: $\triangle BAN \cong \triangle NOB$

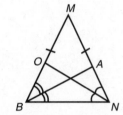

15. Given: Isosceles $\triangle IAE$ with $\overline{IA} \cong \overline{IE}$, $\overline{AG} \perp \overline{IE}$, $\overline{EK} \perp \overline{IA}$

Prove: $\triangle IGA \cong \triangle IKE$

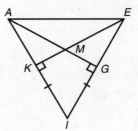

16. Given: Isosceles $\triangle GQR$ with $\overline{GR} \cong \overline{GQ}$,
Isosceles $\triangle QGH$ with $\overline{GQ} \cong \overline{QH}$,
$\overline{GJ} \perp \overline{QR}$, $\overline{QP} \perp \overline{GH}$, and $\overline{GJ} \parallel \overline{QP}$

Prove: $\overline{RJ} \cong \overline{HP}$

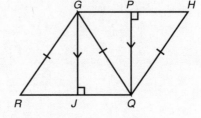

Name _____ Date _____

Use the given information to answer each question.

17. The front of an A-frame house is in the shape of an isosceles triangle, as shown in the diagram. In the diagram, $\overline{HK} \perp \overline{GJ}$, $\overline{GH} \cong \overline{JH}$, and $m\angle HGJ = 68.5°$. Use this information to determine the measure of $\angle GHJ$. Explain.

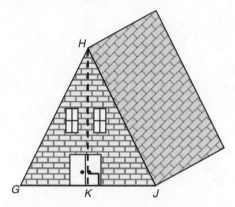

The measure of $\angle GHJ$ is 43°.

By the Triangle Sum Theorem, $m\angle GHK = 180° - (90° + 68.5°) = 21.5°$.

By the Isosceles Triangle Vertex Angle Theorem, $m\angle GHK = m\angle JHK$.
Therefore, $m\angle GHJ = 21.5° + 21.5° = 43°$.

18. When building a house, rafters are used to support the roof. The rafter shown in the diagram has the shape of an isosceles triangle. In the diagram, $\overline{NP} \perp \overline{RQ}$, $\overline{NR} \cong \overline{NQ}$, $NP = 12$ feet, and $RP = 16$ feet. Use this information to determine the length of $\overline{NQ}$. Explain.

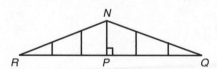

19. Stained glass windows are constructed using different pieces of colored glass held together by lead. The stained glass window in the diagram is rectangular with six different colored glass pieces represented by △TBS, △PBS, △PBQ, △QBR, △NBR, and △NBT. Triangle *TBP* with altitude $\overline{SB}$ and △QBN with altitude $\overline{RB}$, are congruent isosceles triangles. If the measure of ∠NBR is 20°, what is the measure of ∠STB? Explain.

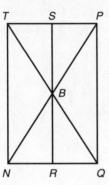

20. While growing up, Nikki often camped out in her back yard in a pup tent. A pup tent has two rectangular sides made of canvas, and a front and back in the shape of two isosceles triangles also made of canvas. The zipper in front, represented by $\overline{MG}$ in the diagram, is the height of the pup tent and the altitude of isosceles △EMH. If the length of $\overline{EG}$ is 2.5 feet, what is the length of $\overline{HG}$? Explain.

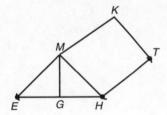

6

Name _____ Date _____

21. A beaded purse is in the shape of an isosceles triangle. In the diagram, $\overline{TN} \cong \overline{TV}$, $\overline{VM} \perp \overline{TN}$, and $\overline{NU} \perp \overline{TV}$. How long is the line of beads represented by $\overline{NU}$, if TV is 13 inches and TM is 5 inches? Explain.

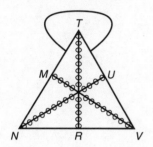

22. A kaleidoscope is a cylinder with mirrors inside and an assortment of loose colored beads. When a person looks through the kaleidoscope, different colored shapes and patterns are created as the kaleidoscope is rotated. Suppose that the diagram represents the shapes that a person sees when they look into the kaleidoscope. Triangle *AEI* is an isosceles triangle with $\overline{AE} \cong \overline{AI}$. $\overline{EK}$ bisects $\angle AEI$ and $\overline{IC}$ bisects $\angle AIE$. What is the length of $\overline{IC}$, if one half the length of $\overline{EK}$ is 14 centimeters? Explain.

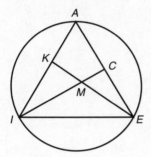

Name _____ Date _____

Making Some Assumptions
Inverse, Contrapositive, Direct Proof, and Indirect Proof

Vocabulary

Define each term in your own words.

1. inverse

2. contrapositive

3. direct proof

4. indirect proof (or proof by contradiction)

5. Hinge Theorem

6. Hinge Converse Theorem

Problem Set

Write the converse of each conditional statement. Then, determine whether the converse is true.

1. If two lines do not intersect and are not parallel, then they are skew lines.

   The converse of the conditional would be:

   If two lines are skew lines, then they do not intersect and are not parallel.

   The converse is true.

2. If two lines are coplanar and do not intersect, then they are parallel lines.

3. If a triangle has one angle whose measure is greater than 90°, then the triangle is obtuse.

4. If a triangle has two sides with equal lengths, then it is an isosceles triangle.

5. If the lengths of the sides of a triangle measure 5 mm, 12 mm, and 13 mm, then it is a right triangle.

Name _____ Date _____

6. If the lengths of the sides of a triangle are 3 cm, 4 cm, and 5 cm, then the triangle is a right triangle.

7. If the corresponding sides of two triangles are congruent, then the triangles are congruent.

8. If the corresponding angles of two triangles are congruent, then the triangles are similar.

Write the inverse of each conditional statement. Then, determine whether the inverse is true.

9. If a triangle is an equilateral triangle, then it is an isosceles triangle.

The inverse of the conditional would be:

If a triangle is not an equilateral triangle, then it is not an isosceles triangle.

The inverse is not true.

10. If a triangle is a right triangle, then the sum of the measures of its acute angles is 90°.

6

11. If the sum of the internal angles of a polygon is 180°, then the polygon is a triangle.

12. If a polygon is a triangle, then the sum of its exterior angles is 360°.

13. If two angles are the acute angles of a right triangle, then they are complementary.

14. If two angles are complementary, then the sum of their measures is 90°.

15. If a polygon is a square, then it is a rhombus.

6

16. If a polygon is a trapezoid, then it is a quadrilateral.

Name _____ Date _____

Write the contrapositive of each conditional statement. Then, determine whether the contrapositive is true.

17. If one of the acute angles of a right triangle measures 45°, then it is an isosceles right triangle.

The contrapositive of the conditional would be:

If a triangle is not an isosceles right triangle, then it is not a right triangle with an acute angle that measures 45°.

The contrapositive is true.

18. If one of the acute angles of a right triangle measures 30°, then it is a 30°−60°−90° triangle.

19. If a quadrilateral is a rectangle, then it is a parallelogram.

20. If a quadrilateral is an isosceles trapezoid, then it has two pairs of congruent base angles.

21. If the sum of the measures of two angles is 180°, then the angles are supplementary.

22. If two angles are supplementary, then the sum of their measures is 180°.

23. If the radius of a circle is 8 meters, then the diameter of the circle is 16 meters.

24. If the diameter of a circle is 12 inches, then the radius of the circle is 6 inches.

6

Name _____ Date _____

Create an indirect proof to prove each statement.

25. Given: $\overline{WY}$ bisects $\angle XYZ$ and $\overline{XW} \not\cong \overline{ZW}$

Prove: $\overline{XY} \not\cong \overline{ZY}$

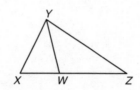

Statements	Reasons
1. $\overline{XY} \cong \overline{ZY}$	1. Assumption
2. $\overline{WY}$ bisects $\angle XYZ$	2. Given
3. $\angle XYW \cong \angle ZYW$	3. Definition of angle bisector
4. $\overline{YW} \cong \overline{YW}$	4. Reflexive Property of $\cong$
5. $\triangle XYW \cong \triangle ZYW$	5. SAS Congruence Theorem
6. $\overline{XW} \cong \overline{ZW}$	6. CPCTC
7. $\overline{XW} \not\cong \overline{ZW}$	7. Given
8. $\overline{XY} \cong \overline{ZY}$ is false.	8. Step 7 contradicts Step 6. The assumption is false.
9. $\overline{XY} \not\cong \overline{ZY}$ is true.	9. Proof by contradiction

26. Given: $m\angle EBX \neq m\angle EBZ$

Prove: $\overline{EB}$ is not an altitude of $\triangle EZX$.

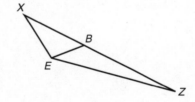

27. Given: $\angle OMP \cong \angle MOP$ and $\overline{NP}$ does not bisect $\angle ONM$.

Prove: $\overline{NM} \not\cong \overline{NO}$

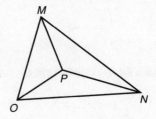

28. Given: $\overline{ET} \cong \overline{DT}$ and $\overline{EU} \not\cong \overline{DU}$

Prove: $\overline{EX} \not\cong \overline{DX}$

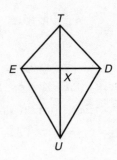

Name _____ Date _____

For each pair of triangles, use the Hinge Theorem or its converse to write a conclusion using an inequality.

29.

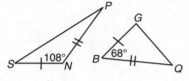

SP > GQ

30.

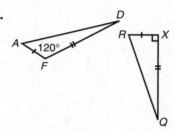

31.

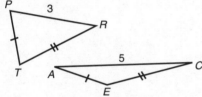

32.

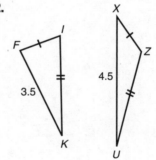

6

Name _____ Date _____

Squares and Rectangles
Properties of Squares and Rectangles

Vocabulary

Define the term in your own words.

1. Explain the Perpendicular/Parallel Line Theorem in your own words.

Problem Set

Use the given statements and the Perpendicular/Parallel Line Theorem to identify the pair of parallel lines in each figure.

1. Given: $l \perp m$ and $l \perp r$

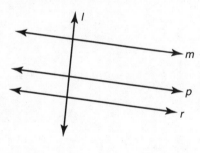

$m \parallel r$

2. $k \perp b$ and $g \perp b$

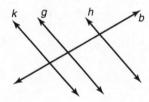

3. Given: $z \perp g$ and $z \perp p$

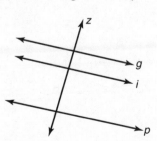

4. Given: $c \perp t$ and $t \perp e$

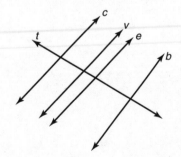

5. Given: $n \perp r$ and $r \perp q$

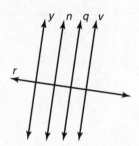

6. Given: $b \perp x$ and $k \perp b$

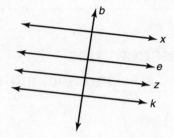

Complete each statement for square *GKJH*.

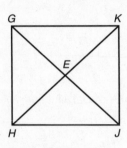

7. $\overline{GK} \cong \underline{\overline{KJ}} \cong \underline{\overline{JH}} \cong \underline{\overline{HG}}$

8. $\angle KGH \cong \angle \underline{\quad} \cong \angle \underline{\quad} \cong \angle \underline{\quad} \cong \angle \underline{\quad} \cong \angle \underline{\quad} \cong \angle \underline{\quad} \cong \angle \underline{\quad}$

9. $\angle GEK$, $\angle \underline{\quad}$, $\angle \underline{\quad}$, $\angle \underline{\quad}$, $\angle \underline{\quad}$, $\angle \underline{\quad}$, $\angle \underline{\quad}$, and $\angle \underline{\quad}$ are right angles.

10. $\overline{GK} \parallel \underline{\quad}$ and $\overline{GH} \parallel \underline{\quad}$

11. $\overline{GE} \cong \underline{\quad} \cong \underline{\quad} \cong \underline{\quad}$

12. $\angle \underline{KGE} \cong \angle \underline{\quad} \cong \angle \underline{\quad} \cong \angle \underline{\quad} \cong \angle \underline{\quad} \cong \angle \underline{\quad} \cong \angle \underline{\quad} \cong \angle \underline{\quad}$

7

Name _____ Date _____

Complete each statement for rectangle *TMNU*.

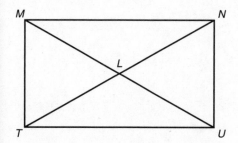

13. $\overline{MN} \cong \underline{\ \ TU\ \ }$ and $\overline{MT} \cong \underline{\ \ NU\ \ }$

14. $\angle NMT \cong \angle\underline{\ \ \ \ \ } \cong \angle\underline{\ \ \ \ \ } \cong \angle\underline{\ \ \ \ \ }$

15. $\angle MTU$, $\angle\underline{\ \ \ \ \ }$, $\angle\underline{\ \ \ \ \ }$, and $\angle\underline{\ \ \ \ \ }$ are right angles.

16. $\overline{MN} \parallel \underline{\ \ \ \ }$ and $\overline{MT} \parallel \underline{\ \ \ \ }$

17. $\overline{MU} \cong \underline{\ \ \ \ }$

18. $\overline{ML} \cong \underline{\ \ \ \ } \cong \underline{\ \ \ \ } \cong \underline{\ \ \ \ }$

Construct each quadrilateral using the given information.

19. Use $\overline{AB}$ to construct square *ABCD* with diagonals $\overline{AC}$ and $\overline{BD}$ intersecting at point *E*.

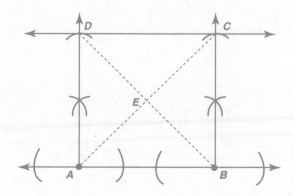

7

20. Use $\overline{WX}$ to construct square WXYZ with diagonals $\overline{WY}$ and $\overline{XZ}$ intersecting at point P.

W   X

21. Use $\overline{OP}$ to construct square OPQR with diagonals $\overline{OQ}$ and $\overline{PR}$ intersecting at point T.

O   P

Name _____ Date _____

22. Use $\overline{RE}$ to construct rectangle *RECT* with diagonals $\overline{RC}$ and $\overline{ET}$ intersecting at point *A*. Do not construct a square.

●————————————●
R   E

23. Use $\overline{QR}$ to construct rectangle *QRST* with diagonals $\overline{QS}$ and $\overline{RT}$ intersecting at point *P*. Do not construct a square.

●—————————●
Q   R

7

24. Use $\overline{MN}$ to construct rectangle *MNOP* with diagonals $\overline{MO}$ and $\overline{NP}$ intersecting at point *G*. Do not construct a square.

M   N

Create each proof.

25. Write a paragraph proof to prove $\overline{AC} \cong \overline{BD}$ in square *ABCD*.

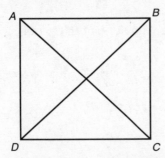

You are given square *ABCD* with diagonals $\overline{AC}$ and $\overline{DB}$. By definition of a square, $\angle ADC$ and $\angle BCD$ are right angles. Because all right angles are congruent, you can conclude that $\angle ADC \cong \angle BCD$. Also by definition of a square, $\overline{AD} \cong \overline{BC}$. By the Reflexive Property, $\overline{DC} \cong \overline{DC}$. Therefore, $\triangle ADC \cong \triangle BCD$ by the SAS Congruence Theorem. So, $\overline{AC} \cong \overline{BD}$ by CPCTC.

Name _____ Date _____

26. Write a paragraph proof to prove $\overline{GL} \cong \overline{IL}$ and $\overline{HL} \cong \overline{JL}$ in square *GHIJ*.

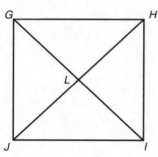

27. Create a two-column proof to prove $\overline{ML} \perp \overline{NP}$ in square *MNLP*.

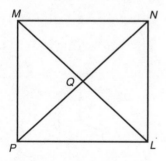

28. Create a two-column proof to prove $\overline{RT} \cong \overline{SU}$ in rectangle *RSTU*.

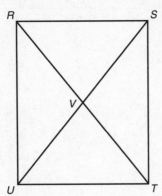

Name _____ Date _____

29. Create a two-column proof to prove $\overline{LK} \cong \overline{KN}$ and $\overline{OK} \cong \overline{KM}$ in rectangle *LMNO*.

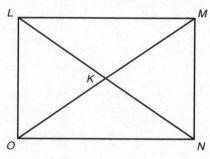

30. Write a paragraph proof to prove opposite sides are parallel in rectangle *WXYZ*.

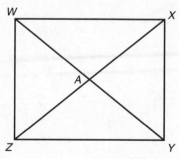

7

Name _____ Date _____

Parallelograms and Rhombi
Properties of Parallelograms and Rhombi

Vocabulary

1. Explain how the Parallelogram/Congruent-Parallel Side Theorem can be used to determine if a quadrilateral is a parallelogram.

Problem Set

Complete each statement for parallelogram *MNPL*.

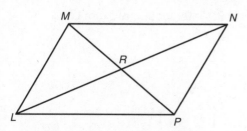

1. $\overline{MN} \cong \underline{\ \overline{LP}\ }$ and $\overline{ML} \cong \underline{\ \overline{NP}\ }$

2. $\angle NML \cong \angle$ _____ and $\angle MLP \cong \angle$ _____

3. $\overline{MN} \parallel$ _____ and $\overline{ML} \parallel$ _____

4. $\overline{MR} \cong$ _____ and $\overline{LR} \cong$ _____

7

Complete each statement for rhombus *UVWX*.

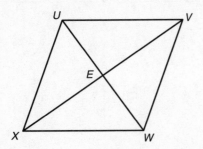

5. $\overline{UV} \cong \underline{\overline{VW}} \cong \underline{\overline{WX}} \cong \underline{\overline{XU}}$

6. $\angle UVW \cong \angle \underline{\hspace{1cm}}$ and $\angle XUV \cong \angle \underline{\hspace{1cm}}$

7. $\overline{UV} \parallel \underline{\hspace{1cm}}$ and $\overline{UX} \parallel \underline{\hspace{1cm}}$

8. $\overline{UE} \cong \underline{\hspace{1cm}}$ and $\overline{XE} \cong \underline{\hspace{1cm}}$

Construct each quadrilateral using the given information.

9. Use $\overline{RS}$ to construct parallelogram *RSTU* with diagonals $\overline{RT}$ and $\overline{SU}$ intersecting at point *G*.

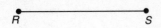

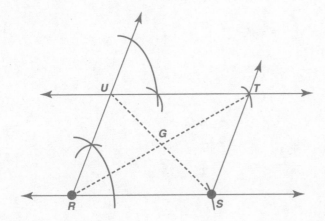

Name _____ Date _____

10. Use $\overline{AB}$ to construct parallelogram *ABCD* with diagonals $\overline{AC}$ and $\overline{BD}$ intersecting at point *F*.

11. Use $\overline{WX}$ to construct parallelogram *WXYZ* with diagonals $\overline{WY}$ and $\overline{XZ}$ intersecting at point *H*.

12. Use $\overline{AB}$ to construct rhombus *ABCD* with diagonals $\overline{AC}$ and $\overline{BD}$ intersecting at point *K*. Do not construct a square.

7

13. Use $\overline{WX}$ to construct rhombus *WXYZ* with diagonals $\overline{WY}$ and $\overline{XZ}$ intersecting at point *V*. Do not construct a square.

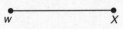

14. Use $\overline{EF}$ to construct rhombus *EFGH* with diagonals $\overline{EG}$ and $\overline{FH}$ intersecting at point *T*. Do not construct a square.

Determine the missing statement needed to prove each quadrilateral is a parallelogram by the Parallelogram/Congruent-Parallel Side Theorem.

15. $\overline{XY} \parallel \overline{ZW}$

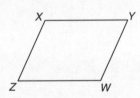

$\overline{XY} \cong \overline{ZW}$

16. $\overline{PS} \cong \overline{QR}$

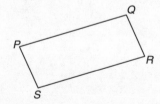

Name _____ Date _____

17. $\overline{MN} \cong \overline{PQ}$

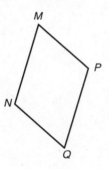

18. $\overline{CF} \parallel \overline{DE}$

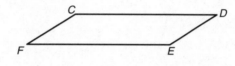

19. $\overline{ST} \parallel \overline{VU}$

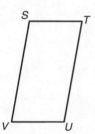

20. $\overline{KG} \cong \overline{HL}$

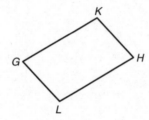

Create each proof.

21. Write a paragraph proof to prove $\angle BAD \cong \angle DCB$ in parallelogram *ABCD*.

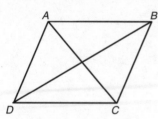

We are given parallelogram *ABCD* with diagonals $\overline{AC}$ and $\overline{DB}$. By definition of a parallelogram, $\overline{AB} \parallel \overline{CD}$ and $\overline{AD} \parallel \overline{BC}$. So, $\angle ABD \cong \angle CDB$ and $\angle ADB \cong \angle DBC$ by the Alternate Interior Angle Theorem. By the Reflexive Property, $\overline{DB} \cong \overline{DB}$. Therefore, $\triangle ABD \cong \triangle CDB$ by the ASA Congruence Theorem. So, $\angle BAD \cong \angle DCB$ by CPCTC.

22. Create a two-column proof to prove $\overline{GL} \cong \overline{IL}$ and $\overline{JL} \cong \overline{HL}$ in parallelogram *GHIJ*.

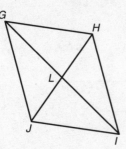

23. Write a paragraph proof to prove opposite sides are congruent in parallelogram *HIJK*.

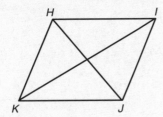

Name _____ Date _____

24. Create a two-column proof to prove $\overline{RT} \perp \overline{SU}$ in rhombus *RSTU*.

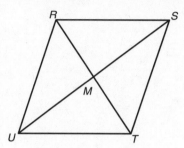

25. Create a two-column proof to prove ∠*QPR* ≅ ∠*SPR*, ∠*QRP* ≅ ∠*SRP*, ∠*PSQ* ≅ ∠*RSQ*, and ∠*PQS* ≅ ∠*RQS* in rhombus *PQRS*.

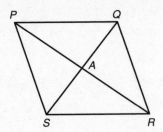

Name _____ Date _____

26. Create a two-column proof to prove rhombus *RSTU* is a parallelogram.

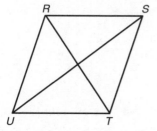

Use the given information to answer each question.

27. Tommy drew a quadrilateral. He used a protractor to measure all four angles of the quadrilateral. How many pairs of angles must be congruent for the quadrilateral to be a parallelogram? Explain.

Opposite angles are congruent in a parallelogram, so both pairs of opposite angles must be congruent.

28. Khyree cut a quadrilateral out of a piece of cardstock, but is not sure if the figure is a parallelogram or a rhombus. He measures the lengths of the opposite sides and determines them to be congruent. He measures the opposite angles of the quadrilateral and determines them also to be congruent. He measures one angle and is able to determine that the quadrilateral is a rhombus. What angle did he measure? Explain.

29. Penny makes the following statement: "Every rhombus is a parallelogram." Do you agree? Explain.

30. Sally plans to make the base of her sculpture in the shape of a rhombus. She cuts out four pieces of wood to create a mold for concrete. The pieces of wood are the following lengths: 5 inches, 5 inches, 3 inches, and 3 inches. Will the base of Sally's sculpture be a rhombus? Explain.

31. Ronald has a picture in the shape of a quadrilateral that he cut out of a magazine. How could Ronald use a ruler to prove that the picture is a parallelogram?

32. Three angles of a parallelogram have the following measures: 58°, 122°, and 58°. What is the measure of the fourth angle? How do you know?

7

Name _____ Date _____

Kites and Trapezoids
Properties of Kites and Trapezoids

Vocabulary

Write the term from the box that best completes each statement.

base angles of a trapezoid	biconditional statement
midsegment	isosceles trapezoid

1. The _____ are either pair of angles of a trapezoid that share a base as a common side.

2. A(n) _____ is a trapezoid with congruent non-parallel sides.

3. A(n) _____ is a statement that contains *if and only if*.

4. The _____ of a trapezoid is a segment formed by connecting the midpoints of the legs of the trapezoid.

Problem Set

Complete each statement for kite *PRSQ*.

1. $\overline{PQ} \cong$ $\underline{QS}$ and $\overline{PR} \cong$ $\underline{SR}$

2. $\angle QPR \cong \angle$ _____

3. $\overline{PT} \cong$ _____

4. $\angle PQT \cong \angle$ _____ and $\angle PRT \cong \angle$ _____

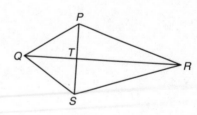

7

Complete each statement for trapezoid *UVWX*.

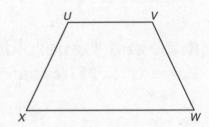

5. The bases are $\overline{UV}$ and $\overline{WX}$.

6. The pairs of base angles are ∠_____ and ∠_____, and ∠_____ and ∠_____.

7. The legs are ____ and ____.

8. The vertices are _____, _____, _____, and _____.

Construct each quadrilateral using the given information.

9. Construct kite *QRST* with diagonals $\overline{QS}$ and $\overline{RT}$ intersecting at point *M*.

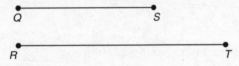

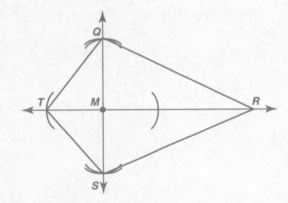

Name _____ Date _____

10. Construct kite *LMNO* with diagonals $\overline{MO}$ and $\overline{LN}$ intersecting at point *A*.

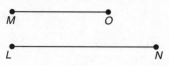

11. Construct kite *UVWX* with diagonals $\overline{UW}$ and $\overline{XV}$ intersecting at point *K*.

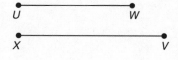

7

12. Construct trapezoid *ABCD* with $\overline{AB}$ as a base.

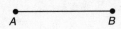

13. Construct trapezoid *HGYU* with $\overline{HG}$ as a base.

14. Construct trapezoid *BNJI* with $\overline{BN}$ as a base.

7

Name _____ Date _____

Use the given figure to answer each question.

15. The figure shown is a kite with ∠*DAB* ≅ ∠*DCB*. Which sides of the kite are congruent?

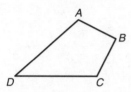

$\overline{AB}$ and $\overline{CB}$ are congruent.
$\overline{AD}$ and $\overline{CD}$ are congruent.

16. The figure shown is a kite with $\overline{FG}$ ≅ $\overline{FE}$. Which of the kite's angles are congruent?

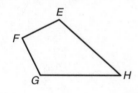

17. Given that *IJLK* is a kite, what kind of triangles are formed by diagonal $\overline{IL}$?

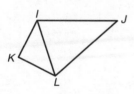

18. Given that *LMNO* is a kite, what is the relationship between the triangles formed by diagonal $\overline{MO}$?

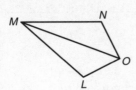

19. Given that *PQRS* is a kite, which angles are congruent?

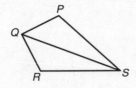

20. Given that *TUVW* is a kite, which angles are congruent?

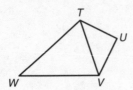

7

Name _____ Date _____

Use the given figure to answer each question.

21. The figure shown is an isosceles trapezoid with $\overline{AB} \parallel \overline{CD}$. Which sides are congruent?

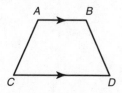

$\overline{AC}$ and $\overline{BD}$ are congruent.

22. The figure shown is an isosceles trapezoid with $\overline{EH} \cong \overline{FG}$. Which sides are parallel?

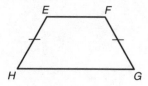

23. The figure shown is an isosceles trapezoid with $\overline{IJ} \cong \overline{KL}$. What are the bases?

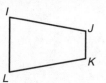

24. The figure shown is an isosceles trapezoid with $\overline{MP} \cong \overline{NO}$. What are the pairs of base angles?

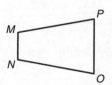

25. The figure shown is an isosceles trapezoid with $\overline{PQ} \parallel \overline{RS}$. Which sides are congruent?

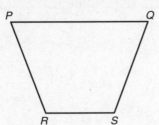

26. The figure shown is an isosceles trapezoid with $\overline{LM} \parallel \overline{KN}$. What are the pairs of base angles?

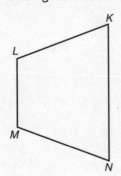

Create each proof.

27. Write a paragraph proof to prove $\angle ABC \cong \angle ADC$ in kite *ABCD*.

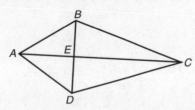

You are given kite *ABCD* with diagonals $\overline{BD}$ and $\overline{AC}$ intersecting at point *E*. By definition of a kite, we know that $\overline{AB} \cong \overline{AD}$ and $\overline{BC} \cong \overline{CD}$. By the Reflexive Property, you know that $\overline{AC} \cong \overline{AC}$. Therefore, $\triangle ABC \cong \triangle ADC$ by the SSS Congruence Theorem. So, $\angle ABC \cong \angle ADC$ by CPCTC.

7

Name _____ Date _____

28. Write a two-column proof to prove $\overline{HF} \cong \overline{JF}$ in kite *GHIJ*.

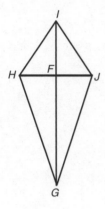

29. Write a paragraph proof to prove $\overline{WZ}$ bisects $\angle XWY$ and $\angle XZY$ in kite *WYZX*.

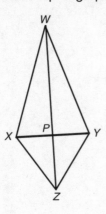

30. Write a paragraph proof to prove $\angle U \cong \angle T$ in isosceles trapezoid *RSTU*.

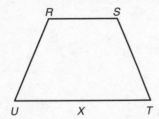

Name _____ Date _____

31. Write a two-column proof to prove $\angle K \cong \angle L$ in isosceles trapezoid *JKLM*.

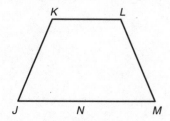

32. Write a two-column proof to prove that diagonals $\overline{RT}$ and $\overline{SU}$ in isosceles trapezoid *RSTU* are congruent if $\overline{RU} \cong \overline{ST}$.

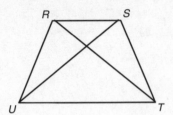

Construct each isosceles trapezoid using the given information.

33. Construct isosceles trapezoid *ABCD* if $\overline{PS}$ is the perimeter of the trapezoid.

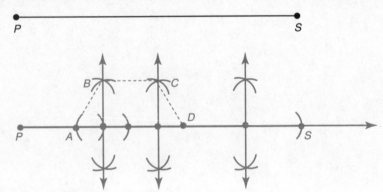

Name _____ Date _____

34. Construct isosceles trapezoid *WXYZ* if $\overline{AD}$ is the perimeter of the trapezoid.

35. Construct isosceles trapezoid *EFGH* if $\overline{WZ}$ is the perimeter of the trapezoid.

36. Construct isosceles trapezoid *PQRS* if $\overline{FJ}$ is the perimeter of the trapezoid.

37. Construct isosceles trapezoid *JKLM* if $\overline{TW}$ is the perimeter of the trapezoid.

T ●————————————————————● W

38. Construct isosceles trapezoid *STUV* if $\overline{EH}$ is the perimeter of the trapezoid.

E ●————————————————● H

Use the given information to answer each question.

39. Alice created a kite out of two sticks and some fabric. The sticks were 10 inches and 15 inches long. She tied the sticks together so they were perpendicular and attached the fabric. When she measured the kite, she noticed that the distance from where the sticks meet to the top of the kite was 5 inches. What is the area of the kite Alice created?

$A = 2\left(\frac{1}{2}\right)(5)(5) + 2\left(\frac{1}{2}\right)(5)(10)$

$A = 25 + 50$

$A = 75$

The area of the kite is 75 square inches.

7

Name _____ Date _____

40. Simon connected a square and two congruent right triangles together to form an isosceles trapezoid. Draw a diagram to represent the isosceles trapezoid.

41. Magda told Sam that an isosceles trapezoid must also be a parallelogram because there is a pair of congruent sides in an isosceles trapezoid. Is Magda correct? Explain.

42. Sylvia drew what she thought was an isosceles trapezoid. She measured the base angles and determined that they measured 81°, 79°, 101° and 99°. Could her drawing be an isosceles trapezoid? Explain.

43. Joanne constructed a kite with a perimeter of 38 centimeters so that the sum of the two shorter sides is 10 centimeters. What are the lengths of each of the two longer sides?

44. Ilyssa constructed a kite that has side lengths of 8 inches and 5 inches. What are the lengths of the other two sides? Explain.

7

7

Name _____ Date _____

Interior Angles of a Polygon
Sum of the Interior Angle Measures of a Polygon

Vocabulary

Give an example of the term.

1. Draw an example of a polygon. Label the interior angles of the polygon.

Problem Set

Draw all possible diagonals from vertex *A* for each polygon. Then write the number of triangles formed by the diagonals.

1.

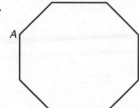

2 triangles

2.

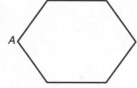

3.

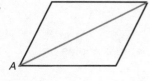

4.

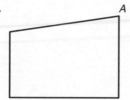

7

LESSON 7.4 **Skills Practice**   *page 2*

5.

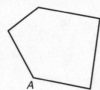

6.

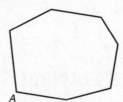

Use the triangles formed by diagonals to calculate the sum of the interior angle measures of each polygon.

7. Draw all of the diagonals that connect to vertex *A*. What is the sum of the interior angles of square *ABCD*?

The diagonal divides the figure into two triangles. The sum of the interior angles of each triangle is 180°, so I multiplied 180° by 2 to determine the sum of the interior angles of the figure:

180° × 2 = 360°

The sum of the interior angles is 360°.

8. Draw all of the diagonals that connect to vertex *E*. What is the sum of the interior angles of figure *EFGHI*?

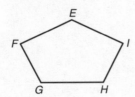

7

664 ■ **Chapter 7** Skills Practice

Name _____ Date _____

9. Draw all of the diagonals that connect to vertex *J*. What is the sum of the interior angles of figure *JKMONL*?

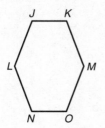

10. Draw all of the diagonals that connect to vertex *P*. What is the sum of the interior angles of the figure *PQRSTUV*?

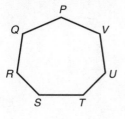

7

11. Draw all of the diagonals that connect to vertex *W*. What is the sum of the interior angles of the figure *WXYZABCD*?

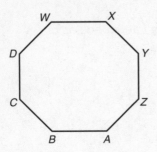

12. Draw all of the diagonals that connect to vertex *H*. What is the sum of the interior angles of the figure *HIJKLMNOP*?

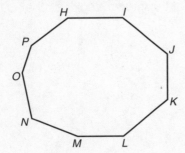

Name _____ Date _____

Calculate the sum of the interior angle measures of each polygon.

13. A polygon has 8 sides.

The sum is equal to $(n - 2) \cdot 180°$:

$(8 - 2) \cdot 180° = 6 \cdot 180° = 1080°$

The sum of the interior angles of the polygon is 1080°.

14. A polygon has 9 sides.

15. A polygon has 13 sides.

16. A polygon has 16 sides.

17. A polygon has 20 sides.

18. A polygon has 25 sides.

The sum of the measures of the interior angles of a polygon is given. Determine the number of sides for each polygon.

19. 1080°

    $180°(n - 2) = 1080°$

           $n - 2 = 6$

               $n = 8$

    8 sides

20. 1800°

21. 540°

22. 1260°

23. 3780°

24. 6840°

For each regular polygon, calculate the measure of each of its interior angles.

25.

$$\frac{(n - 2)180°}{n} = \frac{(8 - 2)180°}{8}$$

$$= \frac{(6)180°}{8}$$

$$= \frac{1080°}{8}$$

$$= 135°$$

The measure of each interior angle is 135°.

26.

7

Name _____ Date _____

27.

28.

29.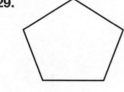

30.

7

Calculate the number of sides for each polygon.

31. The measure of each angle of a regular polygon is 108°.

$$108° = \frac{(n-2)180°}{n}$$

$108°n = (n-2)(180°)$

$108°n = 180°n - 360°$

$72°n = 360°$

$n = 5$

The regular polygon has 5 sides.

32. The measure of each angle of a regular polygon is 156°.

33. The measure of each angle of a regular polygon is 160°.

34. The measure of each angle of a regular polygon is 162°.

Name _____ Date _____

35. The measure of each angle of a regular polygon is 144°.

36. The measure of each angle of a regular polygon is 165.6°.

7

Name _____ Date _____

Exterior and Interior Angle Measurement Interactions
Sum of the Exterior Angle Measures of a Polygon

Vocabulary

Identify the term in the diagram.

1. Identify the term that is illustrated by the arrow in the diagram below.

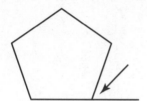

Problem Set

Extend each vertex of the polygon to create one exterior angle at each vertex.

1.

2.

3.

4.

7

5.

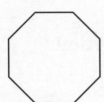

6.

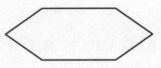

Calculate the sum of the measures of the exterior angles for each polygon.

7. pentagon

360°

8. hexagon

9. triangle

10. nonagon

11. 20-gon

12. 150-gon

Given the measure of an interior angle of a polygon, calculate the measure of the adjacent exterior angle.

13. What is the measure of an exterior angle if it is adjacent to an interior angle of a polygon that measures 90°?

Interior and exterior angles are supplementary. So subtract 90°, the measure of the interior angle, from 180°.

180° − 90° = 90°

7

Name _____ Date _____

14. What is the measure of an exterior angle if it is adjacent to an interior angle of a polygon that measures 120°?

15. What is the measure of an exterior angle if it is adjacent to an interior angle of a polygon that measures 108°?

16. What is the measure of an exterior angle if it is adjacent to an interior angle of a polygon that measures 135°?

17. What is the measure of an exterior angle if it is adjacent to an interior angle of a polygon that measures 115°?

18. What is the measure of an exterior angle if it is adjacent to an interior angle of a polygon that measures 124°?

Given the regular polygon, calculate the measure of each of its exterior angles.

19. What is the measure of each exterior angle of a square?

$\frac{360}{4} = 90°$

20. What is the measure of each exterior angle of a regular pentagon?

7

21. What is the measure of each exterior angle of a regular hexagon?

22. What is the measure of each exterior angle of a regular octagon?

23. What is the measure of each exterior angle of a regular decagon?

24. What is the measure of each exterior angle of a regular 12-gon?

Calculate the number of sides of the regular polygon given the measure of each exterior angle.

25. 45°

$$\frac{360}{n} = 45$$

$$45n = 360$$

$$n = 8$$

8 sides

26. 90°

27. 36°

28. 60°

29. 40°

30. 30°

Name _____ Date _____

Quadrilateral Family
Categorizing Quadrilaterals Based on Their Properties

Problem Set

List all of the quadrilaterals that have the given characteristic.

1. all sides congruent

square and rhombus

2. diagonals congruent

3. no parallel sides

4. diagonals bisect each other

5. two pairs of parallel sides

6. all angles congruent

Identify all of the terms from the following list that apply to each figure: quadrilateral, parallelogram, rectangle, square, trapezoid, rhombus, kite.

7.

rhombus

parallelogram

quadrilateral

8.

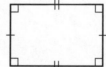

9.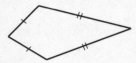

10.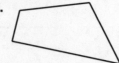

11.

12.

Name the type of quadrilateral that best describes each figure. Explain your answer.

13.

Rectangle. The quadrilateral has two pairs of parallel sides and four right angles, but the four sides are not all congruent.

14.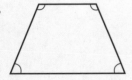

7

Name _____ Date _____

15.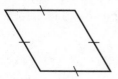

16.

17.

18.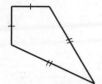

7

Draw the part of the Venn diagram that is described.

19. Suppose that part of a Venn diagram has two circles. One circle represents all types of quadrilaterals with four congruent sides. The other circle represents all types of quadrilaterals with four congruent angles. Draw this part of the Venn diagram and label it with the appropriate types of quadrilaterals.

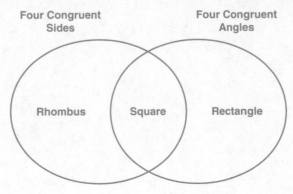

Four Congruent Sides   Four Congruent Angles

Rhombus   Square   Rectangle

20. Suppose that part of a Venn diagram has two circles. One circle represents all types of quadrilaterals with two pairs of congruent sides (adjacent or opposite). The other circle represents all types of quadrilaterals with at least one pair of parallel sides. Draw this part of the Venn diagram and label it with the appropriate types of quadrilaterals.

7

Name _____ Date _____

21. Suppose that part of a Venn diagram has two circles. One circle represents all types of quadrilaterals with two pairs of parallel sides. The other circle represents all types of quadrilaterals with four congruent sides. Draw this part of the Venn diagram and label it with the appropriate types of quadrilaterals.

22. Suppose that part of a Venn diagram has two circles. One circle represents all types of quadrilaterals with four right angles. The other circle represents all types of quadrilaterals with two pairs of parallel sides. Draw this part of the Venn diagram and label it with the appropriate types of quadrilaterals.

23. Suppose that a Venn diagram has two circles. One circle represents all types of quadrilaterals with four congruent sides. The other circle represents all types of quadrilaterals with congruent diagonals. Draw this part of the Venn diagram and label it with the appropriate types of quadrilaterals.

24. Suppose that a Venn diagram has two circles. One circle represents all types of quadrilaterals with diagonals that bisect the vertex angles. The other circle represents all types of quadrilaterals with perpendicular diagonals. Draw this part of the Venn diagram and label it with the appropriate types of quadrilaterals.

Name _____ Date _____

Tell whether the statement is true or false. If false, explain why.

25. A trapezoid is also a parallelogram.

False. Parallelograms have two pairs of parallel sides. Trapezoids only have one pair.

26. A square is also a rhombus.

27. Diagonals of a rectangle are perpendicular.

28. A parallelogram has exactly one pair of opposite angles congruent.

29. A square has diagonals that are perpendicular and congruent.

30. All quadrilaterals have supplementary consecutive angles.

List the steps to tell how you would construct the quadrilateral with the given information.

31. Rectangle *HIJK* given only diagonal $\overline{HJ}$.

1. Duplicate $\overline{HJ}$ and bisect it to determine the midpoint.

2. Duplicate $\overline{HJ}$ again, labeling it $\overline{IK}$, and bisecting it to determine the midpoint.

3. Draw segments $\overline{HJ}$ and $\overline{IK}$ so that their midpoints intersect.

4. Connect the endpoints of the segments to form rectangle *HIJK*.

7

32. Square *ABCD* given only diagonal $\overline{AC}$.

33. Kite *RTSU* given only diagonal $\overline{RS}$.

34. Rhombus *MNOP* given only diagonal $\overline{MO}$.

35. Parallelogram *JKLM* given only diagonal $\overline{JL}$.

36. Isosceles trapezoid *BCDE* given only diagonal $\overline{BD}$.

Name _____ Date _____

Three Angle Measure
Introduction to Trigonometry

Vocabulary

Use the diagram to complete each sentence.

1. If b is the opposite side, then x is the _____.
2. If y is the reference angle, then b is the _____.
3. If x is the reference angle, then b is the _____.

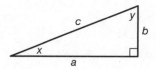

Problem Set

Determine the ratio $\dfrac{\text{opposite}}{\text{hypotenuse}}$ using $\angle A$ as the reference angle in each triangle. Write your answers as fractions in simplest form.

1.

$\dfrac{\text{opposite}}{\text{hypotenuse}} = \dfrac{6}{10} = \dfrac{3}{5}$

2.

3.

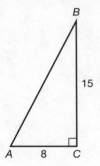

4.

5.

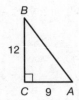

6.

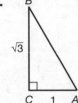

Determine the ratio $\dfrac{\text{adjacent}}{\text{hypotenuse}}$ using $\angle A$ as the reference angle in each triangle. Write your answers as fractions in simplest form.

7.

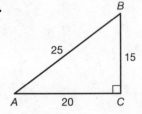

$$\dfrac{\text{adjacent}}{\text{hypotenuse}} = \dfrac{20}{25} = \dfrac{4}{5}$$

8.

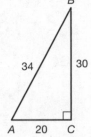

Name _____ Date _____

9.

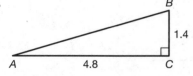

10.

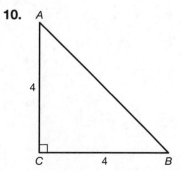

11.

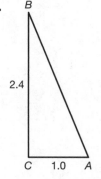

12.

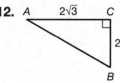

Determine the ratios $\dfrac{\text{opposite}}{\text{hypotenuse}}$, $\dfrac{\text{adjacent}}{\text{hypotenuse}}$, and $\dfrac{\text{opposite}}{\text{adjacent}}$ using $\angle A$ as the reference angle in each triangle. Write your answers as fractions in simplest form.

13.

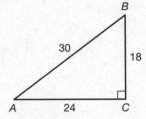

$$\frac{\text{opposite}}{\text{hypotenuse}} = \frac{18}{30} = \frac{3}{5}$$

$$\frac{\text{adjacent}}{\text{hypotenuse}} = \frac{24}{30} = \frac{4}{5}$$

$$\frac{\text{opposite}}{\text{adjacent}} = \frac{18}{24} = \frac{3}{4}$$

14.

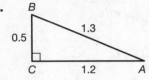

15.

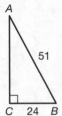

16.

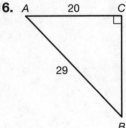

Name _____ Date _____

17.

A   C

5√2   5

B

18.

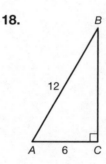

In each figure, triangles *ABC* and *DEF* are similar by the *AA* Similarity Theorem. Calculate the indicated ratio twice, first using △*ABC* and then using △*ADE*.

19. $\dfrac{\text{opposite}}{\text{hypotenuse}}$ for reference angle *A*

20. $\dfrac{\text{adjacent}}{\text{hypotenuse}}$ for reference angle *A*

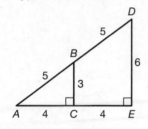

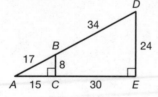

$AE = 4 + 4 = 8$

$AD = 5 + 5 = 10$

In △*ABC*, $\dfrac{\text{opposite}}{\text{hypotenuse}} = \dfrac{3}{5}$.

In △*ADE*, $\dfrac{\text{opposite}}{\text{hypotenuse}} = \dfrac{6}{10} = \dfrac{3}{5}$.

21. $\dfrac{\text{opposite}}{\text{hypotenuse}}$ for reference angle *A*

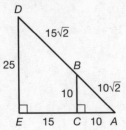

22. $\dfrac{\text{adjacent}}{\text{hypotenuse}}$ for reference angle *A*

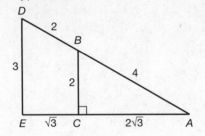

23. $\dfrac{\text{opposite}}{\text{adjacent}}$ for reference angle *A*

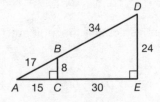

24. $\dfrac{\text{opposite}}{\text{adjacent}}$ for reference angle *A*

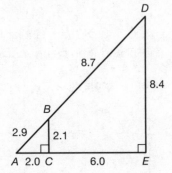

Name _____ Date _____

The Tangent Ratio
Tangent Ratio, Cotangent Ratio, and Inverse Tangent

Vocabulary

Match each description to its corresponding term for triangle *EFG*.

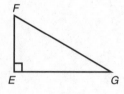

1. $\dfrac{EG}{EF}$ in relation to $\angle G$

 a. tangent

2. $\dfrac{EF}{EG}$ in relation to $\angle G$

 b. cotangent

3. $\tan^{-1}\left(\dfrac{EF}{EG}\right)$ in relation to $\angle G$

 c. inverse tangent

Problem Set

Calculate the tangent of the indicated angle in each triangle. Write your answers in simplest form.

1.

$\tan B = \dfrac{2}{2} = 1$

2.
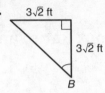

$\tan B =$

3.
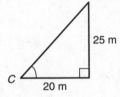

$\tan C =$

4.
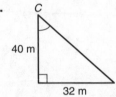

$\tan C =$

5.
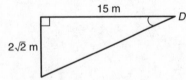

$\tan D =$

6.
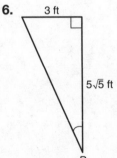

$\tan D =$

Name _____ Date _____

Calculate the cotangent of the indicated angle in each triangle. Write your answers in simplest form.

7.

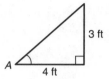

$\cot A = \dfrac{4}{3}$

8. *A*

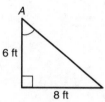

$\cot A =$

9. *F*

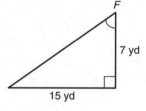

$\cot F =$

10.

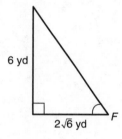

$\cot F =$

11.

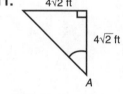

$\cot A =$

12.

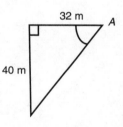

$\cot A =$

Use a calculator to approximate each tangent ratio. Round your answers to the nearest hundredth.

13. tan 30°

0.58

14. tan 45°

15. tan 60°

16. tan 15°

17. tan 75°

18. tan 89°

Use a calculator to approximate each cotangent ratio. Round your answers to the nearest hundredth.

19. cot 60°

0.58

20. cot 15°

21. cot 45°

22. cot 75°

23. cot 10°

24. cot 30°

Use a tangent ratio or a cotangent ratio to calculate the missing length of each triangle. Round your answers to the nearest hundredth.

25.

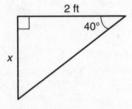

$$\tan 40° = \frac{x}{2}$$

$$2 \tan 40° = x$$

$$x \approx 1.68 \text{ ft}$$

26.

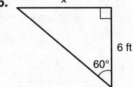

27.

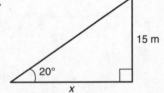

28.

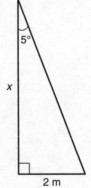

Name _____ Date _____

29.

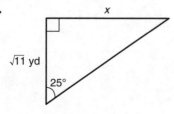

30.

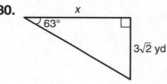

Calculate the measure of angle *X* for each triangle. Round your answers to the nearest hundredth.

31.

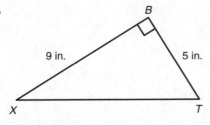

$\tan X = \dfrac{5}{9}$

$m\angle X = \tan^{-1}\left(\dfrac{5}{9}\right) \approx 29.05°$

32.

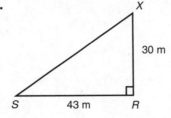

33.

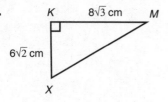

34.

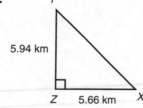

35.

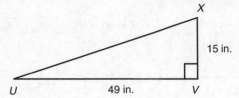

36.

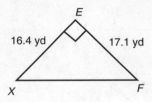

Solve each problem. Round your answers to the nearest hundredth.

37. A boat travels in the following path. How far north did it travel?

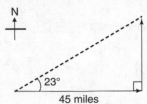

$$\tan 23° = \frac{N}{45}$$

$$45 \tan 23° = N$$

$$N \approx 19.10 \text{ mi}$$

38. During a group hike, a park ranger makes the following path. How far west did they travel?

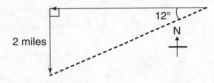

39. A surveyor makes the following diagram of a hill. What is the height of the hill?

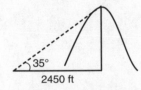

Name _____ Date _____

40. To determine the height of a tree, a botanist makes the following diagram. What is the height of the tree?

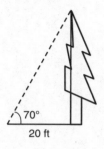

70°

20 ft

41. A moving truck is equipped with a ramp that extends from the back of the truck to the ground. When the ramp is fully extended, it touches the ground 12 feet from the back of the truck. The height of the ramp is 2.5 feet. Calculate the measure of the angle formed by the ramp and the ground.

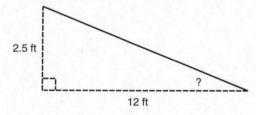

2.5 ft

?

12 ft

42. A park has a skateboard ramp with a length of 14.2 feet and a length along the ground of 12.9 feet. The height is 5.9 feet. Calculate the measure of the angle formed by the ramp and the ground.

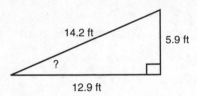

43. A lifeguard is sitting on an observation chair at a pool. The lifeguard's eye level is 6.2 feet from the ground. The chair is 15.4 feet from a swimmer. Calculate the measure of the angle formed when the lifeguard looks down at the swimmer.

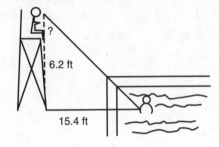

44. A surveyor is looking up at the top of a building that is 140 meters tall. His eye level is 1.4 meters above the ground, and he is standing 190 meters from the building. Calculate the measure of the angle from his eyes to the top of the building.

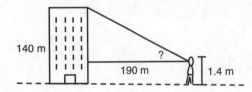

Name _____ Date _____

The Sine Ratio
Sine Ratio, Cosecant Ratio, and Inverse Sine

Vocabulary

Write the term from the box that best completes each statement.

sine	cosecant	inverse sine

1. The _____ of an acute angle in a right triangle is the ratio of the length of the hypotenuse to the length of a side that is opposite the angle.

2. The _____ of x is the measure of an acute angle whose sine is x.

3. The _____ of an acute angle in a right triangle is the ratio of the length of the side that is opposite the angle to the length of the hypotenuse.

Problem Set

Calculate the sine of the indicated angle in each triangle. Write your answers in simplest form.

1.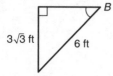

$\sin B = \dfrac{3\sqrt{3}}{6} = \dfrac{\sqrt{3}}{2}$

2.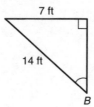

$\sin B =$

3.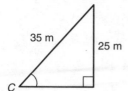

$\sin C =$

4.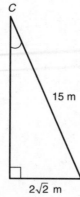

$\sin C =$

5.

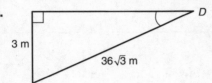

$\sin D =$

6.

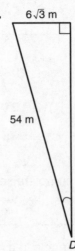

$\sin D =$

Calculate the cosecant of the indicated angle in each triangle. Write your answers in simplest form.

7.

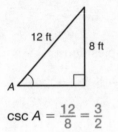

$\csc A = \dfrac{12}{8} = \dfrac{3}{2}$

8.

$\csc A =$

9.

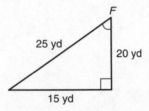

$\csc F =$

10.

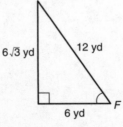

$\csc F =$

11.

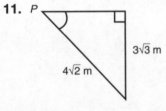

$\csc P =$

12.

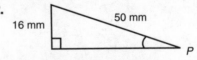

$\csc P =$

8

Name _____ Date _____

Use a calculator to approximate each sine ratio. Round your answers to the nearest hundredth.

13. sin 30°

0.5

14. sin 45°

15. sin 60°

16. sin 15°

17. sin 75°

18. sin 5°

Use a calculator to approximate each cosecant ratio. Round your answers to the nearest hundredth.

19. csc 45°

1.41

20. csc 90°

21. csc 120°

22. csc 30°

23. csc 15°

24. csc 60°

Use a sine ratio or a cosecant ratio to calculate the missing length of each triangle. Round your answers to the nearest hundredth.

25.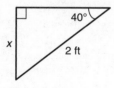

$\sin 40° = \dfrac{x}{2}$

$2 \sin 40° = x$

$x \approx 1.29 \text{ ft}$

26.

27.

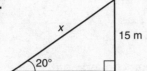

28.

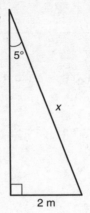

29.

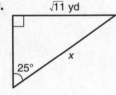

30.

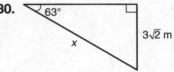

Calculate the measure of angle *X* for each triangle. Round your answers to the nearest hundredth.

31.

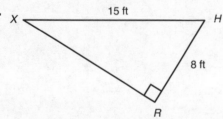

32.

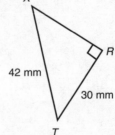

$\sin X = \dfrac{8}{15}$

$m\angle X = \sin^{-1}\left(\dfrac{8}{15}\right) \approx 32.23°$

Name _____ Date _____

33.

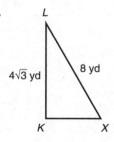

34.

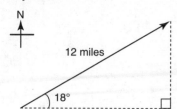

35.

36.

Solve each problem. Round your answers to the nearest hundredth.

37. A scout troop traveled 12 miles from camp, as shown on the map below. How far north did they travel?

$$\sin 18° = \frac{N}{12}$$

$$12 \sin 18° = N$$

$$N \approx 3.71 \text{ mi}$$

38. An ornithologist tracked a Cooper's hawk that traveled 23 miles. How far east did the bird travel?

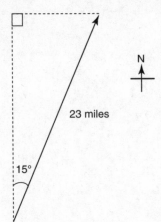

39. An architect needs to use a diagonal support in an arch. Her company drew the following diagram. How long does the diagonal support have to be?

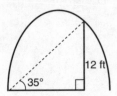

40. A hot air balloon lifts 125 feet into the air. The diagram below shows that the hot air balloon was blown to the side. How long is the piece of rope that connects the balloon to the ground?

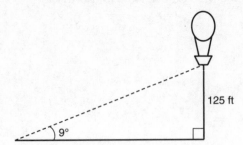

Name _____ Date _____

41. Jerome is flying a kite on the beach. The kite is attached to a 100-foot string and is flying 45 feet above the ground, as shown in the diagram. Calculate the measure of the angle formed by the string and the ground.

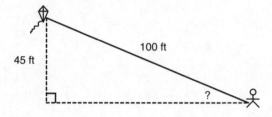

100 ft

45 ft

?

42. An airplane ramp is 58 feet long and reaches the cockpit entrance 19 feet above the ground, as shown in the diagram. Calculate the measure of the angle formed by the ramp and the ground.

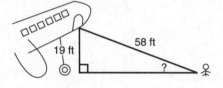

58 ft

19 ft

?

43. Bleachers in a stadium are 4 meters tall and have a length of 12 meters, as shown in the diagram. Calculate the measure of the angle formed by the bleachers and the ground.

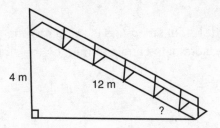

44. A 20-foot flagpole is raised by a 24-foot rope, as shown in the diagram. Calculate the measure of the angle formed by the rope and the ground.

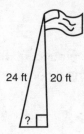

Name _____ Date _____

The Cosine Ratio
Cosine Ratio, Secant Ratio, and Inverse Cosine

Vocabulary

Describe the similarities and differences between the pair of terms.

1. cosine ratio and secant ratio

Define the term in your own words.

2. inverse cosine

Problem Set

Calculate the cosine of the indicated angle in each triangle. Write your answers in simplest form.

1.

$\cos B = \dfrac{3\sqrt{3}}{6} = \dfrac{\sqrt{3}}{2}$

2.

$\cos B =$

3.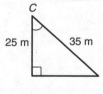

$\cos C =$

4.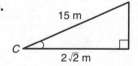

$\cos C =$

5.

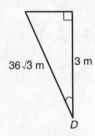

cos D =

6.

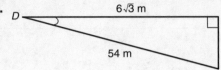

cos D =

Calculate the secant of the indicated angle in each triangle. Write your answers in simplest form.

7.

$\sec A = \dfrac{12}{8} = \dfrac{3}{2}$

8.

sec A =

9.

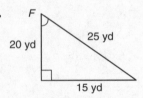

sec F =

10.

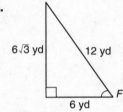

sec F =

11.

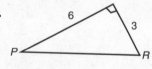

sec P =

12.

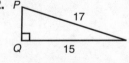

sec P =

Name _____ Date _____

Use a calculator to approximate each cosine ratio. Round your answers to the nearest hundredth.

13. cos 30°

0.87

14. cos 45°

15. cos 60°

16. cos 15°

17. cos 75°

18. cos 89°

Use a calculator to approximate each secant ratio. Round your answers to the nearest hundredth.

19. sec 45°

$\dfrac{1}{\cos(45°)} = 1.41$

20. sec 25°

21. sec 75°

22. sec 30°

23. sec 15°

24. sec 60°

Use a cosine ratio or a secant ratio to calculate the missing length of each triangle. Round your answers to the nearest hundredth.

25.

2 ft

40°

x

$\cos 40° = \dfrac{x}{2}$

$2\cos 40° = x$

$x \approx 1.53 \text{ ft}$

26.

6 ft

60°

x

27.

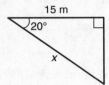

28.

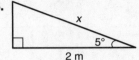

29.

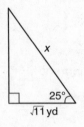

30.

Calculate the measure of angle *X* for each triangle. Round your answers to the nearest hundredth.

31.

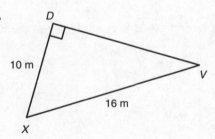

$\cos X = \dfrac{10}{16}$

$m\angle X = \cos^{-1}\left(\dfrac{10}{16}\right) \approx 51.32°$

32.

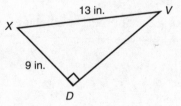

Name _____ Date _____

33.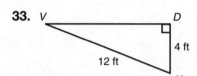

34.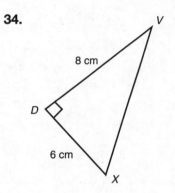

35.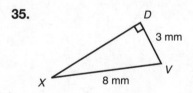

36.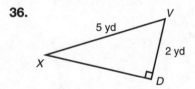

Solve each problem. Round your answers to the nearest hundredth.

37. The path of a model rocket is shown below. How far east did the rocket travel?

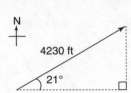

$$\cos 21° = \frac{E}{4230}$$

$$4230 \cos 21° = E$$

$$E \approx 3949.05 \text{ ft}$$

38. An ichthyologist tags a shark and charts its path. Examine his chart below. How far south did the shark travel?

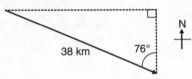

39. A kite is flying 120 feet away from the base of its string, as shown below. How much string is let out?

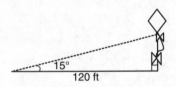

40. A pole has a rope tied to its top and to a stake 15 feet from the base. What is the length of the rope?

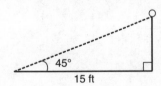

Name _____ Date _____

41. You park your boat at the end of a 20-foot dock. You tie the boat to the opposite end of the dock with a 35-foot rope. The boat drifts downstream until the rope is extended as far as it will go, as shown in the diagram. What is the angle formed by the rope and the dock?

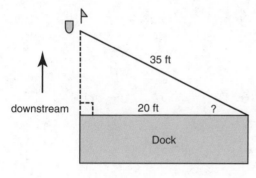

42. Rennie is walking her dog. The dog's leash is 12 feet long and is attached to the dog 10 feet horizontally from Rennie's hand, as shown in the diagram. What is the angle formed by the leash and the horizontal at the dog's collar?

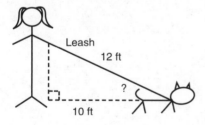

43. A ladder is leaning against the side of a house, as shown in the diagram. The ladder is 24 feet long and makes a 76° angle with the ground. How far from the edge of the house is the base of the ladder?

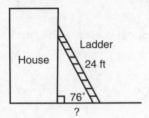

44. A rectangular garden 9 yards long has a diagonal path going through it, as shown in the diagram. The path makes a 34° angle with the longer side of the garden. Determine the length of the path.

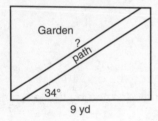

Name _____ Date _____

We Complement Each Other!
Complement Angle Relationships

Problem Set

For each right triangle, name the given ratio in two different ways.

1.

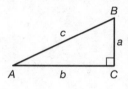

$\dfrac{a}{c}$

sin $\angle A = \dfrac{a}{c}$

cos $\angle B = \dfrac{a}{c}$

2.

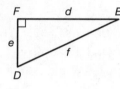

$\dfrac{d}{e}$

3.

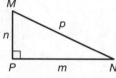

$\dfrac{p}{m}$

4.

$\dfrac{s}{r}$

5.

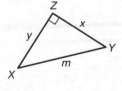

$\dfrac{y}{z}$

6.

$\dfrac{w}{v}$

Determine the trigonometric ratio that you would use to solve for *x* in each triangle. Explain your reasoning. You do not need to solve for *x*.

7.

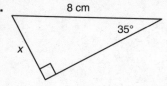

8 cm
35°
x

8.

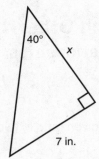

40°
x
7 in.

I would use the sine ratio because the hypotenuse is given and the length of the side opposite the given angle needs to be determined.

9.

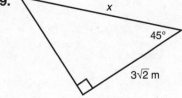

x
45°
3√2 m

10.

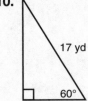

17 yd
60°
x

11.

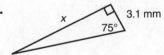

x
3.1 mm
75°

12.

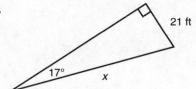

21 ft
17°
x

Name _____ Date _____

Solve each problem. Round your answers to the nearest hundredth.

13. You are standing 40 feet away from a building. The angle of elevation from the ground to the top of the building is 57°. What is the height of the building?

$$\tan 57° = \frac{h}{40}$$

$$40 \tan 57° = h$$

$$h \approx 61.59 \text{ ft}$$

14. A surveyor is 3 miles from a mountain. The angle of elevation from the ground to the top of the mountain is 15°. What is the height of the mountain?

15. The angle of elevation from a ship to a 135-foot-tall lighthouse is 2°. How far is the ship from the lighthouse?

16. The Statue of Liberty is about 151 feet tall. If the angle of elevation from a tree in Liberty State Park to the statue's top is 1.5°, how far is the tree from the statue?

17. The angle of elevation from the top of a person's shadow on the ground to the top of the person is 45°. The top of the shadow is 50 inches away from the person. How tall is the person?

18. A plane is spotted above a hill that is 12,000 feet away. The angle of elevation to the plane is 28°. How high is the plane?

19. During the construction of a house, a 6-foot-long board is used to support a wall. The board has an angle of elevation from the ground to the wall of 67°. How far is the base of the wall from the board?

20. Museums use metal rods to position the bones of dinosaurs. If an angled rod needs to be placed 1.3 meters away from a bone, with an angle of elevation from the ground of 51°, what must the length of the rod be?

Name _____ Date _____

Solve each problem. Round your answers to the nearest hundredth.

21. The angle of depression from the top of a building to a telephone line is 34°. If the building is 25 feet tall, how far from the building does the telephone line reach the ground?

$$\tan 34° = \frac{25}{d}$$

$$d = \frac{25}{\tan 34°}$$

$$d \approx 37.06 \text{ ft}$$

22. An airplane flying 3500 feet from the ground sees an airport at an angle of depression of 77°. How far is the airplane from the airport?

23. To determine the depth of a well's water, a hydrologist measures the diameter of the well to be 3 feet. She then uses a flashlight to point down to the water on the other side of the well. The flashlight makes an angle of depression of 79°. What is the depth of the well water?

24. A zip wire from a tree to the ground has an angle of depression of 18°. If the zip wire ends 250 feet from the base of the tree, how far up the tree does the zip wire start?

25. From a 50-foot-tall lookout tower, a park ranger sees a fire at an angle of depression of 1.6°. How far is the fire from the tower?

26. The Empire State Building is 448 meters tall. The angle of depression from the top of the Empire State Building to the base of the UN building is 74°. How far is the UN building from the Empire State Building?

27. A factory conveyor has an angle of depression of 18° and drops 10 feet. How long is the conveyor?

28. A bicycle race organizer needs to put up barriers along a hill. The hill is 300 feet tall and from the top makes an angle of depression of 26°. How long does the barrier need to be?

Name _____ Date _____

Time to Derive!
Deriving the Triangle Area Formula, the Law of Sines, and the Law of Cosines

Vocabulary

Define each term in your own words.

1. Law of Sines

2. Law of Cosines

Problem Set

Determine the area of each triangle. Round your answers to the nearest tenth.

1.

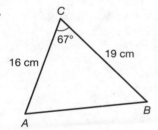

$A = \frac{1}{2} ab \sin C$

$A = \frac{1}{2} (19)(16)(\sin 67°)$

$A \approx 139.9$

The area of the triangle is approximately 139.9 square centimeters.

2.

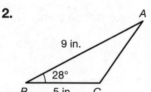

3.

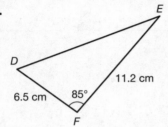

4.

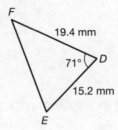

5.

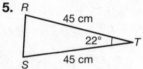

6.

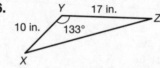

Determine the unknown side length *x* by using the Law of Sines. Round your answers to the nearest tenth.

7.

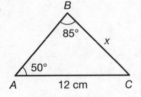

$$\frac{\sin A}{a} = \frac{\sin B}{b}$$

$$\frac{\sin 50°}{x} = \frac{\sin 85°}{12}$$

$$12 \sin 50° = x \sin 85°$$

$$x = \frac{12 \sin 50°}{\sin 85°}$$

$$x \approx 9.2 \text{ cm}$$

8.

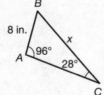

Name _____ Date _____

9.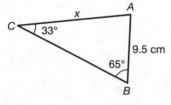

10.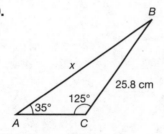

11.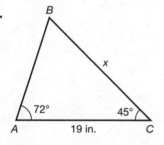

12.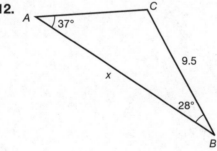

Determine $m\angle B$ by using the Law of Sines. Round your answers to the nearest tenth.

13.
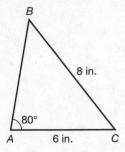

$$\frac{\sin B}{b} = \frac{\sin A}{a}$$

$$\frac{\sin B}{6} = \frac{\sin 80°}{8}$$

$$8 \sin B = 6 \sin 80°$$

$$\sin B = \frac{6 \sin 80°}{8} \approx 0.739$$

$$m\angle B = \sin^{-1}(0.739) \approx 47.6°$$

14.
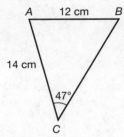

15.
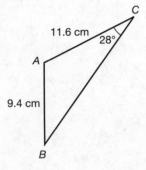

16.
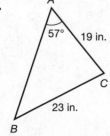

Name _____ Date _____

17.

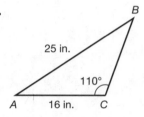

18.

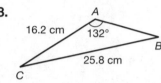

Determine the unknown side length by using the Law of Cosines. Round your answers to the nearest tenth.

19.

20.

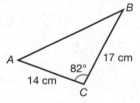

$b^2 = a^2 + c^2 - 2ac \cos B$

$b^2 = 5^2 + 7^2 - 2(5)(7)\cos 42°$

$b^2 = 25 + 49 - 70 \cos 42° ≈ 21.98$

$b = \sqrt{21.98}$

$b ≈ 4.7$ in.

21.

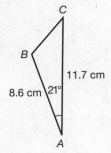

22.

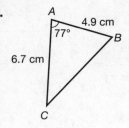

23.

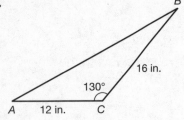

24.

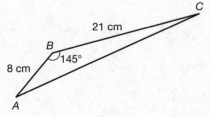

Name _____ Date _____

7. ∠SQR

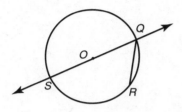

8. ∠TOU

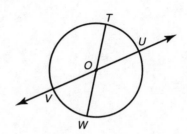

Identify each angle as an inscribed angle or a central angle.

9. ∠URE

Angle *URE* is an inscribed angle.

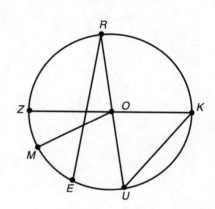

10. ∠ZOM

11. ∠KOM

12. ∠ZKU

13. ∠MOU

14. ∠ROK

Classify each arc as a major arc, a minor arc, or a semicircle.

15. $\overparen{AC}$

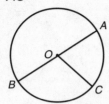

Arc *AC* is a minor arc.

16. $\overparen{DE}$

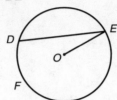

17. $\overparen{FHI}$

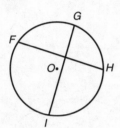

18. $\overparen{JML}$

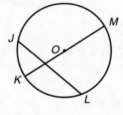

19. $\overparen{NPQ}$

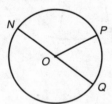

20. $\overparen{TRS}$

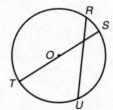

Draw the part of a circle that is described.

21. Draw chord $\overline{AB}$.

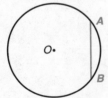

22. Draw radius $\overline{OE}$.

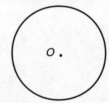

Name _____ Date _____

23. Draw secant $\overleftrightarrow{GH}$.

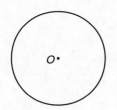

24. Draw a tangent at point J.

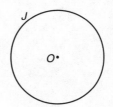

25. Label the point of tangency A.

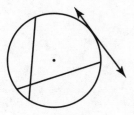

26. Label center C.

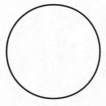

27. Draw inscribed angle $\angle FDG$.

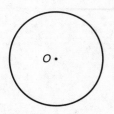

28. Draw central angle $\angle HOI$.

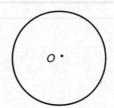

Name _____ Date _____

Determine the measure of each intercepted arc.

19. $m\widehat{KM}$

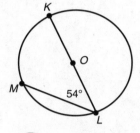

$m\widehat{KM} = 108°$

20. $m\widehat{IU}$

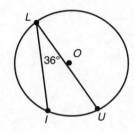

21. $m\widehat{QW}$

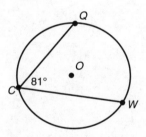

22. $m\widehat{TV}$

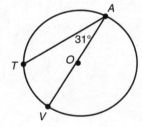

23. $m\widehat{ME}$

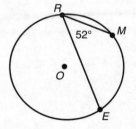

24. $m\widehat{DS}$

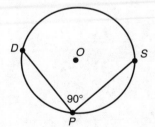

Calculate the measure of each angle.

25. The measure of ∠*AOB* is 62°. What is the measure of ∠*ACB*?

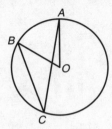

$$m\angle ACB = \frac{1}{2}(m\angle AOB) = \frac{62°}{2} = 31°$$

26. The measure of ∠*COD* is 98°. What is the measure of ∠*CED*?

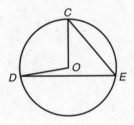

27. The measure of ∠*EOG* is 128°. What is the measure of ∠*EFG*?

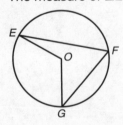

Name _____ Date _____

28. The measure of ∠*GOH* is 74°. What is the measure of ∠*GIH*?

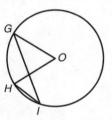

29. The measure of ∠*JOK* is 168°. What is the measure of ∠*JIK*?

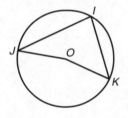

30. The measure of ∠*KOL* is 148°. What is the measure of ∠*KML*?

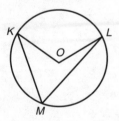

Use the given information to answer each question.

31. In circle C, $m\widehat{XZ}$ = 86°. What is $m\widehat{WY}$?

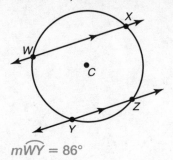

$m\widehat{WY}$ = 86°

32. In circle C, $m\angle WCX$ = 102°. What is $m\widehat{YZ}$?

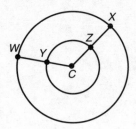

33. In circle C, $m\widehat{WZ}$ = 65° and $m\widehat{XZ}$ = 38°. What is $m\angle WCX$?

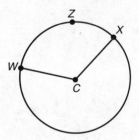

Name _____ Date _____

34. In circle C, $m\angle WCX = 105°$. What is $m\angle WYX$?

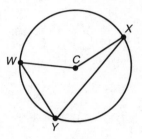

35. In circle C, $m\angle WCY = 83°$. What is $m\angle XCZ$?

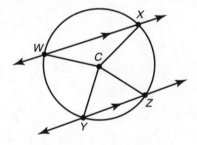

36. In circle C, $m\angle WYX = 50°$ and $m\angle XYZ = 30°$. What is $m\widehat{WXZ}$?

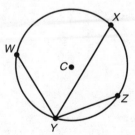

Name _____ Date _____

Manhole Covers
Measuring Angles Inside and Outside of Circles

Vocabulary

Define each theorem in your own words.

1. Interior Angles of a Circle Theorem

2. Exterior Angles of a Circle Theorem

3. Tangent to a Circle Theorem

Problem Set

Write an expression for the measure of the given angle.

1. $m\angle RPM$

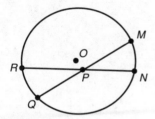

$$m\angle RPM = \frac{1}{2}\left(m\widehat{RM} + m\widehat{QN}\right)$$

2. $m\angle ACD$

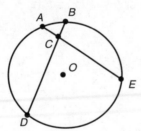

9

3. *m∠JNK*

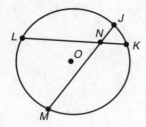

4. *m∠UWV*

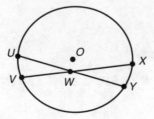

5. *m∠SWT*

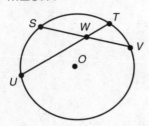

6. *m∠HJI*

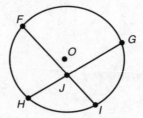

List the intercepted arc(s) for the given angle.

7. ∠QMR

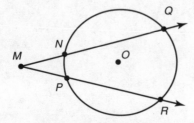

$\overarc{NP}$, $\overarc{QR}$

8. ∠RSU

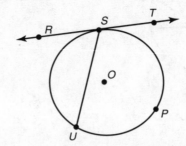

Name _____ Date _____

9. ∠FEH

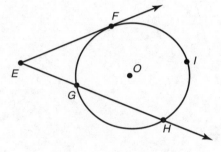

10. ∠ZWA

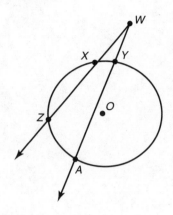

11. ∠BDE

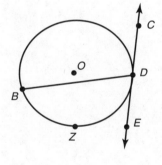

12. ∠JLM

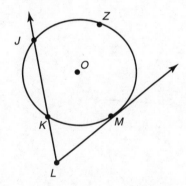

Write an expression for the measure of the given angle.

13. m∠DAC

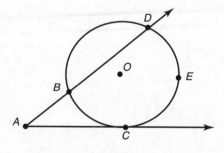

14. m∠UXY

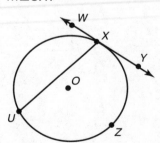

$m\angle DAC = \frac{1}{2}\left(m\overset{\frown}{DEC} - m\overset{\frown}{BC}\right)$

15. *m∠SRT*

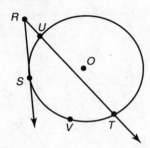

16. *m∠FJG*

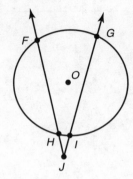

17. *m∠ECG*

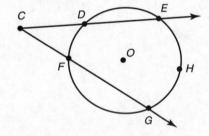

18. *m∠LPN*

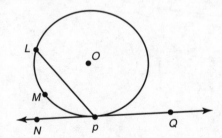

Name _____ Date _____

Create a proof to prove each statement.

19. Given: Chords $\overline{AE}$ and $\overline{BD}$ intersect at point C.

Prove: $m\angle ACB = \frac{1}{2}\left(m\widehat{AB} + m\widehat{DE}\right)$

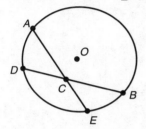

Statements	Reasons
1. Chords $\overline{AE}$ and $\overline{BD}$ intersect at point C.	1. Given
2. Draw chord $\overline{AD}$	2. Construction
3. $m\angle ACB = m\angle D + m\angle A$	3. Exterior Angle Theorem
4. $m\angle A = \frac{1}{2}m\widehat{DE}$	4. Inscribed Angle Theorem
5. $m\angle D = \frac{1}{2}m\widehat{AB}$	5. Inscribed Angle Theorem
6. $m\angle ACB = \frac{1}{2}m\widehat{DE} + \frac{1}{2}m\widehat{AB}$	6. Substitution
7. $m\angle ACB = \frac{1}{2}\left(m\widehat{AB} + m\widehat{DE}\right)$	7. Distributive Property

20. Given: Secant $\overleftrightarrow{QT}$ and tangent $\overleftrightarrow{SR}$ intersect at point S.

Prove: $m\angle QSR = \frac{1}{2}\left(m\widehat{QR} - m\widehat{RT}\right)$

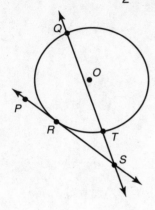

Name _____ Date _____

21. Given: Tangents $\overleftrightarrow{VY}$ and $\overleftrightarrow{XY}$ intersect at point Y.

Prove: $m\angle Y = \frac{1}{2}(m\widehat{VWX} - m\widehat{VX})$

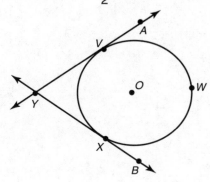

22. Given: Chords $\overline{FI}$ and $\overline{GH}$ intersect at point J.

Prove: $m\angle FJH = \frac{1}{2}\left(m\widehat{FH} + m\widehat{GI}\right)$

Name _____ Date _____

23. Given: Secant $\overleftrightarrow{JL}$ and tangent $\overleftarrow{NL}$ intersect at point L.

Prove: $m\angle L = \frac{1}{2}\left(m\widehat{JM} - m\widehat{KM}\right)$

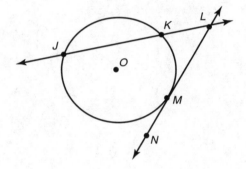

24. Given: Tangents $\overleftrightarrow{SX}$ and $\overleftrightarrow{UX}$ intersect at point X.

Prove: $m\angle X = \frac{1}{2}\left(m\widehat{VTW} - m\widehat{VW}\right)$

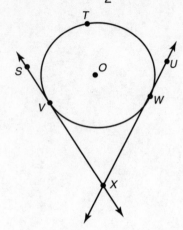

9

Name _____ Date _____

Use the diagram shown to determine the measure of each angle or arc.

25. Determine $m\widehat{FI}$.

$m\angle K = 20°$

$m\widehat{GJ} = 80°$

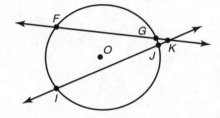

The measure of arc FI is 120 degrees.

$m\angle K = \frac{1}{2}(m\widehat{FI} = m\widehat{GJ})$

$20 = \frac{1}{2}(m\widehat{FI} - 80)$

$40 = m\widehat{FI} - 80$

$m\widehat{FI} = 120$

26. Determine $m\angle KLJ$.

$m\widehat{KM} = 120°$

$m\widehat{JN} = 100°$

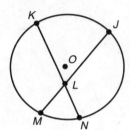

9

27. Determine $m\angle X$.

$m\widehat{VW} = 50°$

$m\widehat{TU} = 85°$

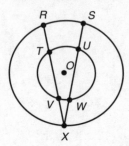

28. Determine $m\angle WYX$.

$m\widehat{WUY} = 300°$

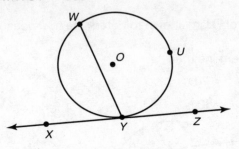

Name _____ Date _____

29. Determine $m\overset{\frown}{RS}$.

$m\overset{\frown}{UV} = 30°$

$m\angle RTS = 80°$

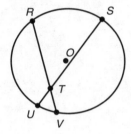

30. Determine $m\angle D$.

$m\overset{\frown}{ZXC} = 150°$

$m\overset{\frown}{CB} = 30°$

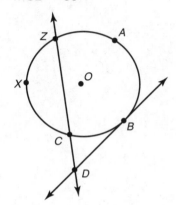

9

Name _____ Date _____

Color Theory
Chords

Vocabulary

Match each definition with its corresponding term.

1. Diameter–Chord Theorem

a. If two chords of the same circle or congruent circles are congruent, then their corresponding arcs are congruent.

2. Equidistant Chord Theorem

b. The segments formed on a chord when two chords of a circle intersect

3. Equidistant Chord Converse Theorem

c. If two chords of the same circle or congruent circles are congruent, then they are equidistant from the center of the circle.

4. Congruent Chord–Congruent Arc Theorem

d. If two arcs of the same circle or congruent circles are congruent, then their corresponding chords are congruent.

5. Congruent Chord–Congruent Arc Converse Theorem

e. If two chords of the same circle or congruent circles are equidistant from the center of the circle, then the chords are congruent.

6. segments of a chord

f. If two chords of a circle intersect, then the product of the lengths of the segments of one chord is equal to the product of the lengths of the segments in the second chord.

7. Segment–Chord Theorem

g. If a diameter of a circle is perpendicular to a chord, then the diameter bisects the chord and bisects the arc determined by the chord.

Problem Set

Use the given information to answer each question. Explain your answer.

1. If diameter $\overline{BD}$ bisects $\overline{AC}$, what is the angle of intersection?

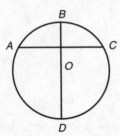

   The angle of intersection is 90° because diameters that bisect chords are perpendicular bisectors.

2. If diameter $\overline{FH}$ intersects $\overline{EG}$ at a right angle, how does the length of $\overline{EI}$ compare to the length of $\overline{IG}$?

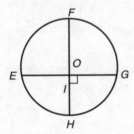

3. How does the measure of $\overset{\frown}{KL}$ and $\overset{\frown}{LM}$ compare?

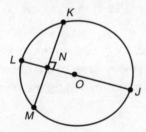

Name _____ Date _____

4. If $\overline{KP} \cong \overline{LN}$, how does the length of $\overline{QO}$ compare to the length of $\overline{RO}$?

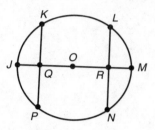

5. If $\overline{YO} \cong \overline{ZO}$, what is the relationship between $\overline{TU}$ and $\overline{XV}$?

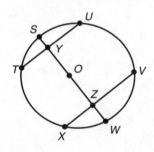

6. If $\overline{GO} \cong \overline{HO}$ and diameter $\overline{EJ}$ is perpendicular to both, what is the relationship between $\overline{GF}$ and $\overline{HK}$?

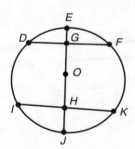

Determine each measurement.

7. If $\overline{BD}$ is a diameter, what is the length of $\overline{EC}$?

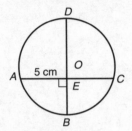

$EC = EA = 5$ cm

8. If the length of $\overline{AB}$ is 13 millimeters, what is the length of $\overline{CD}$?

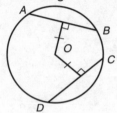

9. If the length of $\overline{AB}$ is 24 centimeters, what is the length of $\overline{CD}$?

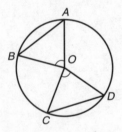

10. If the length of $\overline{BF}$ is 32 inches, what is the length of $\overline{CH}$?

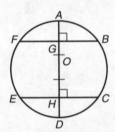

Name _____ Date _____

11. If the measure of ∠*AOB* = 155°, what is the measure of ∠*DOC*?

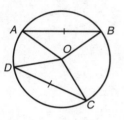

12. If segment $\overline{AC}$ is a diameter, what is the measure of ∠*AED*?

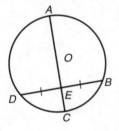

Compare each measurement. Explain your answer.

13. If $\overline{DE} \cong \overline{FG}$, how does the measure of $\overset{\frown}{DE}$ and $\overset{\frown}{FG}$ compare?

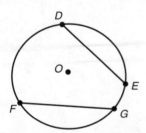

The measure of $\overset{\frown}{DE}$ is equal to the measure of $\overset{\frown}{FG}$ because the corresponding arcs of congruent chords are congruent.

14. If $\overset{\frown}{KM} \cong \overset{\frown}{JL}$, how does the measure of $\overline{JL}$ and $\overline{KM}$ compare?

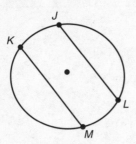

15. If $\overline{QR} \cong \overline{PS}$, how does the measure of $\overset{\frown}{QPR}$ and $\overset{\frown}{PRS}$ compare?

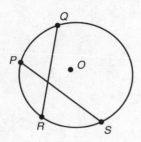

16. If $\overset{\frown}{EDG} \cong \overset{\frown}{DEH}$, how does the measure of $\overline{EG}$ and $\overline{DH}$ compare?

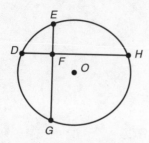

Name _____ Date _____

17. If $\angle AOB \cong \angle DOC$, what is the relationship between $\overline{AB}$ and $\overline{DC}$?

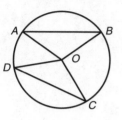

18. If $\angle EOH \cong \angle GOF$, what is the relationship between $\overset{\frown}{EH}$ and $\overset{\frown}{FG}$?

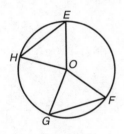

Use each diagram and the Segment Chord Theorem to write an equation involving the segments of the chords.

19.

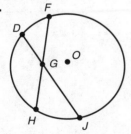

$DG \cdot GJ = FG \cdot GH$

20.

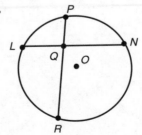

9

21.

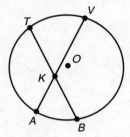

22.

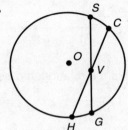

23.

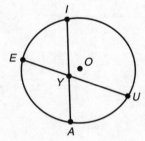

24.

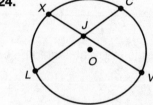

Name _____ Date _____

Solar Eclipses
Tangents and Secants

Vocabulary

Write the term from the box that best completes each statement.

external secant segment	Secant Segment Theorem	tangent segment
secant segment	Secant Tangent Theorem	Tangent Segment Theorem

1. A(n) _____ is the segment that is formed from an exterior point of a circle to the point of tangency.

2. The _____ states that if two tangent segments are drawn from the same point on the exterior of the circle, then the tangent segments are congruent.

3. When two secants intersect in the exterior of a circle, the segment that begins at the point of intersection, continues through the circle, and ends on the other side of the circle is called a(n) _____.

4. When two secants intersect in the exterior of a circle, the segment that begins at the point of intersection and ends where the secant enters the circle is called a(n) _____.

5. The _____ states that if two secants intersect in the exterior of a circle, then the product of the lengths of the secant segment and its external secant segment is equal to the product of the lengths of the second secant segment and its external secant segment.

6. The _____ states that if a tangent and a secant intersect in the exterior of a circle, then the product of the lengths of the secant segment and its external secant segment is equal to the square of the length of the tangent segment.

Problem Set

Calculate the measure of each angle. Explain your reasoning.

1. If $\overline{OA}$ is a radius, what is the measure of $\angle OAB$?

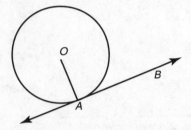

The measure of angle *OAB* is 90 degrees because a tangent line and the radius that ends at the point of tangency are perpendicular.

2. If $\overline{OD}$ is a radius, what is the measure of $\angle ODC$?

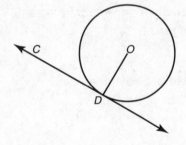

3. If $\overline{YO}$ is a radius, what is the measure of $\angle XYO$?

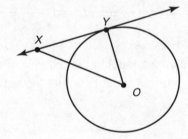

Name _____ Date _____

4. If $\overline{RS}$ is a tangent segment and $\overline{OS}$ is a radius, what is the measure of $\angle ROS$?

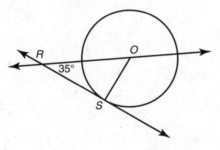

5. If $\overline{UT}$ is a tangent segment and $\overline{OU}$ is a radius, what is the measure of $\angle TOU$?

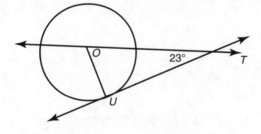

6. If $\overrightarrow{VW}$ is a tangent segment and $\overline{OV}$ is a radius, what is the measure of $\angle VWO$?

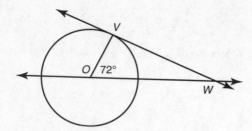

Write a statement to show the congruent segments.

7. $\overleftrightarrow{AC}$ and $\overleftrightarrow{BC}$ are tangent to circle O.

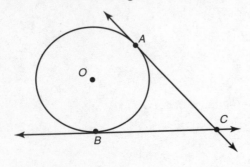

$\overline{AC} \cong \overline{CB}$

8. $\overleftrightarrow{XZ}$ and $\overleftrightarrow{ZW}$ are tangent to circle O.

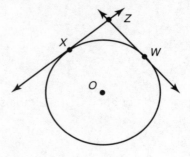

9. $\overleftrightarrow{RS}$ and $\overleftrightarrow{RT}$ are tangent to circle O.

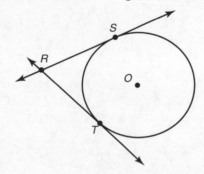

10. $\overleftrightarrow{MP}$ and $\overleftrightarrow{NP}$ are tangent to circle O.

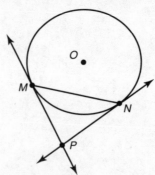

Name _____ Date _____

11. $\overleftrightarrow{DE}$ and $\overrightarrow{FE}$ are tangent to circle O.

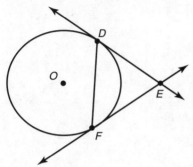

12. $\overleftrightarrow{GH}$ and $\overleftrightarrow{GI}$ are tangent to circle O.

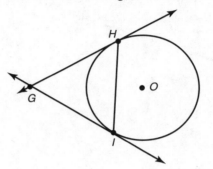

Calculate the measure of each angle. Explain your reasoning.

13. If $\overline{EF}$ and $\overline{GF}$ are tangent segments, what is the measure of $\angle EGF$?

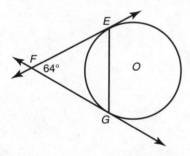

The measure of angle *EGF* is 58 degrees.

I know triangle *EFG* is isosceles and its base angles are congruent.

Let x represent the measure of angle *FEG* and the measure of angle *EGF*.

$m\angle F + x + x = 180$

$\quad\quad 64 + 2x = 180$

$\quad\quad\quad\quad 2x = 116$

$\quad\quad\quad\quad\; x = 58$

14. If $\overline{HI}$ and $\overline{JI}$ are tangent segments, what is the measure of $\angle HJI$?

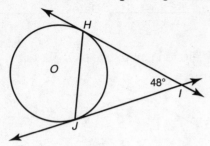

15. If $\overline{KM}$ and $\overline{LM}$ are tangent segments, what is the measure of $\angle KML$?

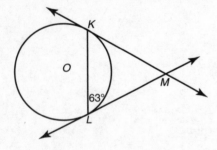

Name _____ Date _____

16. If $\overline{NP}$ and $\overline{QP}$ are tangent segments, what is the measure of $\angle NPQ$?

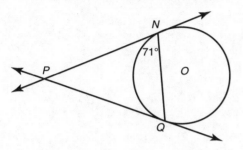

17. If $\overline{AF}$ and $\overline{VF}$ are tangent segments, what is the measure of $\angle AVF$?

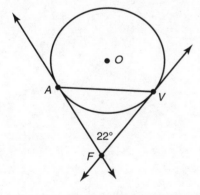

18. If $\overline{RT}$ and $\overline{MT}$ are tangent segments, what is the measure of $\angle RTM$?

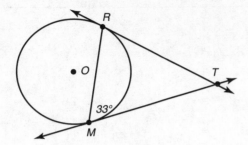

9

Name two secant segments and two external secant segments for circle O.

19.

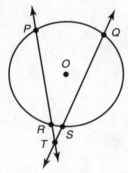

20.

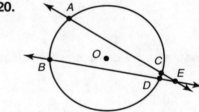

Secant segments: $\overline{PT}$ and $\overline{QT}$

External secant segments: $\overline{RT}$ and $\overline{ST}$

21.

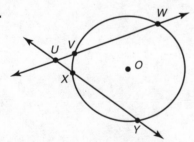

22.

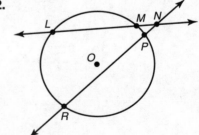

Name _____ Date _____

23.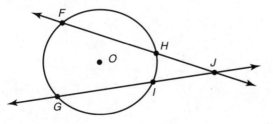

24.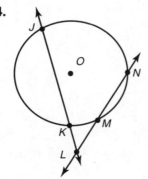

Use each diagram and the Secant Segment Theorem to write an equation involving the secant segments.

25.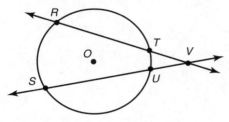

26.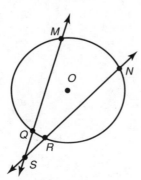

$RV \cdot TV = SV \cdot UV$

27.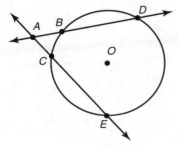

28.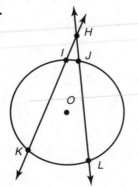

29.

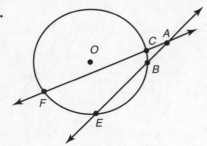

30.

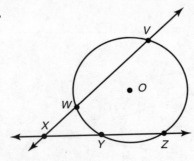

Name a tangent segment, a secant segment, and an external secant segment for circle *O*.

31.

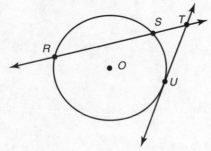

32.

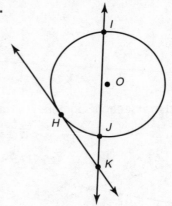

Tangent segment: $\overline{TU}$

Secant segment: $\overline{RT}$

External secant segment: $\overline{ST}$

33.

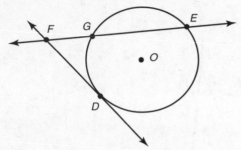

34.

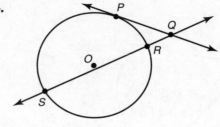

Name _____ Date _____

35.

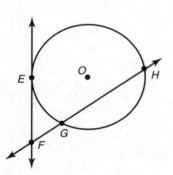

36.

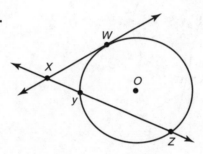

Use each diagram and the Secant Tangent Theorem to write an equation involving the secant and tangent segments.

37.

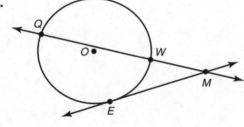

38.

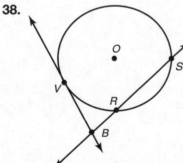

$(EM)^2 = QM \cdot WM$

39.

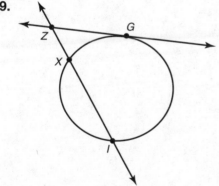

40.

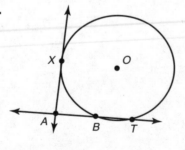

41.

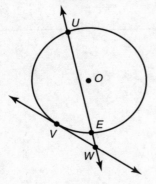

42.

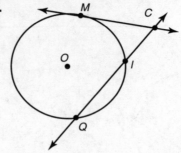

Name _____ Date _____

Replacement for a Carpenter's Square
Inscribed and Circumscribed Triangles and Quadrilaterals

Vocabulary

Answer each question.

1. How are inscribed polygons and circumscribed polygons different?

2. Describe how you can use the Inscribed Right Triangle–Diameter Theorem to show an inscribed triangle is a right triangle.

3. What does the Converse of the Inscribed Right Triangle–Diameter Theorem help to show in a circle?

4. What information about a quadrilateral inscribed in a circle does the Inscribed Quadrilateral–Opposite Angles Theorem give?

Problem Set

Draw a triangle inscribed in the circle through the three points. Then determine if the triangle is a right triangle.

1.

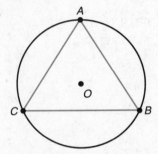

No. The triangle is not a right triangle. None of the sides of the triangle is a diameter of the circle.

2.

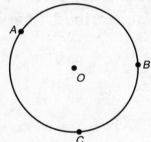

3.

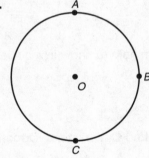

4.

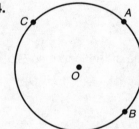

5.

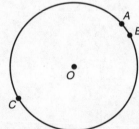

6.

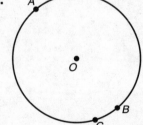

Name _____ Date _____

7.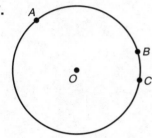

8.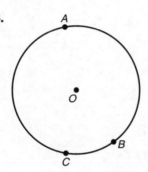

Draw a triangle inscribed in the circle through the given points. Then determine the measure of the indicated angle.

9. In $\triangle ABC$, $m\angle A = 55°$. Determine $m\angle B$.

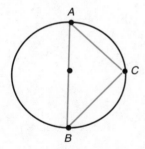

$m\angle B = 180° - 90° - 55° = 35°$

10. In $\triangle ABC$, $m\angle B = 38°$. Determine $m\angle A$.

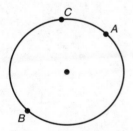

11. In $\triangle ABC$, $m\angle C = 62°$. Determine $m\angle A$.

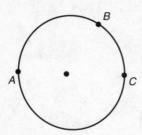

12. In $\triangle ABC$, $m\angle B = 26°$. Determine $m\angle C$.

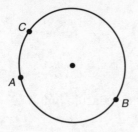

13. In $\triangle ABC$, $m\angle C = 49°$. Determine $m\angle A$.

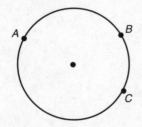

14. In $\triangle ABC$, $m\angle B = 51°$. Determine $m\angle A$.

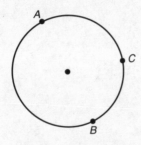

Name _____ Date _____

Draw a quadrilateral inscribed in the circle through the given four points. Then determine the measure of the indicated angle.

15. In quadrilateral *ABCD*, *m*∠*B* = 81°. Determine *m*∠*D*.

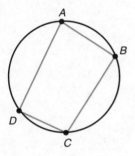

   m∠*D* = 180° − 81° = 99°

16. In quadrilateral *ABCD*, *m*∠*C* = 75°. Determine *m*∠*A*.

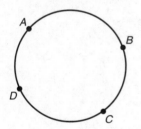

17. In quadrilateral *ABCD*, *m*∠*B* = 112°. Determine *m*∠*D*.

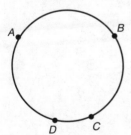

10

18. In quadrilateral *ABCD*, *m*∠*D* = 93°. Determine *m*∠*B*.

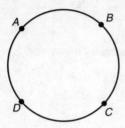

19. In quadrilateral *ABCD*, *m*∠*A* = 72°. Determine *m*∠*C*.

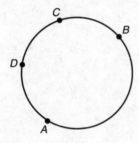

20. In quadrilateral *ABCD*, *m*∠*B* = 101°. Determine *m*∠*D*.

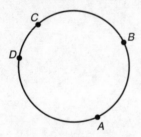

Name _____ Date _____

Construct a circle inscribed in each polygon.

21.

22.

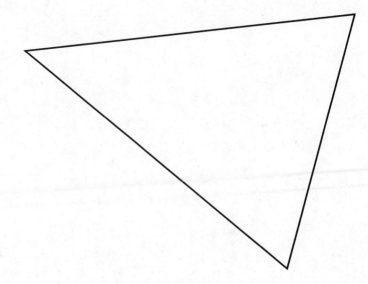

23.

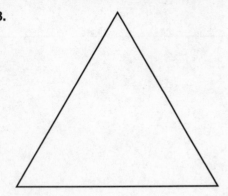

24.

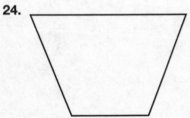

25.

Name _____ Date _____

26.

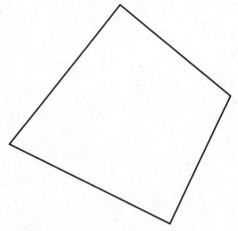

Create a proof to prove each statement.

27. Given: Inscribed $\triangle ABC$ in circle O, $m\widehat{AC} = 40°$, and $m\widehat{BC} = 140°$

Prove: $\overline{AB}$ is a diameter of circle O.

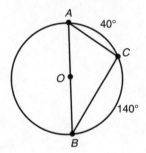

Statements	Reasons
1. $m\widehat{AC} = 40°$, $m\widehat{BC} = 140°$	1. Given
2. $m\widehat{AC} + m\widehat{BC} + m\widehat{AB} = 360°$	2. Arc Addition Postulate
3. $40° + 140° + m\widehat{AB} = 360°$	3. Substitution
4. $m\widehat{AB} = 180°$	4. Subtraction Property of Equality
5. $m\angle C = \frac{1}{2} m\widehat{AB}$	5. Definition of inscribed angle
6. $m\angle C = 90°$	6. Substitution
7. $\triangle ABC$ is a right triangle with right angle C.	7. Definition of right triangle
8. $\overline{AB}$ is the diameter of circle O.	8. Converse of Inscribed Right Triangle-Diameter Theorem

28. Given: Inscribed $\triangle RST$ in circle O with diameter $\overline{RS}$, and $m\widehat{RT} = 60°$

Prove: $m\widehat{ST} = 120°$

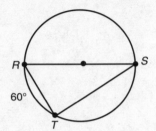

Name _____ Date _____

29. Given: Inscribed quadrilateral *ABCD* in circle *O*, $m\widehat{AB} = 50°$, and $m\widehat{BC} = 90°$

Prove: $m\angle B = 110°$

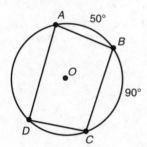

30. Given: Inscribed quadrilateral $MNPQ$ in circle O, $m\widehat{MQ} = 75°$, and $m\angle NMQ = 120°$

Prove: $m\widehat{MN} = 45°$

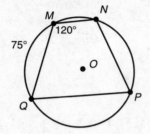

Name _____ Date _____

31. Given: $m\widehat{AB} = 50°$, $m\widehat{BC} = 90°$, and $m\widehat{CD} = 90°$

Prove: $m\angle BCD = 90°$

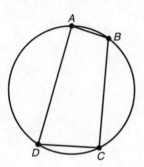

10

32. Given: $\angle BAD$ and $\angle ADC$ are supplementary angles

Prove: $m\angle BAD = m\angle ABC$

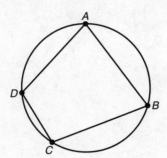

Name _____ Date _____

Gears
Arc Length

Vocabulary

Define the key term in your own words.

1. arc length

2. radian

Problem Set

Calculate the ratio of the length of each arc to the circle's circumference.

1. The measure of $\overset{\frown}{AB}$ is 40°.

$\dfrac{40°}{360°} = \dfrac{1}{9}$

The arc is $\dfrac{1}{9}$ of the circle's circumference.

2. The measure of $\overset{\frown}{CD}$ is 90°.

3. The measure of $\overset{\frown}{EF}$ is 120°.

4. The measure of $\overset{\frown}{GH}$ is 150°.

5. The measure of $\overset{\frown}{IJ}$ is 105°.

6. The measure of $\overset{\frown}{KL}$ is 75°.

Write an expression that you can use to calculate the length of $\overset{\frown}{RS}$. You do not need to simplify the expression.

7.

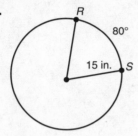

$\frac{80}{360} \cdot 2\pi(15)$

8.

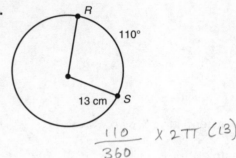

$\frac{110}{360} \times 2\pi(13)$

9.

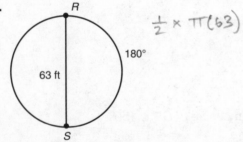

$\frac{1}{4} \times 2\pi(17)$

10.

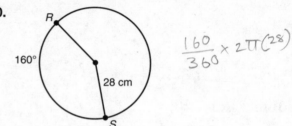

$\frac{160}{360} \times 2\pi(28)$

11.

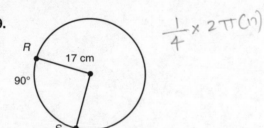

$\frac{1}{2} \times \pi(63)$

12.

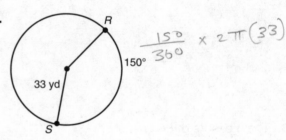

$\frac{150}{360} \times 2\pi(33)$

Calculate each arc length. Write your answer in terms of π.

13. If the measure of $\overset{\frown}{AB}$ is 45° and the radius is 12 meters, what is the arc length of $\overset{\frown}{AB}$?

$C = 2\pi(12) = 24\pi$

Fraction of C: $\dfrac{45°}{360°} = \dfrac{1}{8}$

Arc length of $\overset{\frown}{AB}$: $\dfrac{1}{8}(24\pi) = 3\pi$

The arc length of $\overset{\frown}{AB}$ is 3π meters.

Name _____ Date _____

14. If the measure of $\overset{\frown}{CD}$ is 120° and the radius is 15 centimeters, what is the arc length of $\overset{\frown}{CD}$?

15. If the measure of $\overset{\frown}{EF}$ is 60° and the radius is 8 inches, what is the arc length of $\overset{\frown}{EF}$?

16. If the measure of $\overset{\frown}{GH}$ is 30° and the radius is 6 meters, what is the arc length of $\overset{\frown}{GH}$?

17. If the measure of $\overset{\frown}{IJ}$ is 80° and the diameter is 10 centimeters, what is the arc length of $\overset{\frown}{IJ}$?

18. If the measure of $\overset{\frown}{KL}$ is 15° and the diameter is 18 feet, what is the arc length of $\overset{\frown}{KL}$?

19. If the measure of $\overset{\frown}{MN}$ is 75° and the diameter is 20 millimeters, what is the arc length of $\overset{\frown}{MN}$?

20. If the measure of $\overset{\frown}{OP}$ is 165° and the diameter is 21 centimeters, what is the arc length of $\overset{\frown}{OP}$?

Calculate each arc length. Write your answer in terms of π.

21. If the measure of $\overset{\frown}{AB}$ is 135°, what is the arc length of $\overset{\frown}{AB}$?

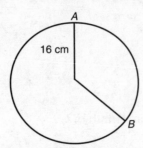

$C = 2\pi(16) = 32\pi$

Fraction of C: $\dfrac{135°}{360°} = \dfrac{3}{8}$

Arc length of $\overset{\frown}{AB}$: $\dfrac{3}{8}(32\pi) = \dfrac{96}{8}\pi = 12\pi$

The arc length of $\overset{\frown}{AB}$ is 12π cm.

Name _____ Date _____

22. If the measure of $\overarc{CD}$ is 45°, what is the arc length of $\overarc{CD}$?

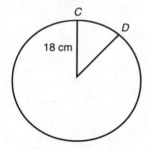

23. If the measure of $\overarc{EF}$ is 90°, what is the arc length of $\overarc{EF}$?

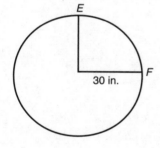

24. If the measure of $\widehat{GH}$ is 120°, what is the arc length of $\widehat{GH}$?

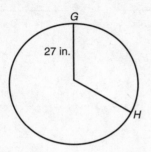

25. If the length of the radius is 4 centimeters, what is the arc length of $\widehat{IJ}$?

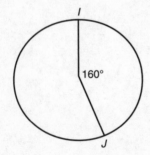

Name _____ Date _____

26. If the length of the radius is 7 centimeters, what is the arc length of $\overset{\frown}{KL}$?

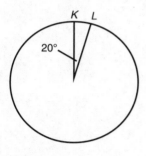

27. If the length of the radius is 11 centimeters, what is the arc length of $\overset{\frown}{MN}$?

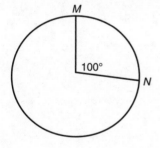

28. If the length of the radius is 17 centimeters, what is the arc length of $\overset{\frown}{OP}$?

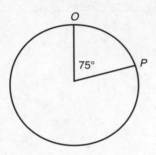

Use the given information to answer each question. Where necessary, use 3.14 to approximate π.

29. Determine the perimeter of the shaded region.

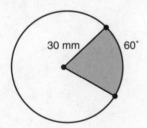

Arc length: $\dfrac{60}{360} \times 2(3.14)(30) = 31.4$ mm

Perimeter of shaded region: $31.4 + 30 + 30 = 91.4$ mm

Name _____ Date _____

30. Determine the perimeter of the figure below.

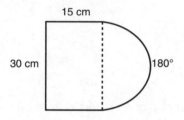

31. A semicircular cut was taken from the rectangle shown. Determine the perimeter of the shaded region.

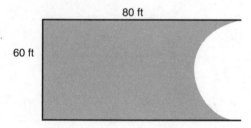

32. A circle has a circumference of 81.2 inches. What is the radius of the circle?

33. Bella used a tape measure and determined the circumference of a flagpole to be 6.2 inches. What is the radius of the flagpole?

34. Carla used a string and a tape measure and determine the circumference of a circular cup to be 12.56 inches. What is the radius of the cup?

Solve for each measure given the information.

35. If $\theta = \frac{\pi}{3}$ and $r = 3$, what is the length of the intercepted arc?

$$\theta = \frac{s}{r}$$

$$\frac{\pi}{3} = \frac{s}{3}$$

$$s = \pi$$

36. If $r = 8$ and the intercepted arc length is 6π, what is the measure of the central angle?

37. The measure of a central angle is 80°. The length of the radius is 40 mm. Determine the arc length using the formula $\frac{\text{measure of angle}}{360°} \cdot 2\pi r$.

Name _____ Date _____

38. If $r = 6$ and the intercepted arc length is 4π, what is the measure of the central angle?

39. The measure of a central angle is 80°. The length of the radius is 40 mm. Determine the arc length using the formula $\dfrac{\text{measure of angle}}{360°} \cdot 2\pi r$.

10

40. The measure of a central angle is 110°. The length of the radius is 15 ft. Determine the arc length using the formula $\dfrac{\text{measure of angle}}{360°} \cdot 2\pi r$.

Name _____ Date _____

Playing Darts
Sectors and Segments of a Circle

Vocabulary

Draw an example of each term.

1. concentric circles

2. sector of a circle

3. segment of a circle

Problem Set

Calculate the area of each sector. Write your answer in terms of π.

1. If the radius of the circle is 9 centimeters, what is the area of sector *AOB*?

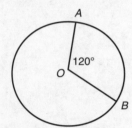

Total area of the circle = $\pi(9^2) = 81\pi$ cm²

Sector *AOB*'s fraction of the circle = $\dfrac{120°}{360°} = \dfrac{1}{3}$

Area of sector $AOB = \dfrac{1}{3}(81\pi) = 27\pi$

The area of sector *AOB* is 27π cm².

2. If the radius of the circle is 16 meters, what is the area of sector *COD*?

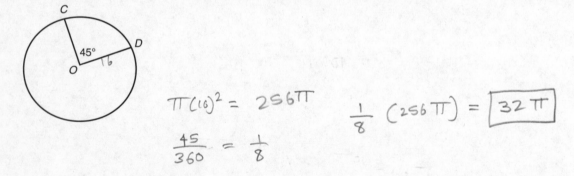

$\pi(16)^2 = 256\pi$

$\dfrac{45}{360} = \dfrac{1}{8}$

$\dfrac{1}{8}(256\pi) = \boxed{32\pi}$

Name _____ Date _____

3. If the radius of the circle is 15 feet, what is the area of sector *EOF*?

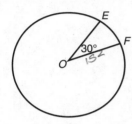

$\pi(15)^2 = 225\pi$

$\dfrac{30}{360} = \dfrac{1}{12}$

$\dfrac{1}{12}(225\pi) = \boxed{18.75\pi}$

4. If the radius of the circle is 10 inches, what is the area of sector *GOH*?

$\pi(10)^2 = 100\pi$

$\dfrac{20}{360} = \dfrac{1}{18}$

$\dfrac{1}{18}(100\pi) = \boxed{5.\overline{5}\pi}$

5. If the radius of the circle is 32 centimeters, what is the area of sector *IOJ*?

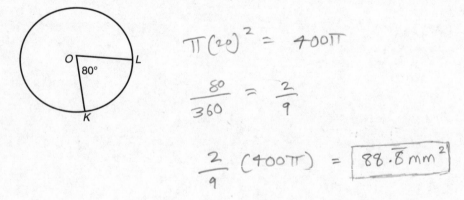

$\pi(32)^2 = 1024\pi$

$\dfrac{18}{360} = \dfrac{1}{20}$

$\dfrac{1}{20}(1024\pi) = \boxed{51.2\ \pi\ cm^2}$

$\dfrac{18}{360}\ \pi(32)^2$

51.2

6. If the radius of the circle is 20 millimeters, what is the area of sector *KOL*?

$\pi(20)^2 = 400\pi$

$\dfrac{80}{360} = \dfrac{2}{9}$

$\dfrac{2}{9}(400\pi) = \boxed{88.\overline{8}\ mm^2}$

Name _____ Date _____

7. If the radius of the circle is 24 centimeters, what is the area of sector *MON*?

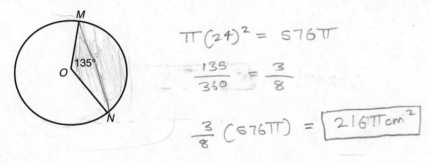

$\pi(24)^2 = 576\pi$

$\dfrac{135}{360} = \dfrac{3}{8}$

$\dfrac{3}{8}(576\pi) = \boxed{216\pi \text{ cm}^2}$

8. If the radius of the circle is 21 meters, what is the area of sector *POQ*?

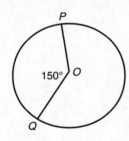

$\pi(21)^2 = 441\pi$

$\dfrac{150}{360} = \dfrac{5}{12}$

$\dfrac{5}{12}(441\pi) = 183.75 \text{ m}^2$

Calculate the area of each segment. Round your answer to the nearest tenth, if necessary. Use 3.14 to estimate π.

9. If the radius of the circle is 6 centimeters, what is the area of the shaded segment?

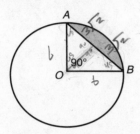

$$\pi (6)^2 = 36\pi$$

$$\frac{1}{4}(36\pi) = 9\pi$$

$$18$$

$$9\pi - 18 = 10.3$$

Total area of the circle = $\pi(6^2) = 36\pi$ cm²

Sector *AOB*'s fraction of the circle = $\dfrac{90°}{360°} = \dfrac{1}{4}$

Area of sector $AOB = \dfrac{1}{4}(36\pi) = 9\pi$ cm²

Area of $\triangle AOB = \dfrac{1}{2}(6 \cdot 6) = 18$ cm²

Area of the segment: $9\pi - 18 \approx 28.3 - 18 = 10.3$

The area of the shaded segment is approximately 10.3 cm².

10. If the radius of the circle is 14 inches, what is the area of the shaded segment?

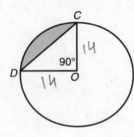

$$\pi(14)^2 = 196\pi$$

$$\frac{1}{4}(196\pi) = 49\pi$$

$$\frac{1}{2}(14 \cdot 14) = 98$$

$$49\pi - 98 = \boxed{55.9 \text{ in}^2}$$

Name _____ Date _____

11. If the radius of the circle is 17 feet, what is the area of the shaded segment?

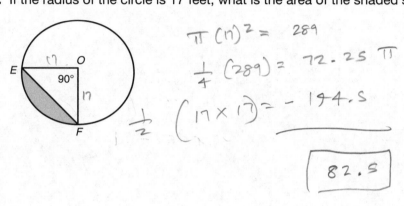

$\pi (17)^2 = 289$

$\frac{1}{4}(289) = 72.25\ \pi$

$\frac{1}{2}(17 \times 17) = - 144.5$ _____

$\boxed{82.5}$

12. If the radius of the circle is 22 centimeters, what is the area of the shaded segment?

$\pi(22)^2 = 484\pi$

$\frac{1}{4} \cdot x\ 484\pi = 121\pi$

$\frac{1}{2}(22 \times 22) = -242$ _____

$\boxed{138.1}$

10

13. If the radius of the circle is 25 meters, what is the area of the shaded segment?

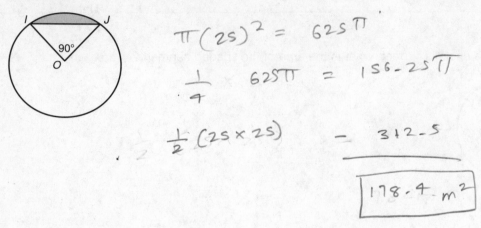

$$\pi(25)^2 = 625\pi$$

$$\frac{1}{4} \times 625\pi = 156-25\pi$$

$$\frac{1}{2}(25 \times 25) \qquad - \quad 312.5$$

$$\boxed{178.4 \, m^2}$$

14. If the radius of the circle is 30 centimeters, what is the area of the shaded segment?

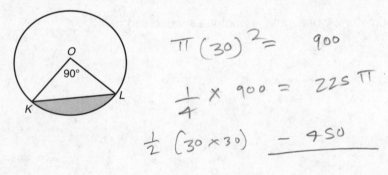

$$\pi(30)^2 = 900$$

$$\frac{1}{4} \times 900 = 225\pi$$

$$\frac{1}{2}(30 \times 30) \qquad - \quad 450$$

$$\boxed{256.9 \, cm^2}$$

Name _____ Date _____

In circle O below, $m\overarc{AB} = 90°$. Use the given information to determine the length of the radius of circle O.

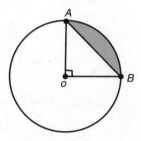

10

15. If the area of the segment is $16\pi - 32$ square feet, what is the length of the radius of circle O?

$$16\pi = \frac{90°}{360°}(\pi r^2)$$
$$16\pi = \frac{1}{4}(\pi r^2)$$
$$64 = r^2$$
$$8 = r$$

The length of the radius is 8 feet.

16. If the area of the segment is $25\pi - 50$ square inches, what is the length of the radius of circle O?

17. If the area of the segment is $\pi - 2$ square meters, what is the length of the radius of circle O?

18. If the area of the segment is $56.25\pi - 112.5$ square yards, what is the length of the radius of circle *O*?

19. If the area of the segment is $121\pi - 242$ square feet, what is the length of the radius of circle *O*?

20. If the area of the segment is $90.25\pi - 180.5$ square millimeters, what is the length of the radius of circle *O*?

Name _____ Date _____

Circle K. Excellent!
Circle Problems

Vocabulary

Define the key term in your own words.

1. linear velocity

2. angular velocity

Problem Set

Use the given arc measures to determine the measures of the indicated angles.

1.

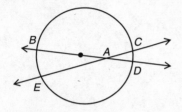

$m\widehat{ED} = 140°$

$m\widehat{CD} = 10°$

$m\angle EAD = \underline{\quad 155° \quad}$

$m\angle CAD = \underline{\quad 25° \quad}$

Because arc *BCD* is a semicircle, its measure is 180°.

$m\widehat{BCD} = m\widehat{BC} + m\widehat{CD}$

$180° = m\widehat{BC} + 10°$

$m\widehat{BC} = 170°$

$m\angle EAD = \frac{1}{2}(m\widehat{ED} + m\widehat{BC})$

$m\angle EAD = \frac{1}{2}(140° + 170°)$

$m\angle EAD = \frac{1}{2}(310°)$

$m\angle EAD = 155°$

$m\angle CAD = 180° - 155°$

$\qquad = 25°$

2.

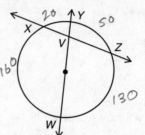

$m\widehat{XY} = 20°$

$m\widehat{YZ} = 50°$

$m\angle XVY = \underline{\quad 75 \quad}$

$m\angle YVZ = \underline{\quad 105 \quad}$

$130 + 20 = \frac{150}{2}$

$= 75$

$\begin{array}{r} 180 \\ -\ 75 \\ \hline 105 \end{array}$

Name _____ Date _____

3.

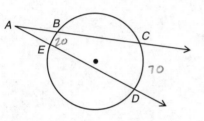

70 − 20 = 50
      ÷ 2
    ———
      25

$m\overarc{BE} = 20°$

$m\overarc{CD} = 70°$

$m\angle A = \underline{\ 25\ }$

4.

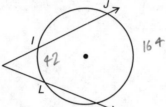

164 − 42 =

122 ÷ 2 =

61

$m\overarc{JK} = 164°$

$m\overarc{IL} = 42°$

$m\angle H = \underline{\ 61\ }$

10

5.

170 − 20 = 150
         ÷ 2
      —————

$m\overarc{AE} = 170°$

$m\overarc{BD} = 20°$

$m\angle C = \underline{\ 75\ }$

6.

50 − 12 = 38
       ÷ 2
     ————
       19

$m\overarc{MQ} = 50°$

$m\overarc{NP} = 12°$

$m\angle O = \underline{\ 19\ }$

Calculate the area of each sector. Use 3.14 for π. Round to the nearest hundredth, if necessary.

7.

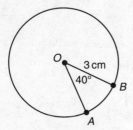

$A = \dfrac{40}{360}\pi r^2$

$A = \dfrac{1}{9}\pi(3)^2$

$A = \dfrac{1}{9}\pi(9)$

$A = \pi$

$A \approx 3.14$ **square centimeters**

8.

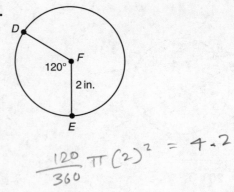

$\dfrac{120}{360}\,\pi(2)^2 = 4.2$

9.

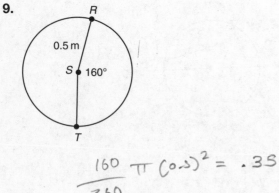

$\dfrac{160}{360}\,\pi(0.5)^2 = .35$

10.

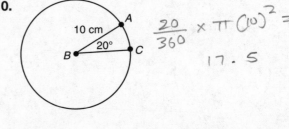

$\dfrac{20}{360} \times \pi(10)^2 =$

17.5

Name _____ Date _____

11.

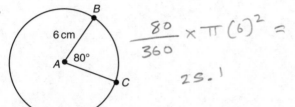

$$\frac{80}{360} \times \pi (6)^2 =$$

$$25.1$$

12.

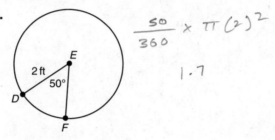

$$\frac{50}{360} \times \pi (2)^2$$

$$1.7$$

Calculate the area of the shaded segment of the circle.

13.

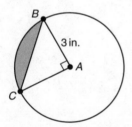

The area of the shaded segment = the area of sector ABC − the area of triangle ABC.

Area of sector $ABC = \dfrac{90}{360}\pi r^2$

$$= \frac{1}{4}\pi(3)^2$$

$$\approx \frac{1}{4}(3.14)(9)$$

$$\approx 7.07 \text{ square inches}$$

Area of $\triangle ABC = \dfrac{1}{2}bh$

$$= \frac{1}{2}(3)(3)$$

$$= \frac{9}{2} = 4.5 \text{ square inches}$$

Area of segment $\approx 7.07 - 4.5 \approx 2.57$ square inches

14.

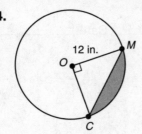

Name _____ Date _____

15.

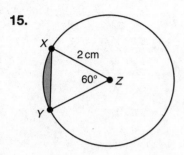

16.

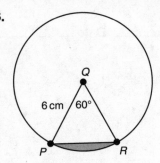

Determine each linear or angular velocity.

17. Determine the linear velocity if $s = 12$ cm and $t = 2$ sec.

$$v = \frac{s}{t}$$

$$= \frac{12 \text{ cm}}{2 \text{ sec}}$$

$$= 6 \text{ cm/sec}$$

18. Determine the angular velocity if $\theta = 12\pi$ and $t = 5\pi$ seconds.

Name _____ Date _____

19. Determine the linear velocity if $s = 4.2$ in. and $t = 12$ s.

20. Determine the angular velocity if $\theta = 9\pi$ and $t = 16$ seconds.

21. Determine the linear velocity if $s = 25$ ft and $t = 120$ s.

22. Determine the angular velocity if $\theta = \frac{3}{4}\pi$ and $t = 10\pi$ seconds.

10

Name _____ Date _____

Whirlygigs for Sale!
Rotating Two-Dimensional Figures through Space

Vocabulary

Describe the term in your own words.

1. disc

Problem Set

Write the name of the solid figure that would result from rotating the plane figure shown around the axis shown.

1.

sphere

2.

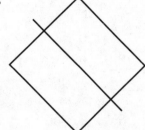

3.

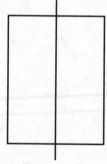

4.

5.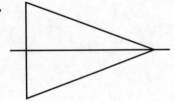

6.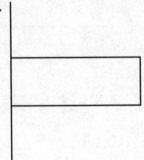

Relate the dimensions of the plane figure to the solid figure that results from its rotation around the given axis.

7.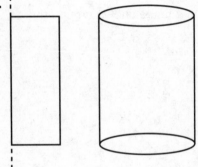

The base of the rectangle is equal to the radius of the cylinder's base.

8.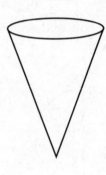

9.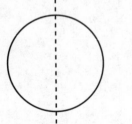

10.

Name _____ Date _____

11.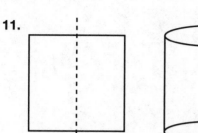

12.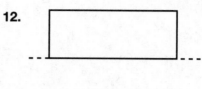

11

Name _____ Date _____

Cakes and Pancakes
Translating and Stacking Two-Dimensional Figures

Vocabulary

Match each definition to its corresponding term.

1. oblique triangular prism

    A. dotted paper used to show three-dimensional diagrams

2. oblique rectangular prism

    B. a prism with rectangles as bases whose lateral faces are not perpendicular to those bases

3. oblique cylinder

    C. a 3-dimensional object with two parallel, congruent, circular bases, and a lateral face not perpendicular to those bases

4. isometric paper

    D. a prism with triangles as bases whose lateral faces are not perpendicular to those bases

5. right triangular prism

    E. a 3-dimensional object with two parallel, congruent, circular bases, and a lateral face perpendicular to those bases

6. right rectangular prism

    F. a prism with triangles as bases whose lateral faces are perpendicular to those bases

7. right cylinder

    G. a prism with rectangles as bases whose lateral faces are perpendicular to those bases

11

Problem Set

Connect the corresponding vertices of the figure and the translated figure. Name the shape that was translated and name the resulting solid figure.

1.

right triangle; right triangular prism

2.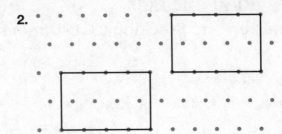

3.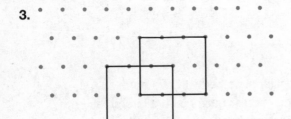

4.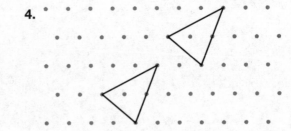

5.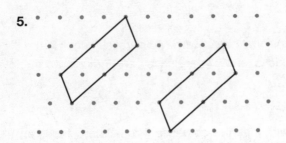

6.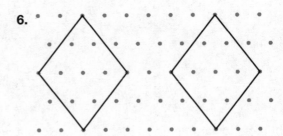

Name _____ Date _____

Name the solid formed by stacking 1000 of the congruent shapes shown.

7.

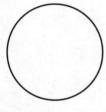

cylinder

8.

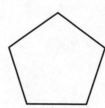

9.

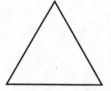

10.

11.

12.

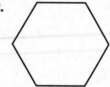

11

Name the solid formed by stacking similar shapes so that each layer of the stack is composed of a slightly smaller shape than the previous layer.

13.

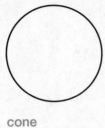

cone

14.

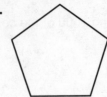

15.

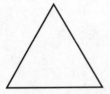

16.

17.

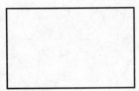

18.

Name _____ Date _____

Relate the dimensions of the given plane shape to the related solid figure. Tell whether the shape was made by stacking congruent or similar shapes.

19.

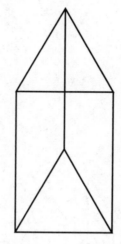

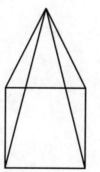

The lengths of the sides of the triangle are the same as the lengths of the sides of the base of the triangular prism. The triangular prism was made by stacking congruent triangles.

20.

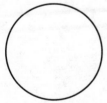

21.

22.

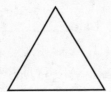 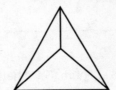

23.

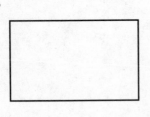 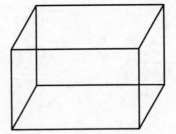

11

24.

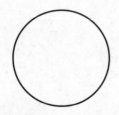 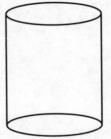

Name _____ Date _____

Cavalieri's Principles
Application of Cavalieri's Principles

Vocabulary

Describe the term in your own words.

1. Cavalieri's principle

Problem Set

Estimate the approximate area or volume each irregular or oblique figure. Round your answers to the nearest tenth, if necessary.

1. The height of each rectangle is 10 yards and the base of each rectangle is 1.5 yards.

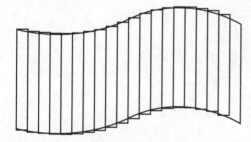

I determined that the area is approximately 300 square yards.

area = base × height
       = (1.5 × 20)(10)
       = (30)(10)
       = 300

I determined the sum of the areas of the rectangles to estimate the area of the figure because Cavalieri's principle says that the area of the irregular figure is equal to the sum of the areas of the multiple rectangles when the base and height of all the rectangles are equal.

2. The height of each rectangle is 0.6 inch and the base of each rectangle is 2 inches.

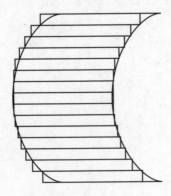

3.

1 cm

10 cm

4.

12 ft

4 ft

Name _____ Date _____

Spin to Win
Volume of Cones and Pyramids

Problem Set

Calculate the volume of each cone. Use 3.14 for π.

1.

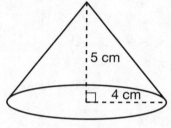

volume $= \frac{1}{3}Bh$

$\quad\quad\quad = \frac{1}{3}\pi r^2 h$

$\quad\quad\quad = \frac{1}{3}\pi(4)^2(5)$

$\quad\quad\quad \approx 83.73$ cubic centimeters

2.

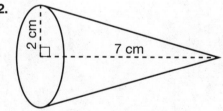

3.

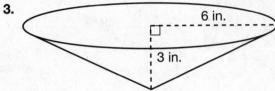

4.

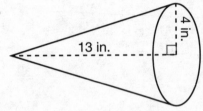

5.

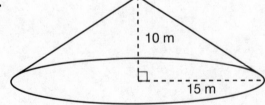

Name _____ Date _____

6.

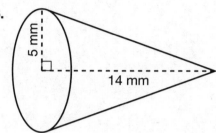

5 mm

14 mm

7.

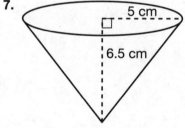

5 cm

6.5 cm

8.

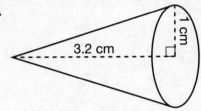

9.

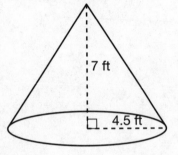

10.

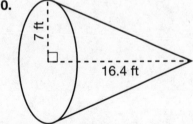

Name _____ Date _____

Calculate the volume of the square pyramid.

11.

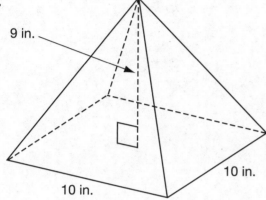

9 in.

10 in.

10 in.

Volume $= \frac{1}{3}Bh$

$= \frac{1}{3}s^2h$

$= \frac{1}{3}(10)^2(9)$

$= 300$ cubic inches

11

12. 9 ft

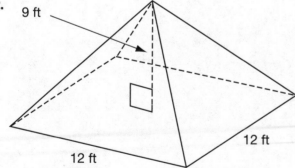

12 ft

12 ft

13.

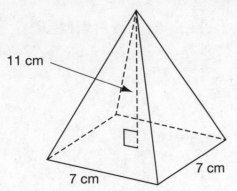

11 cm

7 cm   7 cm

14.

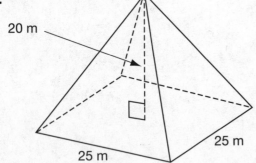

20 m

25 m   25 m

Name _____ Date _____

15.

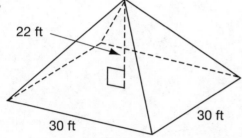

16.

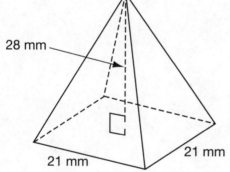

17.

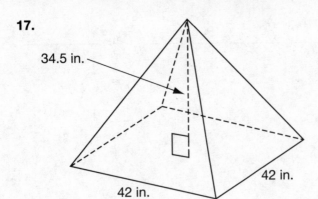

34.5 in.

42 in.

42 in.

18. 75 cm

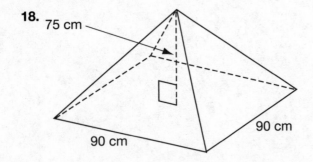

90 cm

90 cm

Name _____ Date _____

19.

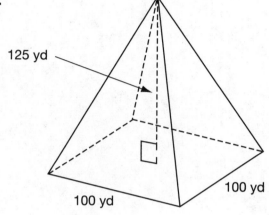

125 yd

100 yd

100 yd

20.

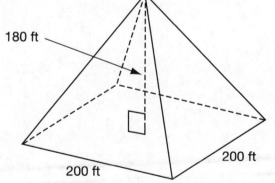

180 ft

200 ft

200 ft

Name _____ Date _____

Spheres à la Archimedes
Volume of a Sphere

Vocabulary

Describe a similarity and a difference between each term.

1. radius of a sphere and diameter of a sphere

2. cross section of a sphere and great circle of a sphere

3. hemisphere and sphere

Describe the term in your own words.

4. annulus

Problem Set

Calculate the volume of each sphere. Use 3.14 for π. Round decimals to the nearest tenth, if necessary.

1. $r = 7$ meters

$$\text{Volume} = \frac{4}{3}\pi r^3$$

$$= \frac{4}{3}\pi(7)^3$$

$$= \frac{1372}{3}\pi$$

$$\approx 1436.0 \text{ cubic meters}$$

2. $r = 6$ inches

3. $d = 20$ inches

4. $d = 16$ meters

5. $r = 2.5$ centimeters

6. $r = 11.25$ millimeters

Name _____ Date _____

7. The radius of the great circle of a sphere is 8 meters.

8. The radius of the great circle of a sphere is 12 feet.

9. The diameter of the great circle of a sphere is 20 centimeters.

10. The diameter of the great circle of a sphere is 15 yards.

11

Name _____ Date _____

Turn Up the . . .
Using Volume Formulas

Problem Set

Calculate the volume of each pyramid.

1.

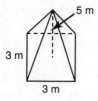

$V = \frac{1}{3}Bh$

$\quad = \frac{1}{3}(3)(3)(5)$

$\quad = 15$ cubic meters

2.

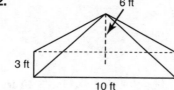

3.

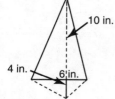

4.

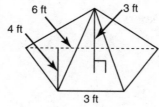

5.

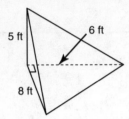

5 ft
6 ft
8 ft

6.

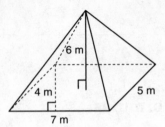

6 m
4 m
5 m
7 m

Calculate the volume of each cylinder. Use 3.14 for π. Round decimals to the nearest tenth, if necessary.

7. 5.5 m

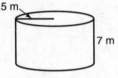

7 m

$V = \pi r^2 h$

$= \pi (5.5)^2 (7)$

$= 211.75\pi$

≈ 664.9 cubic meters

8. 30 yd

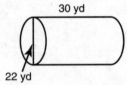

22 yd

9. 20 m

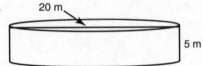

5 m

10. 10 ft

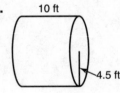

4.5 ft

Name _____ Date _____

11.

12.

13.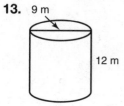

14.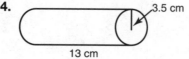

Calculate the volume of each cone. Use 3.14 for π. Round decimals to the nearest tenth, if necessary.

15.

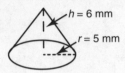

$V = \frac{1}{3}\pi r^2 h$

$= \frac{1}{3}\pi(5)^2(6)$

$= 50\pi$

≈ 157 cubic millimeters

16.

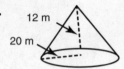

17.

18.

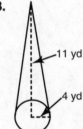

Name _____ Date _____

19.

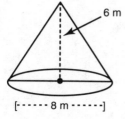

6 m

[------ 8 m ------]

20. [------ 3 ft ------]

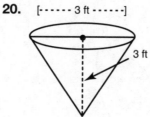

3 ft

21.

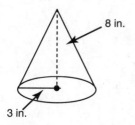

8 in.

3 in.

22.

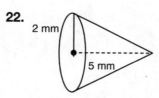

2 mm

5 mm

Calculate the volume of each sphere. Use 3.14 for π. Round decimals to the nearest tenth, if necessary.

23.

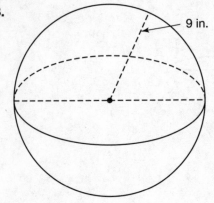

9 in.

$V = \dfrac{4}{3}\pi r^3$

$= \dfrac{4}{3}\pi(9)^3$

$= 972\pi$

≈ 3052.08 cubic inches

24.

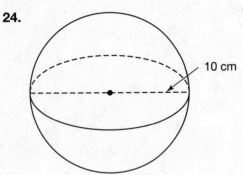

10 cm

Name _____ Date _____

25.

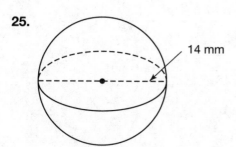

14 mm

26.

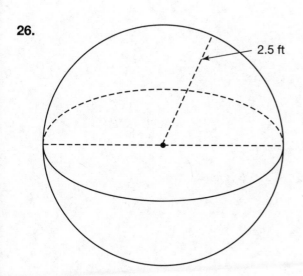

2.5 ft

11

Name _____ Date _____

Tree Rings
Cross Sections

Problem Set

Describe the shape of each cross section shown.

1.

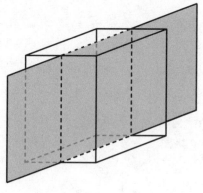

2.

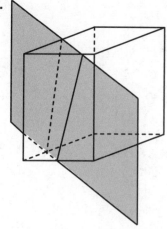

The cross section is a rectangle.

3.

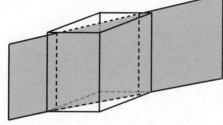

4.

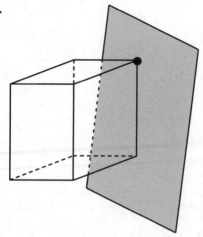

5.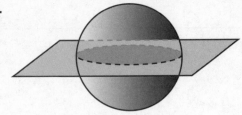

6.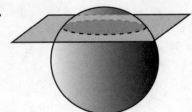

7.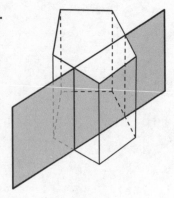

8.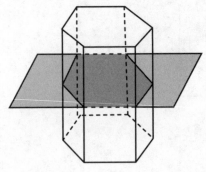

9.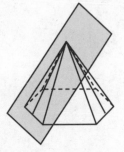

10.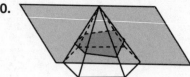

Name _____ Date _____

Use the given information to sketch and describe the cross sections.

11. Consider a cylinder. Sketch and describe three different cross sections formed when a plane intersects a cylinder.

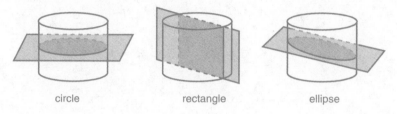

circle   rectangle   ellipse

12. Consider a rectangular prism. Sketch and describe three different cross sections formed when a plane intersects a rectangular prism.

13. Consider a pentagonal prism. Sketch and describe three different cross sections formed when a plane intersects a pentagonal prism.

14. Consider a triangular prism. Sketch and describe three different cross sections formed when a plane intersects a triangular prism.

15. Consider a triangular pyramid. Sketch and describe three different cross sections formed when a plane intersects a triangular pyramid.

16. Consider a hexagonal pyramid. Sketch and describe three different cross sections formed when a plane intersects a hexagonal pyramid.

Name _____ Date _____

Consider two cross sections of the given solid. One cross section is parallel to the base of the solid, and the other cross section is perpendicular to the base of the solid. Determine the shape of each of these cross sections.

17.

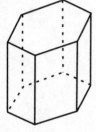

A cross section that is parallel to the base is a hexagon congruent to the hexagonal bases.

A cross section that is perpendicular to the base is a rectangle.

18.

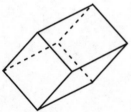

19.

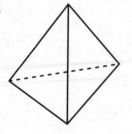

20.

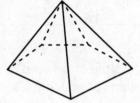

21.

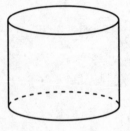

22.

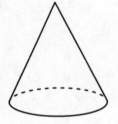

Name _____ Date _____

23.

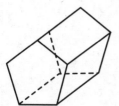

24.

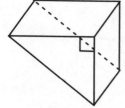

Draw a solid that could have each cross section described.

25. cross section parallel to the base

   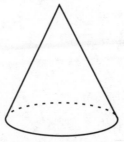

The solid is a cone. (The solid could also be a cylinder.)

26. cross section perpendicular to the base

27. cross section parallel to the base

11

28. cross section parallel to the base

Name _____ Date _____

29. cross section perpendicular to the base

30. cross section parallel to the base

11

11

Name _____   Date _____

Two Dimensions Meet Three Dimensions
Diagonals in Three Dimensions

Problem Set

Draw all of the sides you cannot see in each rectangular solid using dotted lines. Then, draw a three-dimensional diagonal using a solid line.

1.
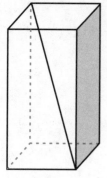

2.
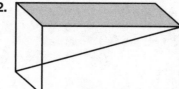

3.
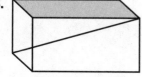

4.
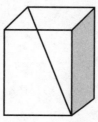

5.
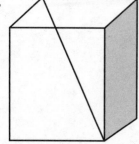

6.
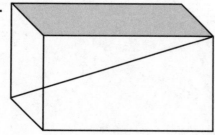

Determine the length of the diagonal of each rectangular solid.

7.

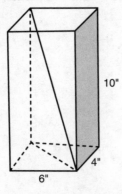

The length of the diagonal of the rectangular solid is about 12.33 inches.

The length of the first leg is 10 inches.

Length of Second Leg:

$d^2 = 6^2 + 4^2$

$\quad = 36 + 16$

$d = \sqrt{52} \approx 7.21$

Length of Diagonal:

$d = 7.21^2 + 10^2$

$\quad = 51.98 + 100$

$d = \sqrt{151.98} \approx 12.33$

8.

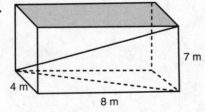

Name _____ Date _____

9.

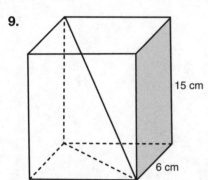

15 cm

6 cm

10 cm

10.

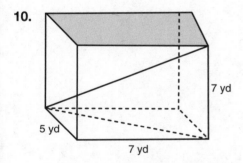

7 yd

5 yd

7 yd

11.

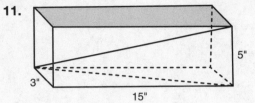

12.

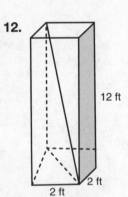

Name _____ Date _____

Diagonals are shown on the front panel, side panel, and top panel of each rectangular solid. Sketch three triangles using the diagonals from each of the three panels and some combination of the length, width, and height of the solid.

13.

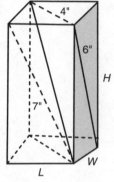

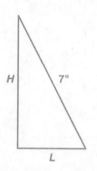 

14.

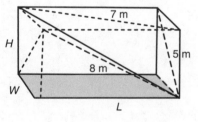

15.

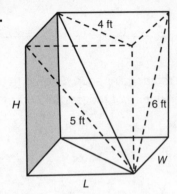

16.

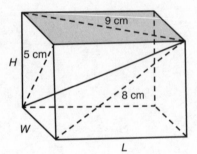

17.

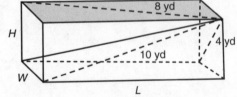

Name _____ Date _____

18.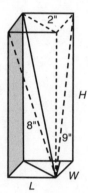

A rectangular solid is shown. Use the diagonals across the front panel, the side panel, and the top panel of each solid to determine the length of the three-dimensional diagonal.

19.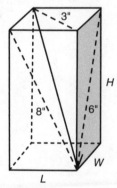

$SD^2 = \frac{1}{2}(8^2 + 6^2 + 3^2)$

$SD^2 = \frac{1}{2}(64 + 36 + 9)$

$SD^2 = \frac{1}{2}(109)$

$SD^2 = 54.5$

$SD = \sqrt{54.5} \approx 7.4$

The length of the three-dimensional diagonal is $\sqrt{54.5}$ or approximately 7.4 inches.

20.

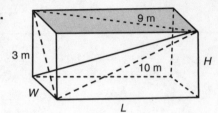

21.

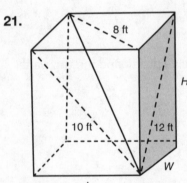

Name _____ Date _____

22.

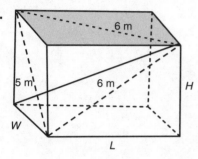

23.

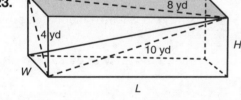

24.

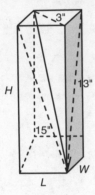

Use a formula to answer each question. Show your work and explain your reasoning.

25. A packing company is in the planning stages of creating a box that includes a diagonal support. The box has a width of 5 feet, a length of 6 feet, and a height of 8 feet. How long will the diagonal support need to be?

The diagonal support should be approximately 11.18 feet. I determined the answer by calculating the length of the box's diagonal.

$d^2 = 5^2 + 6^2 + 8^2$

$d^2 = 25 + 36 + 64$

$d^2 = 125$

$d \approx 11.18$

Name _____ Date _____

26. A plumber needs to transport a 12-foot pipe to a jobsite. The interior of his van is 90 inches in length, 40 inches in width, and 40 inches in height. Will the pipe fit inside the plumber's van?

27. You are landscaping the flower beds in your front yard. You choose to plant a tree that measures 5 feet from the root ball to the top. The interior of your car is 60 inches in length, 45 inches in width, and 40 inches in height. Will the tree fit inside your car?

11

28. Julian is constructing a box for actors to stand on during a school play. To make the box stronger, he decides to include diagonals on all sides of the box and a three-dimensional diagonal through the center of the box. The diagonals across the front and back of the box are each 2 feet, the diagonals across the sides of the box are each 3 feet, and the diagonals across the top and bottom of the box are each 7 feet. How long is the diagonal through the center of the box?

29. Carmen has a cardboard box. The length of the diagonal across the front of the box is 9 inches. The length of the diagonal across the side of the box is 7 inches. The length of the diagonal across the top of the box is 5 inches. Carmen wants to place a 10-inch stick into the box and be able to close the lid. Will the stick fit inside the box?

30. A technician needs to pack a television in a cardboard box. The length of the diagonal across the front of the box is 17 inches. The length of the diagonal across the side of the box is 19 inches. The length of the diagonal across the top of the box is 20 inches. The three-dimensional diagonal of the television is 24 inches. Will the television fit in the box?

Name _____ Date _____

Up and Down or Down and Up
Exploring Quadratic Functions

Vocabulary

Write the given quadratic function in standard form. Then describe the shape of the graph and whether it has an absolute maximum or absolute minimum. Explain your reasoning.

$2x^2 = x + 4$

Problem Set

Write each quadratic function in standard form.

1. $f(x) = x(x + 3)$

   $f(x) = x(x + 3)$

   $f(x) = x \cdot x + x \cdot 3$

   $f(x) = x^2 + 3x$

2. $f(x) = 3x(x - 8) + 5$

3. $g(s) = (s + 4)s - 2$

4. $d(t) = (20 + 3t)t$

5. $f(n) = \dfrac{2n(3n - 6)}{3}$

6. $m(s) = \dfrac{s(s + 3)}{4}$

Write a quadratic function in standard form that represents each area as a function of the width. Remember to define your variables.

7. A builder is designing a rectangular parking lot. She has 300 feet of fencing to enclose the parking lot around three sides.

Let x = the width of the parking lot

The length of the parking lot = $300 - 2x$

Let A = the area of the parking lot

Area of a rectangle = width $\times$ length

$A = w \cdot l$

$A(x) = x \cdot (300 - 2x)$

$ = x \cdot 300 - x \cdot 2x$

$ = 300x - 2x^2$

$ = -2x^2 + 300x$

8. Aiko is enclosing a new rectangular flower garden with a rabbit garden fence. She has 40 feet of fencing.

9. Pedro is building a rectangular sandbox for the community park. The materials available limit the perimeter of the sandbox to at most 100 feet.

Name _____ Date _____

10. Lea is designing a rectangular quilt. She has 16 feet of piping to finish the quilt around three sides.

11. Kiana is making a rectangular vegetable garden alongside her home. She has 24 feet of fencing to enclose the garden around the three open sides.

12. Nelson is building a rectangular ice rink for the community park. The materials available limit the perimeter of the ice rink to at most 250 feet.

Use your graphing calculator to determine the absolute maximum of each function. Describe what the *x*- and *y*-coordinates of this point represent in terms of the problem situation.

13. A builder is designing a rectangular parking lot. He has 400 feet of fencing to enclose the parking lot around three sides. Let x = the width of the parking lot. Let A = the area of the parking lot. The function $A(x) = -2x^2 + 400x$ represents the area of the parking lot as a function of the width.

The absolute maximum of the function is at (100, 20,000).

The *x*-coordinate of 100 represents the width in feet that produces the maximum area.

The *y*-coordinate of 20,000 represents the maximum area in square feet of the parking lot.

14. Joelle is enclosing a portion of her yard to make a pen for her ferrets. She has 20 feet of fencing. Let x = the width of the pen. Let A = the area of the pen. The function $A(x) = -x^2 + 10x$ represents the area of the pen as a function of the width.

15. A baseball is thrown upward from a height of 5 feet with an initial velocity of 42 feet per second. Let t = the time in seconds after the baseball is thrown. Let h = the height of the baseball. The quadratic function $h(t) = -16t^2 + 42t + 5$ represents the height of the baseball as a function of time.

16. Hector is standing on top of a playground set at a park. He throws a water balloon upward from a height of 12 feet with an initial velocity of 25 feet per second. Let t = the time in seconds after the balloon is thrown. Let h = the height of the balloon. The quadratic function $h(t) = -16t^2 + 25t + 12$ represents the height of the balloon as a function of time.

17. Franco is building a rectangular roller-skating rink at the community park. The materials available limit the perimeter of the skating rink to at most 180 feet. Let x = the width of the skating rink. Let A = the area of the skating rink. The function $A(x) = -x^2 + 90x$ represents the area of the skating rink as a function of the width.

18. A football is thrown upward from a height of 6 feet with an initial velocity of 65 feet per second. Let t = the time in seconds after the football is thrown. Let h = the height of the football. The quadratic function $h(t) = -16t^2 + 65t + 6$ represents the height of the football as a function of time.

Name _____ Date _____

Just U and I
Comparing Linear and Quadratic Functions

Vocabulary

Write a definition for each term in your own words.

1. leading coefficient

2. second differences

Problem Set

Graph each table of values. Describe the type of function represented by the graph.

1.

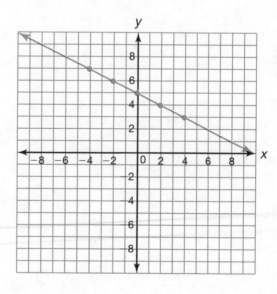

x	y
−4	7
−2	6
0	5
2	4
4	3

The function represented by the graph is a linear function.

2.

x	y
−3	−2
−2	0
−1	2
0	4
1	6

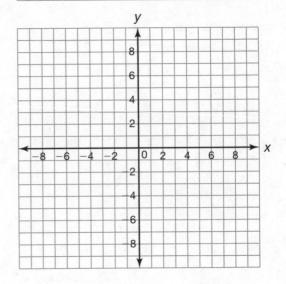

3.

x	y
−2	−8
0	0
2	4
4	4
6	0

4.

x	y
−6	6
−4	0
−2	−2
0	0
2	6

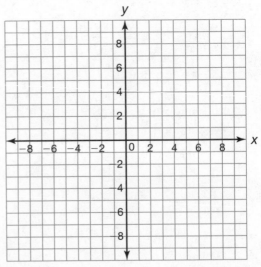

Name _____ Date _____

5.

x	y
1	6
2	3
3	0
4	−3
5	−6

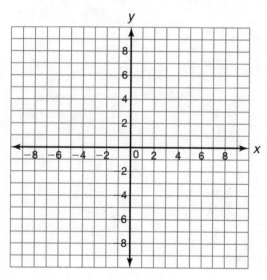

6.

x	y
−3	−9
0	0
3	3
6	0
9	−9

12

Calculate the first and second differences for each table of values. Describe the type of function represented by the table.

7.

x	y	First Differences	Second Differences
−2	−6		
		3	
−1	−3		0
		3	
0	0		0
		3	
1	3		0
		3	
2	6		

The function represented by the table
is a linear function.

8.

x	y	First Differences	Second Differences
−2	12		
−1	3		
0	0		
1	3		
2	12		

9.

x	y	First Differences	Second Differences
−3	3		
−2	4		
−1	5		
0	6		
1	7		

10.

x	y	First Differences	Second Differences
−1	1		
0	0		
1	3		
2	10		
3	21		

Name _____ Date _____

11.

x	y	First Differences		Second Differences
−4	−48			
−3	−27			
−2	−12			
−1	−3			
0	0			

12.

x	y	First Differences		Second Differences
−1	10			
0	8			
1	6			
2	4			
3	2			

12

12

Name _____ Date _____

Walking the . . . Curve?
Domain, Range, Zeros, and Intercepts

Vocabulary

Choose the term that best completes each sentence.

zeros	vertical motion model	interval	open interval
closed interval	half-closed interval	half-open interval	

1. An _____ is defined as the set of real numbers between two given numbers.

2. The x-intercepts of a graph of a quadratic function are also called the _____ of the quadratic function.

3. An _____ (a, b) describes the set of all numbers between a and b, but not including a or b.

4. A _____ or _____ (a, b] describes the set of all numbers between a and b, including b but not including a. Or, [a, b) describes the set of all numbers between a and b, including a but not including b.

5. A quadratic equation that models the height of an object at a given time is a _____.

6. A _____ [a, b] describes the set of all numbers between a and b, including a and b.

Problem Set

Graph the function that represents each problem situation. Identify the absolute maximum, zeros, and the domain and range of the function in terms of both the graph and problem situation. Round your answers to the nearest hundredth, if necessary.

1. A model rocket is launched from the ground with an initial velocity of 120 feet per second. The function $g(t) = -16t^2 + 120t$ represents the height of the rocket, $g(t)$, t seconds after it was launched.

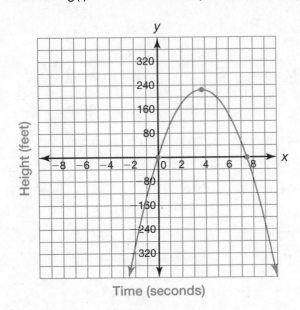

Absolute maximum: (3.75, 225)

Zeros: (0, 0), (7.5, 0)

Domain of graph: The domain is all real numbers from negative infinity to positive infinity.

Domain of the problem: The domain is all real numbers greater than or equal to 0 and less than or equal to 7.5.

Range of graph: The range is all real numbers less than or equal to 225.

Range of the problem: The range is all real numbers less than or equal to 225 and greater than or equal to 0.

2. A model rocket is launched from the ground with an initial velocity of 60 feet per second. The function $g(t) = -16t^2 + 60t$ represents the height of the rocket, $g(t)$, t seconds after it was launched.

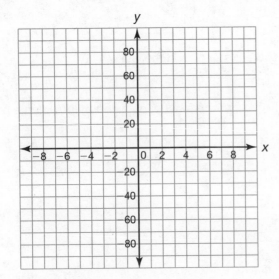

Name _____ Date _____

3. A baseball is thrown into the air from a height of 5 feet with an initial vertical velocity of 15 feet per second. The function $g(t) = -16t^2 + 15t + 5$ represents the height of the baseball, $g(t)$, t seconds after it was thrown.

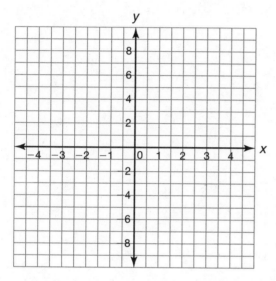

4. A football is thrown into the air from a height of 6 feet with an initial vertical velocity of 50 feet per second. The function $g(t) = -16t^2 + 50t + 6$ represents the height of the football, $g(t)$, t seconds after it was thrown.

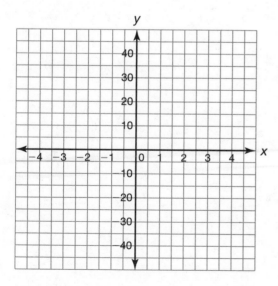

5. A tennis ball is dropped from a height of 25 feet. The initial velocity of an object that is dropped is 0 feet per second. The function $g(t) = -16t^2 + 25$ represents the height of the tennis ball, $g(t)$, t seconds after it was dropped.

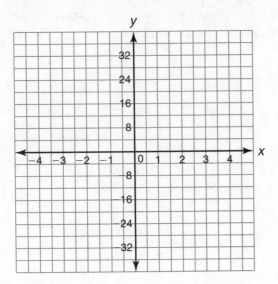

6. A tennis ball is dropped from a height of 150 feet. The initial velocity of an object that is dropped is 0 feet per second. The function $g(t) = -16t^2 + 150$ represents the height of the tennis ball, $g(t)$, t seconds after it was dropped.

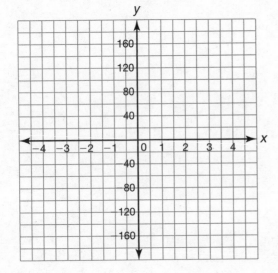

Name _____ Date _____

Use interval notation to represent each interval described.

7. All real numbers greater than or equal to −3 but less than 5.

[−3, 5)

8. All real numbers greater than or equal to −100.

9. All real numbers greater than −36 and less than or equal to 14.

10. All real numbers less than or equal to b.

11. All real numbers greater than or equal to c and less than or equal to d.

12. All real numbers greater than or equal to n.

Identify the intervals of increase and decrease for each function.

13. $f(x) = x^2 + 6x$

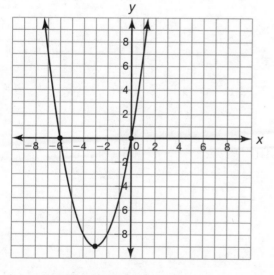

Interval of increase: (−3, ∞)

Interval of decrease: (−∞, −3)

14. $f(x) = 3x^2 − 6x$

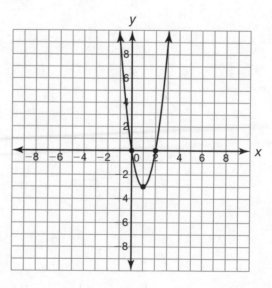

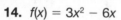

15. $f(x) = -x^2 + 2x + 8$

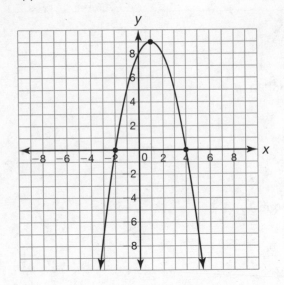

16. $f(x) = -6x^2 + 24x$

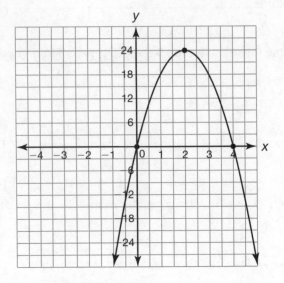

17. $f(x) = x^2 - 9$

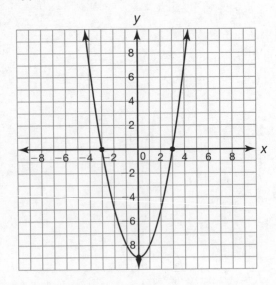

18. $f(x) = x^2 - 4x + 6$

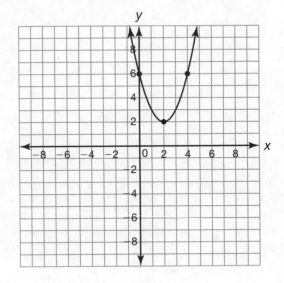

Name _____ Date _____

Are You Afraid of Ghosts?
Factored Form of a Quadratic Function

Vocabulary

Write a definition for each term in your own words.

1. factor an expression

2. factored form

Problem Set

Factor each expression.

1. $6x - 24$

$6x - 24 = 6(x) - 6(4)$

$\qquad = 6(x - 4)$

2. $3x + 36$

3. $10x + 15$

4. $42x - 35$

5. $-x - 9$

6. $-2x + 14$

Determine the *x*-intercepts of each quadratic function in factored form.

7. $f(x) = (x - 2)(x - 8)$

The *x*-intercepts are (2, 0) and (8, 0).

8. $f(x) = (x + 1)(x - 6)$

9. $f(x) = 3(x + 4)(x - 2)$

10. $f(x) = 0.25(x - 1)(x - 12)$

11. $f(x) = 0.5(x + 15)(x + 5)$

12. $f(x) = 4(x - 1)(x - 9)$

Write a quadratic function in factored form with each set of given characteristics.

13. Write a quadratic function that represents a parabola that opens downward and has *x*-intercepts (−2, 0) and (5, 0).

Answers will vary but functions should be in the form:

$f(x) = a(x + 2)(x - 5)$ for $a < 0$

14. Write a quadratic function that represents a parabola that opens downward and has *x*-intercepts (2, 0) and (14, 0).

15. Write a quadratic function that represents a parabola that opens upward and has *x*-intercepts (−8, 0) and (−1, 0).

16. Write a quadratic function that represents a parabola that opens upward and has *x*-intercepts (3, 0) and (7, 0).

Name _____ Date _____

17. Write a quadratic function that represents a parabola that opens downward and has x-intercepts $(-5, 0)$ and $(2, 0)$.

18. Write a quadratic function that represents a parabola that opens upward and has x-intercepts $(-12, 0)$ and $(-4, 0)$.

Determine the x-intercepts for each function using your graphing calculator. Write the function in factored form.

19. $f(x) = x^2 - 8x + 7$

x-intercepts: $(1, 0)$ and $(7, 0)$

factored form: $f(x) = (x - 1)(x - 7)$

20. $f(x) = 2x^2 - 10x - 48$

21. $f(x) = -x^2 - 20x - 75$

22. $f(x) = x^2 + 8x + 12$

23. $f(x) = -3x^2 - 9x + 12$

24. $f(x) = x^2 - 6x$

12

Determine the *x*-intercepts for each function. If necessary, rewrite the function in factored form.

25. $f(x) = (3x + 18)(x - 2)$

factored form: $f(x) = 3(x + 6)(x - 2)$

x-intercepts: $(-6, 0)$ and $(2, 0)$

26. $f(x) = (x + 8)(3 - x)$

27. $f(x) = (-2x + 8)(x - 14)$

28. $f(x) = (x + 16)(2x + 16)$

29. $f(x) = x(x + 7)$

30. $f(x) = (-3x + 9)(x + 3)$

12

Name _____ Date _____

Just Watch that Pumpkin Fly!
Investigating the Vertex of a Quadratic Function

Vocabulary

Graph the quadratic function. Plot and label the vertex. Then draw and label the axis of symmetry. Explain how you determine each location.

$h(t) = t^2 + 2t - 3$

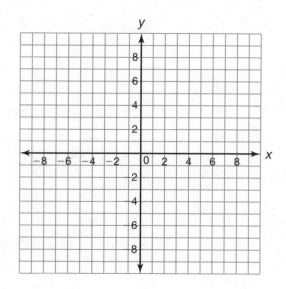

Problem Set

Write a function that represents the vertical motion described in each problem situation.

1. A catapult hurls a watermelon from a height of 36 feet at an initial velocity of 82 feet per second.

   $h(t) = -16t^2 + v_0 t + h_0$
   $h(t) = -16t^2 + 82t + 36$

2. A catapult hurls a cantaloupe from a height of 12 feet at an initial velocity of 47 feet per second.

12

3. A catapult hurls a pineapple from a height of 49 feet at an initial velocity of 110 feet per second.

4. A basketball is thrown from a height of 7 feet at an initial velocity of 58 feet per second.

5. A soccer ball is thrown from a height of 25 feet at an initial velocity of 46 feet per second.

6. A football is thrown from a height of 6 feet at an initial velocity of 74 feet per second.

Identify the vertex and the equation of the axis of symmetry for each vertical motion model.

7. A catapult hurls a grapefruit from a height of 24 feet at an initial velocity of 80 feet per second. The function $h(t) = -16t^2 + 80t + 24$ represents the height of the grapefruit $h(t)$ in terms of time t.
   The vertex of the graph is (2.5, 124).
   The axis of symmetry is $x = 2.5$.

8. A catapult hurls a pumpkin from a height of 32 feet at an initial velocity of 96 feet per second. The function $h(t) = -16t^2 + 96t + 32$ represents the height of the pumpkin $h(t)$ in terms of time t.

9. A catapult hurls a watermelon from a height of 40 feet at an initial velocity of 64 feet per second. The function $h(t) = -16t^2 + 64t + 40$ represents the height of the watermelon $h(t)$ in terms of time t.

10. A baseball is thrown from a height of 6 feet at an initial velocity of 32 feet per second. The function $h(t) = -16t^2 + 32t + 6$ represents the height of the baseball $h(t)$ in terms of time t.

Name _____ Date _____

11. A softball is thrown from a height of 20 feet at an initial velocity of 48 feet per second. The function $h(t) = -16t^2 + 48t + 20$ represents the height of the softball $h(t)$ in terms of time t.

12. A rocket is launched from the ground at an initial velocity of 112 feet per second. The function $h(t) = -16t^2 + 112t$ represents the height of the rocket $h(t)$ in terms of time t.

Determine the axis of symmetry of each parabola.

13. The x-intercepts of a parabola are (3, 0) and (9, 0).

$$\frac{3 + 9}{2} = \frac{12}{2} = 6$$

The axis of symmetry is $x = 6$.

14. The x-intercepts of a parabola are (−3, 0) and (1, 0).

15. The x-intercepts of a parabola are (−12, 0) and (−2, 0).

16. Two symmetric points on a parabola are (−1, 4) and (5, 4).

17. Two symmetric points on a parabola are (−4, 8) and (2, 8).

12

18. Two symmetric points on a parabola are (3, 1) and (15, 1).

Determine the vertex of each parabola.

19. $f(x) = x^2 + 2x - 15$

axis of symmetry: $x = -1$

The axis of symmetry is $x = -1$.
The x-coordinate of the vertex is -1.
The y-coordinate when $x = -1$ is:
$f(-1) = (-1)^2 + 2(-1) - 15$
$\qquad = 1 - 2 - 15$
$\qquad = -16$
The vertex is $(-1, -16)$.

20. $f(x) = x^2 - 8x + 7$

axis of symmetry: $x = 4$

21. $f(x) = x^2 + 4x - 12$

x-intercepts: (2, 0) and (−6, 0)

22. $f(x) = -x^2 - 14x - 45$

x-intercepts: (−9, 0) and (−5, 0)

23. $f(x) = -x^2 + 8x + 20$

two symmetric points on the parabola:
(−1, 11) and (9, 11)

24. $f(x) = -x^2 + 16$

two symmetric points on the parabola:
(−3, 7) and (3, 7)

Name _____ Date _____

Determine another point on each parabola.

25. The axis of symmetry is $x = 3$.

A point on the parabola is (1, 4).

Another point on the parabola is a symmetric point that has the same y-coordinate as (1, 4). The x-coordinate is:

$$\frac{1 + a}{2} = 3$$

$$1 + a = 6$$

$$a = 5$$

Another point on the parabola is (5, 4).

26. The axis of symmetry is $x = -4$.

A point on the parabola is (0, 6).

27. The axis of symmetry is $x = 1$.

A point on the parabola is (−3, 2).

28. The vertex is (5, 2).

A point on the parabola is (3, −1).

29. The vertex is (−1, 6).

A point on the parabola is (2, 3).

30. The vertex is (3, −1).

A point on the parabola is (4, 1).

12

Name _____ Date _____

The Form Is "Key"
Vertex Form of a Quadratic Function

Vocabulary

Write a definition for the term in your own words.

1. vertex form

Problem Set

Determine the vertex of each quadratic function given in vertex form.

1. $f(x) = (x - 3)^2 + 8$

   The vertex is (3, 8).

2. $f(x) = (x + 4)^2 + 2$

3. $f(x) = -2(x - 1)^2 - 8$

4. $f(x) = \frac{1}{2}(x - 2)^2 + 6$

5. $f(x) = -(x + 9)^2 - 1$

6. $f(x) = (x - 5)^2$

Determine the vertex of each quadratic function given in standard form. Use your graphing calculator. Rewrite the function in vertex form.

7. $f(x) = x^2 - 6x - 27$

   The vertex is (3, −36).

   The function in vertex form is
   $f(x) = (x - 3)^2 - 36$.

8. $f(x) = -x^2 - 2x + 15$

9. $f(x) = 2x^2 - 4x - 6$

10. $f(x) = x^2 - 10x + 24$

12

11. $f(x) = -x^2 + 15x - 54$

12. $f(x) = -2x^2 - 14x - 12$

Determine the x-intercepts of each quadratic function given in standard form. Use your graphing calculator. Rewrite the function in factored form.

13. $f(x) = x^2 + 2x - 8$

The x-intercepts are (2, 0) and (−4, 0).

The function in factored form is

$f(x) = (x - 2)(x + 4)$.

14. $f(x) = -x^2 - x + 12$

15. $f(x) = -4x^2 + 12x - 8$

16. $f(x) = 2x^2 + 18x + 16$

17. $f(x) = \frac{1}{2}x^2 - \frac{1}{2}x - 3$

18. $f(x) = \frac{1}{3}x^2 - 2x$

Identify the form of each quadratic function as either standard form, factored form, or vertex form. Then state all you know about the quadratic function's key characteristics, based only on the given equation of the function.

19. $f(x) = 5(x - 3)^2 + 12$

The function is in vertex form.

The parabola opens up and the vertex is (3, 12).

20. $f(x) = -(x - 8)(x - 4)$

21. $f(x) = -3x^2 + 5x$

22. $f(x) = \frac{2}{3}(x + 6)(x - 1)$

23. $f(x) = -(x + 2)^2 - 7$

24. $f(x) = 2x^2 - 1$

Name _____ Date _____

Write an equation for a quadratic function with each set of given characteristics.

25. The vertex is $(-1, 4)$ and the parabola opens down.

Answers will vary but functions should be in the form:

$f(x) = a(x - h)^2 + k$

$f(x) = a(x + 1)^2 + 4$, for $a < 0$

26. The x-intercepts are -3 and 4 and the parabola opens down.

27. The vertex is $(3, -2)$ and the parabola opens up.

28. The vertex is $(0, 8)$ and the parabola opens up.

12

29. The x-intercepts are 5 and 12 and the parabola opens up.

30. The x-intercepts are 0 and 7 and the parabola opens down.

12

Name _____ Date _____

More Than Meets the Eye
Transformations of Quadratic Functions

Vocabulary

Write a definition for each term in your own words.

1. vertical dilation

2. dilation factor

Problem Set

Describe the transformation performed on each function $g(x)$ to result in $d(x)$.

1. $g(x) = x^2$

$d(x) = x^2 - 5$

The graph of $g(x)$ is translated down 5 units.

2. $g(x) = x^2$

$d(x) = x^2 + 2$

3. $g(x) = 3x^2$

$d(x) = 3x^2 + 6$

4. $g(x) = \frac{1}{2}x^2$

$d(x) = \frac{1}{2}x^2 - 1$

5. $g(x) = (x + 2)^2$

$d(x) = (x + 2)^2 - 3$

6. $g(x) = -(x - 2)^2$

$d(x) = -(x - 2)^2 + 5$

Describe the transformation performed on each function $g(x)$ to result in $m(x)$.

7. $g(x) = x^2$

$m(x) = (x + 4)^2$

The graph of $g(x)$ is translated left 4 units.

8. $g(x) = x^2$

$m(x) = (x - 8)^2$

9. $g(x) = x^2$

$m(x) = (x + 1)^2$

10. $g(x) = x^2 - 7$

$m(x) = (x + 2)^2 - 7$

11. $g(x) = x^2 + 8$

$m(x) = (x + 3)^2 + 8$

12. $g(x) = x^2 - 6$

$m(x) = (x - 5)^2 - 6$

Describe the transformation performed on each function $g(x)$ to result in $p(x)$.

13. $g(x) = x^2$

$p(x) = -x^2$

The graph of $p(x)$ is a horizontal reflection of the graph of $g(x)$.

14. $g(x) = x^2$

$p(x) = (-x)^2$

15. $g(x) = x^2 + 2$

$p(x) = -(x^2 + 2)$

16. $g(x) = x^2 - 5$

$p(x) = (-x)^2 - 5$

17. $g(x) = \frac{2}{3}x^2 + 4$

$p(x) = \frac{2}{3}(-x)^2 + 4$

18. $g(x) = 5x^2 - 7$

$p(x) = -(5x^2 - 7)$

Represent each function $n(x)$ as a vertical dilation of $g(x)$ using coordinate notation.

19. $g(x) = x^2$

$n(x) = 4x^2$

$(x, y) \rightarrow (x, 4y)$

20. $g(x) = x^2$

$n(x) = \frac{1}{2}x^2$

Name _____ Date _____

21. $g(x) = -x^2$

  $n(x) = -5x^2$

22. $g(x) = -x^2$

  $n(x) = -\dfrac{3}{4}x^2$

23. $g(x) = (x + 1)^2$

  $n(x) = 2(x + 1)^2$

24. $g(x) = (x - 3)^2$

  $n(x) = \dfrac{1}{2}(x - 3)^2$

Write an equation in vertex form for a function $g(x)$ with the given characteristics. Sketch a graph of each function $g(x)$.

25. The function $g(x)$ is quadratic.

  The function $g(x)$ is continuous.

  The graph of $g(x)$ is a horizontal reflection of the graph of $f(x) = x^2$.

  The function $g(x)$ is translated 3 units up from $f(x) = -x^2$.

  $g(x) = -(x - 0)^2 + 3$

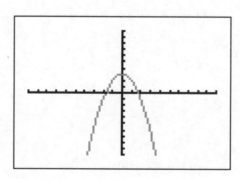

26. The function $g(x)$ is quadratic.

The function $g(x)$ is continuous.

The graph of $g(x)$ is a horizontal reflection of the graph of $f(x) = x^2$.

The function $g(x)$ is translated 2 units down and 5 units left from $f(x) = -x^2$.

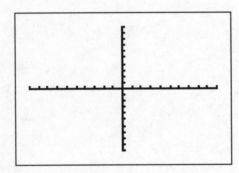

27. The function $g(x)$ is quadratic.

The function $g(x)$ is continuous.

The function $g(x)$ is vertically dilated with a dilation factor of 6.

The function $g(x)$ is translated 1 unit up and 4 units right from $f(x) = 6x^2$.

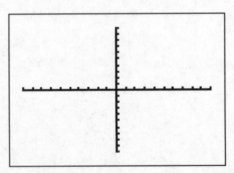

Name _____ Date _____

28. The function $g(x)$ is quadratic.

The function $g(x)$ is continuous.

The function $g(x)$ is vertically dilated with a dilation factor of $\frac{1}{2}$.

The function $g(x)$ is translated 2 units down and 6 units left from $f(x) = \frac{1}{2}x^2$.

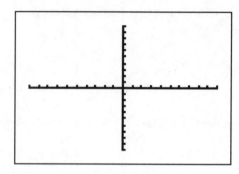

29. The function $g(x)$ is quadratic.

The function $g(x)$ is continuous.

The graph of $g(x)$ is a horizontal reflection of the graph of $f(x) = x^2$.

The function $g(x)$ is vertically dilated with a dilation factor of 3.

The function $g(x)$ is translated 2 units down and 4 units right from $f(x) = -3x^2$.

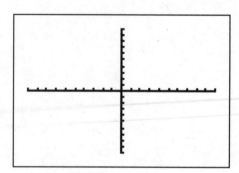

30. The function $g(x)$ is quadratic.

The function $g(x)$ is continuous.

The function $g(x)$ is vertically dilated with a dilation factor of $\frac{1}{4}$.

The function $g(x)$ is translated 3 units up and 2 units left from $f(x) = \frac{1}{4}x^2$.

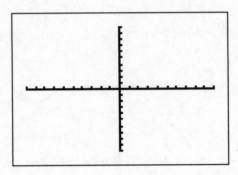

Describe the transformation(s) necessary to translate the graph of the function $f(x) = x^2$ into the graph of each function $g(x)$.

31. $g(x) = x^2 + 7$

The function $g(x)$ is translated 7 units up from $f(x) = x^2$.

32. $g(x) = -x^2 - 4$

33. $g(x) = (x - 2)^2 + 8$

34. $g(x) = 4x^2 + 1$

35. $g(x) = \frac{2}{3}(x + 4)^2 - 9$

36. $g(x) = -(x - 6)^2 + 3$

Name _____ Date _____

Controlling the Population
Adding and Subtracting Polynomials

Vocabulary

Match each definition with its corresponding term.

1. polynomial

2. term

3. coefficient

4. monomial

5. binomial

6. trinomial

7. degree of a term B

8. degree of a polynomial

a. a polynomial with only 1 term

b. the degree of the term with the greatest exponent

c. a mathematical expression involving the sum of powers in one or more variables multiplied by coefficients

d. a polynomial with exactly 3 terms

e. any number being multiplied by a power within a polynomial expression

f. each product in a polynomial expression

g. a polynomial with exactly 2 terms

h. the exponent of a term in a polynomial

Problem Set

Identify the terms and coefficients in each expression.

1. $5x + 8$

The terms are $5x$ and 8. The coefficients are 5 and 8.

2. $2m^3$

2m = T
2 = C

3. $x^2 - 4x$

X, -4X = T
1, 4 = C

4. $-3w^4 + w^2 - 9$

-3w⁴, w², -9 = T
1, -3 = C

5. -18

-18 = T
NA = C

6. $10 - 3x^3 - 6x$

10, -3x³, -6x = T
-3, 6 = C

Determine whether each expression is a polynomial. If the expression is not a polynomial, explain why it is not.

7. $9 + 12x$

The expression is a polynomial.

8. $6m^{\frac{1}{2}}$

yes.

9. $\frac{3}{x} - 8x$

yes

10. $-2w^3 + w^2 - 5$

yes

11. $-2.5m$

yes

12. $\frac{x}{7} + 10$

yes

13. $\sqrt[3]{x} + 12$

NO

14. $\frac{4}{5}m - \frac{1}{5}$

yes

Name _____ Date _____

Determine whether each polynomial is a monomial, binomial, or trinomial. State the degree of the polynomial.

15. $8x + 3$

The polynomial is a binomial with a degree of 1.

16. $5m^2$

monomial

2

17. $x^2 - 7x$

binomial

2

18. $-9n^4 + 6n^2 - 1$

Trinomial

4

19. -12

NOT

20. $4 - 10x^3 + 8x$

Trinomial

4

Write each polynomial in standard form. Classify the polynomial by its number of terms and by its degree.

21. $2x + 6x^2$

$6x^2 + 2x$

The polynomial is a binomial with a degree of 2.

22. $-9m^2 + 4m^3$

$4m^3 - 9m^2$

B   3

23. $10 - 5x$

$-5x + 10$

B 1

24. $7x - 3 + 12x^2$

$12x^2 + 7x - 3$

T   2

25. $15 + 4w - w^3$

$w^3 + 4w + 15$

T   3

26. $5x^2 - 15 + 20x$

$5x^2 + 20x - 15$

T   2

27. $-1 - p^4$

$-p^4 - 1$

B   4

28. $-6t^2 + 4t + 3t^3$

$3t^3 - 6t^2 + 4t$

T   3

29. $-18a^3 + 54a - 22a^2$

T^3

30. $x^3 - x^2 - x^5$

$T \quad s$

Simplify each expression.

31. $(5x - 8) + (7x + 10)$

$5x - 8 + 7x + 10$

$(5x + 7x) + (-8 + 10)$

$12x + 2$

32. $(4m^2 + 9m) - (2m^2 + 6)$

$2m^2 + 9m - 6$

33. $(-x^2 + 5x - 12) + (2x^2 - 6)$

$x^2 + 5x - 18$

34. $(10t^2 - 3t + 9) - (6t^2 + 7t)$

$16 \quad 4t^2 + 4t + 9$

35. $(-5w^2 + 3w - 8) + (15w^2 - 4w + 11)$

$10w^2 - w + 3$

36. $(3x^3 + 10x - 1) - (5x^2 + 10x - 9)$

$-2x^2 + 8$

37. $(-a^2 + 2a - 8) + (2a^2 - 9a + 15)$

$a^2 - 7a + 7$

38. $(14p^4 + 7p^2) + (8p^3 + 7p^2 - p)$

$14p^4 + 8p^3 + 14p^2 - p$

39. $(3x^4 + 3x^2 - 3) - (6x^5 - 9x^3 + 2)$

$-6x^5 + 3x^4 + 9x^3 + 3x^2 - 5$

40. $(-7m^3 - m^2 - m) - (-10m^3 - m - 1)$

13

Name _____ Date _____

The graphs of the functions $f(x) = 2x + 1$, $g(x) = x^2 + x - 3$, and $h(x) = f(x) + g(x)$ are shown. Evaluate the function $h(x)$ for each given value of x. Use the graph of $h(x)$ to verify your answer.

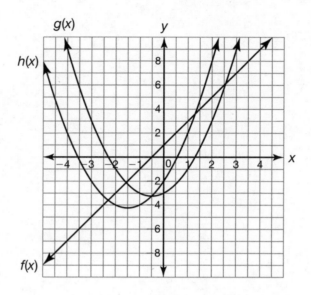

41. Evaluate $h(x)$ at $x = 2$.

$h(x) = f(x) + g(x)$
$\quad\quad = 2x + 1 + x^2 + x - 3$
$\quad\quad = x^2 + 3x - 2$
$h(2) = (2)^2 + 3(2) - 2$
$\quad\quad = 4 + 6 - 2$
$\quad\quad = 8$

42. Evaluate $h(x)$ at $x = -4$.

$x^2 + 3x - 2$

$(-4)^2 + 3(-4) - 2$

$16 \quad -12 \quad -2$

2

43. Evaluate $h(x)$ at $x = 0$.

$(0)^2 + 3(0) - 2$

-2

44. Evaluate $h(x)$ at $x = 1$.

$1^2 + 3 - 2$

$1 + 3 - 2$

$4 - 2$

2

13

45. Evaluate $h(x)$ at $x = -2$.

46. Evaluate $h(x)$ at $x = -1.5$.

Name _____ Date _____

They're Multiplying—Like Polynomials!
Multiplying Polynomials

Problem Set

Determine the product of the binomials using algebra tiles.

1. $x + 1$ and $x + 1$

$(x + 1)(x + 1) = x^2 + 2x + 1$

2. $x + 1$ and $x + 4$

3. $x + 2$ and $x + 2$

4. $x + 3$ and $x + 3$

13

5. $2x + 1$ and $x + 3$

6. $2x + 3$ and $x + 2$

Determine the product of the binomials using multiplication tables.

7. $3x + 4$ and $2x + 2$

8. $5m + 3$ and $4m + 6$

·	$2x$	2
$3x$	$6x^2$	$6x$
4	$8x$	8

$(3x + 4)(2x + 2) = 6x^2 + 6x + 8x + 8$

$= 6x^2 + 14x + 8$

9. $6t + 5$ and $7t - 5$

10. $4x + 2$ and $4x - 2$

Name _____ Date _____

11. $10w - 1$ and $9w + 8$

12. $y + 12$ and $5y + 15$

Determine the product of the polynomials using the Distributive Property.

13. $2x(x + 6)$

$2x(x + 6) = 2x(x) + 2x(6)$
$\qquad = 2x^2 + 12x$

14. $4x^2(x + 2)$

15. $7x(x - 5)$

16. $(2x + 1)(x + 8)$

17. $(x + 3)(x^2 - 1)$

18. $(4x + 4)(5x - 5)$

19. $3x(x^2 + 5x - 1)$

20. $9x(3x^2 - 4x + 2)$

13

21. $(x + 2)(x^2 + 6x - 1)$

22. $(x - 4)(x^2 + 2x - 3)$

Name _____ Date _____

What *Factored* Into It?
Factoring Polynomials

Vocabulary

State the given property.

1. Symmetric Property of Equality

Problem Set

Factor out the greatest common factor of each polynomial, if possible.

1. $x^2 + 9x$

   $x(x + 9)$

2. $m^2 - 4m$

3. $5x^2 + 20x - 15$

4. $24w^2 - 16$

5. $y^3 - 7y$

6. $2x^3 + 10x^2$

7. $3w + 10$

8. $20x^3 + 16x^2 + 8x$

9. $7m^3 - 21$

10. $15x^3 + 4$

13

Factor each trinomial using an area model.

11. $x^2 + 4x + 3$

$x^2 + 4x + 3 = (x + 1)(x + 3)$

12. $x^2 + 5x + 6$

13. $x^2 - x - 6$

Name _____ Date _____

14. $x^2 - x - 12$

15. $x^2 + 7x + 10$

16. $x^2 + 3x - 4$

13

Factor each trinomial completely using multiplication tables. If possible, factor out the greatest common factor first.

17. $x^2 - 2x - 8$

·	x	2
x	x^2	$2x$
-4	$-4x$	-8

$x^2 - 2x - 8 = (x - 4)(x + 2)$

18. $y^2 + 13y + 42$

19. $m^2 + 6m - 7$

20. $x^2 - 9x + 18$

21. $4w^2 + 12w - 40$

22. $2t^3 - 14t^2 + 24t$

23. $3m^3 + 36m^2 + 60m$

24. $2x^2 - 8x - 42$

Name _____ Date _____

Factor each polynomial using the trial and error method. If possible, factor out the greatest common factor first.

25. $x^2 + 11x + 10$

The factors of the constant term, 10, are:

$-1, -10$ $1, 10$

$-2, -5$ $2, 5$

$x^2 + 11x + 10 = (x + 1)(x + 10)$

26. $w^2 + 6w - 16$

27. $m^2 + 2m - 35$

28. $x^2 + 4x - 12$

29. $3n^2 - 27n + 60$

30. $2x^2 + 22x + 60$

Factor each polynomial.

31. $x^2 + 11x + 28 = \underline{\;(x + 4)(x + 7)\;}$

$x^2 - 11x + 28 = \underline{\;(x - 4)(x - 7)\;}$

$x^2 + 3x - 28 = \underline{\;(x - 4)(x + 7)\;}$

$x^2 - 3x + 28 = \underline{\;(x + 4)(x - 7)\;}$

32. $x^2 + 10x + 9 = \underline{\hspace{3cm}}$

$x^2 - 10x + 9 = \underline{\hspace{3cm}}$

$x^2 + 8x - 9 = \underline{\hspace{3cm}}$

$x^2 - 8x - 9 = \underline{\hspace{3cm}}$

33. $x^2 + 12x + 27 = \underline{\hspace{3cm}}$

$x^2 - 12x + 27 = \underline{\hspace{3cm}}$

$x^2 + 6x - 27 = \underline{\hspace{3cm}}$

$x^2 - 6x - 27 = \underline{\hspace{3cm}}$

34. $x^2 + 13x + 40 = \underline{\hspace{3cm}}$

$x^2 - 13x + 40 = \underline{\hspace{3cm}}$

$x^2 + 3x - 40 = \underline{\hspace{3cm}}$

$x^2 - 3x - 40 = \underline{\hspace{3cm}}$

13

35. $x^2 + 12x + 11 =$ _____

$x^2 - 12x + 11 =$ _____

$x^2 + 10x - 11 =$ _____

$x^2 - 10x - 11 =$ _____

36. $x^2 + 13x + 36 =$ _____

$x^2 - 13x + 36 =$ _____

$x^2 + 5x - 36 =$ _____

$x^2 - 5x - 36 =$ _____

Factor each polynomial completely. If possible, factor out the greatest common factor first.

37. $x^2 + 4x + 4$

·	x	2
x	x^2	$2x$
2	$2x$	4

$x^2 + 4x + 4 = (x + 2)(x + 2)$

38. $x^2 - 10x + 25$

39. $-32 - 12m - m^2$

40. $45 + 4w - w^2$

41. $5x^2 + 10x - 15$

42. $4x^2 + 32x + 64$

Name _____ Date _____

Zeroing In
Solving Quadratics by Factoring

Vocabulary

Complete the definition of the Zero Product Property.

1. The Zero Product Property states that if the product of two or more factors is equal to _____ , then at least one factor must be equal to _____ .

If $ab = 0$, then _____ or _____ .

This property is also known as the _____ .

Define the term in your own words.

2. roots

Problem Set

Factor and solve each quadratic equation. Check your answer.

1. $x^2 + 5x + 6 = 0$

$x^2 + 5x + 6 = 0$ Check:

$(x + 3)(x + 2) = 0$ $(-3)^2 + 5(-3) + 6 = 0$ $(-2)^2 + 5(-2) + 6 = 0$

$x + 3 = 0$ or $x + 2 = 0$ $9 - 15 + 6 = 0$ $4 - 10 + 6 = 0$

$x = -3$ or $x = -2$ $0 = 0$ $0 = 0$

The roots are -3 and -2.

2. $x^2 - 3x - 4 = 0$

13

3. $m^2 + 2m - 35 = 0$

4. $-x^2 - 4x + 12 = 0$

5. $x^2 + 8x = 0$

6. $w^2 + 50 = -15w$

7. $-t^2 + 12t = 32$

Name _____ Date _____

8. $x^2 + 2x + 2 = 0$

9. $2t^2 + t - 3 = 0$

10. $w^2 + 5w - 32 = 2w - 4$

13

Determine the zeros of each quadratic function, if possible. Check your answer.

11. $f(x) = x^2 - 5x$

$f(x) = x^2 - 5x$ Check:

$0 = x^2 - 5x$ $(0)^2 - 5(0) \stackrel{?}{=} 0$ $(5)^2 - 5(5) \stackrel{?}{=} 0$

$0 = x(x - 5)$ $0 - 0 \stackrel{?}{=} 0$ $25 - 25 \stackrel{?}{=} 0$

$x = 0$ or $x - 5 = 0$ $0 = 0$ $0 = 0$

$x = 0$ or $x = 5$

The zeros are 0 and 5.

12. $f(x) = 3x^2 + 6x$

13. $f(x) = x^2 + 11x + 30$

14. $f(x) = x^2 - 9x - 36$

Name _____ Date _____

15. $f(x) = 2x^2 + 9x + 10$

16. $f(x) = x^2 + 5x + 14$

17. $f(x) = 3x^2 + 3x - 6$

13

18. $f(x) = \frac{1}{2}x^2 - \frac{3}{4}x$

Name _____ Date _____

What Makes You So Special?
Special Products

Vocabulary

Give an example of each term. Then, factor the expression.

1. perfect square trinomial

2. difference of two squares

3. sum of two cubes

4. difference of two cubes

Problem Set

Factor each binomial completely.

1. $x^2 - 25$

$x^2 - 25 = (x + 5)(x - 5)$

2. $x^3 - 64$

3. $x^3 + 27$

4. $m^2 - 100$

13

5. $5x^3 + 40$ **6.** $t^3 - 125$

7. $8a^3 - 27$ **8.** $x^8 - y^8$

Factor the trinomial completely.

9. $x^2 + 16x + 64$ **10.** $k^2 - 20k + 100$

   $x^2 + 16x + 64 = (x + 8)(x + 8)$

11. $2x^2 - 28x + 98$ **12.** $5x^2 + 10x + 5$

13. $z^3 + 18z^2 + 81z$ **14.** $3x^3 - 30x^2 + 75x$

Determine the root(s) of each quadratic equation. Check your answer(s).

15. $x^2 - 100 = 0$

$$x^2 - 100 = 0$$
$$(x + 10)(x - 10) = 0$$
$$x + 10 = 0 \quad \text{or} \quad x - 10 = 0$$
$$x = -10 \quad \text{or} \quad x = 10$$

The roots are -10 and 10.

Check:

$(-10)^2 - 100 \overset{?}{=} 0$

$100 - 100 \overset{?}{=} 0$

$0 = 0$

$(10)^2 - 100 \overset{?}{=} 0$

$100 - 100 \overset{?}{=} 0$

$0 = 0$

16. $m^2 - 16m + 64 = 0$

13

Name _____ Date _____

17. $6x^2 + 24x + 24 = 0$

18. $4x^2 - 9 = 0$

19. $t^2 + 22t + 121 = 0$

20. $12w^2 - 48w + 48 = 0$

Determine the zero(s) of each quadratic function. Check your answer(s).

21. $f(x) = x^2 - 225$

$$f(x) = x^2 - 225$$
$$0 = x^2 - 225$$
$$0 = (x + 15)(x - 15)$$
$$x + 15 = 0 \quad \text{or} \quad x - 15 = 0$$
$$x = -15 \quad \text{or} \quad x = 15$$

The zeros are -15 and 15.

Check:
$$(-15)^2 - 225 \stackrel{?}{=} 0$$
$$225 - 225 \stackrel{?}{=} 0$$
$$0 = 0$$

$$(15)^2 - 225 \stackrel{?}{=} 0$$
$$225 - 225 \stackrel{?}{=} 0$$
$$0 = 0$$

22. $f(x) = x^2 + x + \dfrac{1}{4}$

23. $f(x) = 9x^2 - 1$

Name _____ Date _____

24. $f(x) = 8x^2 - 48x + 72$

25. $f(x) = 8x^2 - 50$

26. $f(x) = 2x^2 + 52x + 338$

Name _____ Date _____

Could It Be Groovy to Be a Square?
Approximating and Rewriting Radicals

Vocabulary

Choose the word that best completes each statement.

| square root | positive (principal) square root | radicand |
| negative square root | extract the square root | radical expression |

1. When solving certain quadratic equations, it is necessary to _____ from both sides of the equation.
2. Every positive number has both a(n) _____ and a(n) _____.
3. The _____ is the expression enclosed within a radical symbol.
4. A number b is a(n) _____ of a if $b^2 = a$.
5. An expression involving a radical symbol is called a(n) _____.

Problem Set

Rewrite each radical by extracting all perfect squares.

1. $\sqrt{25}$

   $\sqrt{25} = \pm 5$

2. $\sqrt{144}$

3. $\sqrt{400}$

4. $\sqrt{12}$

5. $\sqrt{32}$

6. $\sqrt{45}$

13

7. $\sqrt{300}$

8. $5\sqrt{54}$

Determine the approximate value of each radical expression to the nearest tenth.

9. $\sqrt{7}$

$2.6^2 = 6.76$

$2.7^2 = 7.29$

$\sqrt{7} \approx 2.6$

10. $\sqrt{37}$

11. $\sqrt{96}$

12. $\sqrt{27}$

13. $\sqrt{109}$

14. $\sqrt{405}$

Solve each quadratic equation. Approximate the roots to the nearest tenth.

15. $x^2 = 40$

$x^2 = 40$

$\sqrt{x^2} = \pm\sqrt{40}$

$x = \pm\sqrt{40}$

$6.3^2 = 39.69$

$6.4^2 = 40.96$

$\sqrt{40} \approx \pm 6.3$

$x \approx \pm 6.3$

The roots are approximately 6.3 and −6.3.

16. $m^2 = 68$

Name _____ Date _____

17. $t^2 = 15$ **18.** $x^2 = 83$

19. $(x - 5)^2 = 22$ **20.** $(x + 8)^2 = 29$

Solve each quadratic equation. Rewrite the roots in radical form.

21. $x^2 = 48$ **22.** $x^2 = 52$

$x^2 = 48$

$\sqrt{x^2} = \pm\sqrt{48}$

$x = \pm\sqrt{48}$

$x = \pm\sqrt{16 \cdot 3}$

$x = \pm\sqrt{16} \cdot \sqrt{3}$

$x = \pm 4\sqrt{3}$

The roots are $4\sqrt{3}$ and $-4\sqrt{3}$.

23. $x^2 = 27$

24. $x^2 = 175$

25. $(12 - x)^2 = 8$

26. $(x + 20)^2 = 80$

Name _____ Date _____

Another Method
Completing the Square

Vocabulary

Define the term in your own words.

1. completing the square

Problem Set

Use a geometric figure to complete the square for each expression. Factor the resulting trinomial.

1. $x^2 + 2x$

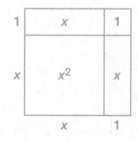

$x^2 + 2x + 1 = (x + 1)^2$

2. $x^2 + 4x$

3. $x^2 + 12x$

4. $x^2 + 9x$

5. $x^2 + 11x$

6. $x^2 + 28x$

Determine the unknown value that would make each trinomial a perfect square.

7. $x^2 - 10x + \underline{\ 25\ }$

8. $x^2 + 14x + \underline{\ \ \ \ \ }$

9. $x^2 + \underline{\ \ \ }x + 9$

10. $x^2 - \underline{\ \ \ \ \ }x + 81$

11. $x^2 + 7x + \underline{\ \ \ \ \ }$

12. $x^2 - 15x + \underline{\ \ \ \ \ }$

13. $x^2 - \underline{\ \ \ \ \ \ }x + 169$

14. $x^2 + \underline{\ \ \ }x + \dfrac{9}{4}$

Determine the roots of each quadratic equation by completing the square. Round your answer to the nearest hundredth. Check your answer.

15. $x^2 + 4x - 6 = 0$

$$x^2 + 4x - 6 = 0$$
$$x^2 + 4x = 6$$
$$x^2 + 4x + 4 = 6 + 4$$
$$(x + 2)^2 = 10$$
$$\sqrt{(x + 2)^2} = \pm\sqrt{10}$$
$$x + 2 = \pm\sqrt{10}$$
$$x = -2 \pm \sqrt{10}$$
$$x \approx 1.16 \quad \text{or} \quad x \approx -5.16$$

Check:

$$(1.16)^2 + 4(1.16) - 6 \overset{?}{=} 0$$
$$1.3456 + 4.64 - 6 \overset{?}{=} 0$$
$$-0.0144 \approx 0$$

$$(-5.16)^2 - 4(-5.16) - 6 \overset{?}{=} 0$$
$$26.6256 - 20.64 - 6 \overset{?}{=} 0$$
$$-0.0144 \approx 0$$

The roots are approximately 1.16 and −5.16.

13

Name _____ Date _____

16. $x^2 - 2x - 4 = 0$

17. $x^2 + 10x + 2 = 0$

18. $x^2 - 12x + 25 = 0$

13

19. $x^2 + 3x - 1 = 0$

20. $x^2 + x - 10 = 0$

13

Name _____ Date _____

Ladies and Gentlemen: Please Welcome the Quadratic Formula!
The Quadratic Formula

Vocabulary

Complete the Quadratic Formula. Then, identify the discriminant and explain what it indicates about the function.

The quadratic equation of the form $ax^2 + bx + c = 0$, can be written as the Quadratic Formula.

$$x =$$

Problem Set

Determine the approximate zeros or roots of each function or equation. Round your answers to the nearest thousandth, if necessary.

1. $f(x) = x^2 + 3x - 5$

$a = 1, b = 3, c = -5$

$x = \dfrac{-b \pm \sqrt{b^2 - 4ac}}{2a}$

$x = \dfrac{-(3) \pm \sqrt{(3)^2 - 4(1)(-5)}}{2(1)}$

$x = \dfrac{-3 \pm \sqrt{9 + 20}}{2}$

$x = \dfrac{-3 \pm \sqrt{29}}{2}$

$x = \dfrac{-3 + 5.385}{2}$ or $x = \dfrac{-3 - 5.385}{2}$

$x \approx 1.193$ or $x \approx -4.193$

2. $f(x) = -3x^2 - x + 7$

14

3. $2x^2 + 6x - 7 = 2$

4. $4x^2 - x - 1 = 5$

5. $f(x) = -8x^2 + 2x + 1$

6. $3x^2 + x + 3 = 5$

Name _____ Date _____

Determine the exact zeros or roots of each function or equation.

7. $f(x) = -2x^2 - 8x + 1$

$a = -2, b = -8, c = 1$

$x = \dfrac{-b \pm \sqrt{b^2 - 4ac}}{2a}$

$x = \dfrac{-(-8) \pm \sqrt{(-8)^2 - 4(-2)(1)}}{2(-2)}$

$x = \dfrac{8 \pm \sqrt{64 + 8}}{-4}$

$x = \dfrac{8 \pm \sqrt{72}}{-4}$

$x = \dfrac{8 \pm \sqrt{36 \cdot 2}}{-4}$

$x = \dfrac{8 \pm 6\sqrt{2}}{-4}$

$x = \dfrac{8 + 6\sqrt{2}}{-4}$ or $x = \dfrac{8 - 6\sqrt{2}}{-4}$

$x = -2 - \dfrac{3}{2}\sqrt{2}$ or $x = -2 + \dfrac{3}{2}\sqrt{2}$

8. $5x^2 + 8x - 3 = 1$

14

9. $-3x^2 + 6x + 2 = -5$

10. $f(x) = x^2 + 6x + 5$

11. $f(x) = -2x^2 + 5x - 1$

12. $-3x^2 + 8x - 2 = -6$

14

Name _____ Date _____

Use the discriminant to determine the number of zeros or roots each function or equation has. Then solve for the zeros or roots.

13. $f(x) = -x^2 + 6x + 7$

$a = -1, b = 6, c = 7$

$b^2 - 4ac = (6)^2 - 4(-1)(7)$

$\qquad = 36 + 28$

$\qquad = 64$

Because $b^2 - 4ac > 0$ the function has two zeros.

$x = \dfrac{-b \pm \sqrt{b^2 - 4ac}}{2a}$

$x = \dfrac{-(6) \pm \sqrt{64}}{2(-1)}$

$x = \dfrac{-6 \pm 8}{-2}$

$x = \dfrac{-6 + 8}{-2}$ or $x = \dfrac{-6 - 8}{-2}$

$x = \dfrac{2}{-2}$ or $x = \dfrac{-14}{-2}$

$x = -1$ or $x = 7$

14. $2x^2 + 8x + 3 = -5$

15. $f(x) = 9x^2 + 5x + 1$

14

16. $6x^2 + 3x - 5 = 2$

17. $f(x) = 5x^2 + 10x + 5$

18. $f(x) = 7x^2 + 9x + 5$

Name _____ Date _____

It's Watching and Tracking!
Using a Calculator-Based Ranger to Model Quadratic Motion

Vocabulary

Define each term in your own words.

1. quadratic regression

2. coefficient of determination

Problem Set

Use your graphing calculator to determine the quadratic regression equation and coefficient of determination for the line of best fit of each given data set. Determine if the equation is a good fit for the data. Round your answers to the nearest hundredth.

1.

x	y
0	0
1	4.05
2	5.50
3	6.25
4	3.50
5	0

$y = -0.97x^2 + 4.84x + 0.03$

$r^2 \approx 0.99$

Because the r^2 value is close to 1, the quadratic regression equation is a good fit for the data.

14

2.

x	y
0	2.1
0.5	3.4
1	4.1
1.5	4.3
2	3.9
2.5	2.3

3.

x	y
−5	−0.5
−4	5
−1	7
0	3
0.5	−1
1	3

14

Name _____ Date _____

4.

x	y
−4	3.05
−3	−1.50
−2	−4.80
−1	−5.18
0	−3.75
1	−1.79

5.

x	y
0	6.2
1	4.5
2	1.5
3	−0.5
4	2.4
5	3.9

14

6.

x	y
−5	7.21
−4	1.80
−3	−2.40
−2	−5.92
−1	−1.40
0	2.73

Name _____ Date _____

They're A Lot More than Just Sparklers!
Solving Quadratic Inequalities

Problem Set

Determine the roots of each quadratic inequality. Use the interval method to determine the solution set of the inequality. Round your answer to the nearest thousandth if necessary.

1. $x^2 - 7x + 16 \geq 10$

$x^2 - 7x + 16 \geq 10$

$x^2 - 7x + 6 \geq 0$

$x^2 - 7x + 6 = 0$

$(x - 6)(x - 1) = 0$

$x - 6 = 0$ or $x - 1 = 0$

$x = 6$ or $x = 1$

Test 0, 2, and 7.

$x^2 - 7x + 16 \geq 10$

$(0)^2 - 7(0) + 16 \geq 10$

$16 \geq 10$ ✔

$x^2 - 7x + 16 \geq 10$

$(2)^2 - 7(2) + 16 \geq 10$

$4 - 14 + 16 \geq 10$

$6 \geq 10$ ✘

$x^2 - 7x + 16 \geq 10$

$(7)^2 - 7(7) + 16 \geq 10$

$49 - 49 + 16 \geq 10$

$16 \geq 10$ ✔

Solution: $x \in (-\infty, 1]$ or $x \in [6, \infty)$

14

2. $x^2 + 7x - 2 < -12$

3. $x^2 + x - 15 < 4$

14

Name _____ Date _____

4. $-x^2 + 11x - 21 \leq 2$

5. $-x^2 + 4x - 5 \leq -2$

6. $-x^2 - 3x + 14 > -3$

A water balloon is thrown upward from a height of 5 feet with an initial velocity of 35 feet per second. The quadratic function $h(t) = -16t^2 + 35t + 5$ represents the height of the balloon, h, in feet t seconds after it is thrown. Use this information to answer each question.

7. How long does it take for the balloon to reach the ground? Round your answer to the nearest thousandth.

$0 = -16t^2 + 35t + 5$

$a = -16, b = 35, c = 5$

$t = \dfrac{-b \pm \sqrt{b^2 - 4ac}}{2a}$

$t = \dfrac{-(35) \pm \sqrt{(35)^2 - 4(-16)(5)}}{2(-16)}$

$t = \dfrac{-35 \pm \sqrt{1225 + 320}}{-32}$

$t = \dfrac{-35 \pm \sqrt{1545}}{-32}$

$t = \dfrac{-35 + 39.306}{-32}$ or $t = \dfrac{-35 - 39.306}{-32}$

$t \approx -0.1346$ or $t \approx 2.322$

It will take just over 2.3 seconds for the balloon to reach the ground.

14

Name _____ Date _____

8. Determine when the balloon is less than 10 feet above the ground. Round your answer to the nearest thousandth.

9. Determine when the balloon is more than 10 feet above the ground. Round your answer to the nearest thousandth.

14

10. Determine when the balloon is less than 20 feet above the ground. Round your answer to the nearest thousandth.

11. Determine when the balloon is more than 20 feet above the ground. Round your answer to the nearest thousandth.

14

Name _____ Date _____

12. Determine when the balloon is less than 30 feet above the ground. Round your answer to the nearest thousandth.

14

Name _____ Date _____

You Must Have a System
Systems of Quadratic Equations

Problem Set

Solve each system of equations algebraically. Then verify each solution graphically.

1. $\begin{cases} y = x^2 - 6x + 7 \\ y = 2x \end{cases}$

2. $\begin{cases} y = x^2 - 3x + 1 \\ y = x - 3 \end{cases}$

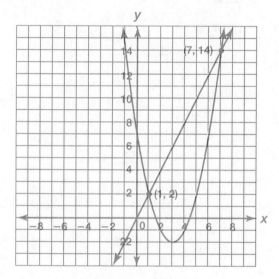

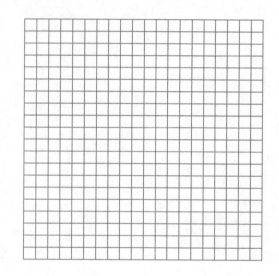

$$2x = x^2 - 6x + 7$$
$$0 = x^2 - 8x + 7$$
$$0 = (x - 7)(x - 1)$$

$x - 7 = 0 \quad$ or $\quad x - 1 = 0$

$\quad x = 7 \qquad\qquad x = 1$

$\quad y = 2(7) \qquad\quad y = 2(1)$

$\quad y = 14 \qquad\qquad y = 2$

The system has two solutions:
(7, 14) and (1, 2).

14

3. $\begin{cases} y = 2x^2 + 16x + 24 \\ y = -x - 2 \end{cases}$

4. $\begin{cases} y = -x^2 + 6x - 6 \\ y = 3x + 1 \end{cases}$

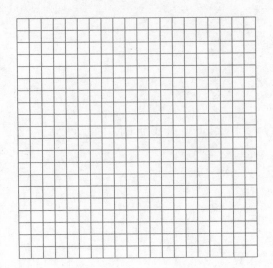

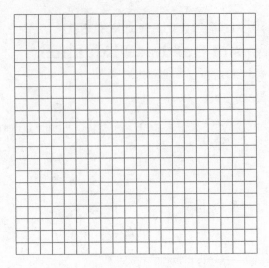

14

Name _____ Date _____

5. $\begin{cases} y = 4x^2 + 6x + 3 \\ y = -6x - 6 \end{cases}$

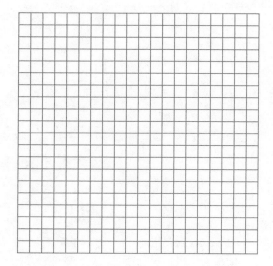

6. $\begin{cases} y = 3x^2 + 24x + 50 \\ y = 4x + 1 \end{cases}$

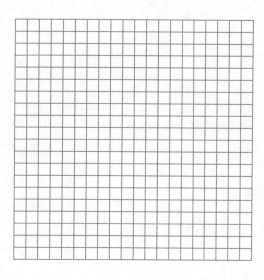

14

Solve each system of equations algebraically. Then verify each solution graphically.

7. $\begin{cases} y = x^2 - 2x + 1 \\ y = -x^2 + 3x + 4 \end{cases}$

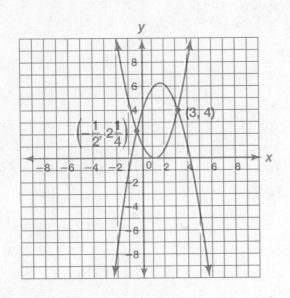

$$-x^2 + 3x + 4 = x^2 - 2x + 1$$
$$0 = 2x^2 - 5x - 3$$
$$0 = (2x + 1)(x - 3)$$
$$2x + 1 = 0 \qquad \text{or}$$
$$2x = -1$$
$$x = -\frac{1}{2}$$

$$y = \left(-\frac{1}{2}\right)^2 - 2\left(-\frac{1}{2}\right) + 1 \qquad x - 3 = 0$$
$$y = \frac{1}{4} + 1 + 1 \qquad\qquad x = 3$$
$$y = \frac{9}{4} = 2\frac{1}{4} \qquad\qquad y = (3)^2 - 2(3) + 1$$
$$y = 9 - 6 + 1$$
$$y = 4$$

The system has two solutions: $\left(-\frac{1}{2}, 2\frac{1}{4}\right)$ and $(3, 4)$.

8. $\begin{cases} y = 2x^2 - x + 3 \\ y = x^2 + 5x - 6 \end{cases}$

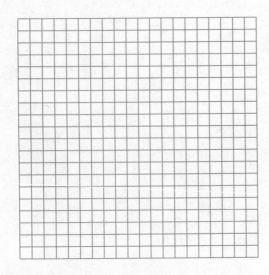

14

Name _____ Date _____

9. $\begin{cases} y = x^2 - 4x + 7 \\ y = -x^2 - 6x - 11 \end{cases}$

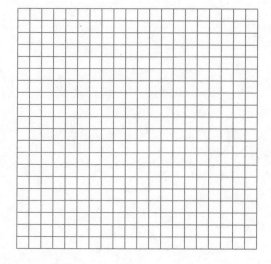

10. $\begin{cases} y = 2x^2 + 4x - 7 \\ y = x^2 + 2x + 1 \end{cases}$

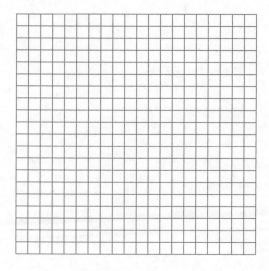

14

11. $\begin{cases} y = x^2 - 8x + 17 \\ y = -x^2 + 6x - 10 \end{cases}$

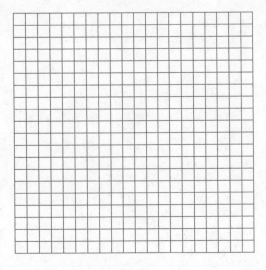

12. $\begin{cases} y = 2x^2 - 3x + 2 \\ y = -2x^2 + x + 1 \end{cases}$

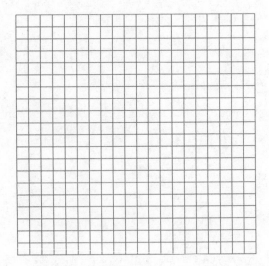

14

Name _____ Date _____

The Real Numbers . . . For Realsies!
The Numbers of the Real Number System

Vocabulary

Choose the word from the box that best completes each sentence.

counterexample	real numbers	whole numbers
natural numbers	closed	integers
rational numbers	Venn diagram	irrational numbers

1. The set of _____ consists of the set of rational numbers and the set of irrational numbers.

2. The set of _____ consists of the numbers used to count objects.

3. A(n) _____ uses circles to show how elements among sets of numbers or objects are related.

4. A set is said to be _____ under an operation when you can perform the operation on any of the numbers in the set and the result is a number that is also in the same set.

5. The set of _____ consists of all numbers that cannot be written as $\frac{a}{b}$, where a and b are integers.

6. The set of _____ consists of the set of whole numbers and their opposites.

7. The set of _____ consists of all numbers that can be written as $\frac{a}{b}$, where a and b are integers, but b is not equal to 0.

8. The set of _____ consists of the set of natural numbers and the number 0.

9. To show that a set is not closed under an operation, one example that shows the result is not part of that set is needed. This example is called a _____ .

Problem Set

For each list of numbers, determine which are included in the given set.

1. The set of natural numbers:

$10, -12, 0, 31, \frac{4}{5}, \sqrt{5}, -\frac{5}{3}, 1970$

The numbers 10, 31, and 1970 are in the set of natural numbers.

2. The set of whole numbers:

$-9, 18, 1, \frac{3}{4}, 0, 92, \sqrt{7}, 2096.5$

3. The set of integers:

$54, \pi, \frac{2}{3}, -16, \sqrt{2}, 3.5, -\frac{7}{10}, -594$

4. The set of rational numbers:

$8, -15, \frac{3}{8}, 0, \sqrt{3}, 9.5, -\frac{4}{5}, 857$

5. The set of irrational numbers:

$-21, \frac{7}{8}, 3, \sqrt{2}, 2.5, 0, 99, \pi$

6. The set of real numbers:

$-18, 18, 1, \frac{2}{3}, \sqrt{3}, 1080, 5.4, -42$

Identify whether each given number set is closed or not closed under the operations addition, subtraction, multiplication, and division. Explain your reasoning.

7. the set of natural numbers

The set of natural numbers is closed under addition and multiplication because when you add or multiply any two natural numbers, the sum or product is always a natural number.

The set of natural numbers is not closed under subtraction because when you subtract a natural number from a natural number, the difference can be 0 or a negative integer.

The set of natural numbers is not closed under division because when you divide a natural number by a natural number, the quotient can be a fraction.

Name _____ Date _____

8. the set of integers

9. the set of rational numbers

10. the set of real numbers

11. the set of whole numbers

12. the set of irrational numbers

Use the given equations to answer each question.

Equation A: $x + 4 = 10$	Equation B: $4x = 24$	Equation C: $x^2 = 16$
Equation D: $8 + x = 8$	Equation E: $x + 7 = 2$	Equation F: $5x = 0$
Equation G: $12x = 3$	Equation H: $x^2 = 3$	Equation J: $5x = 5$

13. Which equations could you solve if the only numbers you knew were natural numbers?

I could solve equations A, B, C, and J.

14. Which equations could you solve if the only numbers you knew were whole numbers?

15. Which equations could you solve if the only numbers you knew were integers?

16. Which equations could you solve if the only numbers you knew were rational numbers?

17. Which equations could you solve if the only numbers you knew were irrational numbers?

18. Which equations could you solve if the only numbers you knew were real numbers?

Represent each given decimal as a fraction.

19. 0.4444 . . .

Let $x = 0.4444 \ldots$

$10x = 4.4444 \ldots$

$-x = 0.4444 \ldots$

$9x = 4$

$\dfrac{9x}{9} = \dfrac{4}{9}$

$x = \dfrac{4}{9}$

The decimal 0.4444 . . . is equal to $\dfrac{4}{9}$.

20. 0.2525 . . .

Name _____ Date _____

21. 0.8181 . . .

22. 0.581581 . . .

23. 0.3939 . . .

24. 0.0909 . . .

25. 0.1212 . . .

26. 0.7373 . . .

27. 0.4848 . . .

28. 1.400400 . . .

Name _____ Date _____

Getting Real, and Knowing How . . .
Real Number Properties

Problem Set

Identify the property demonstrated by each given equation.

1. $4 \cdot (3 \cdot 8) = (4 \cdot 3) \cdot 8$

   Associative Property of Multiplication

2. $9(8 - 5) = 9(8) - 9(5)$

3. $20 + 0 = 20$

4. $10 + 7 + 15 = 10 + 15 + 7$

5. $5 \cdot \frac{1}{5} = 1$

6. $4 \cdot 9 = 9 \cdot 4$

7. $99(1) = 99$

8. $12 + (3 + 8) = (12 + 3) + 8$

9. $5(x + 2) = 5x + 5(2)$

10. $8 + (-8) = 0$

Each expression has been simplified one step at a time. Next to each step, identify the property, transformation, or simplification used in the step.

11. $8x + 4(3x + 7)$

$8x + (12x + 28)$ _____ Distributive Property of Multiplication over Addition

$(8x + 12x) + 28$ _____ Associative Property of Addition

$20x + 28$ _____ Combine like terms

12. $14(2x + 2 + x)$

$14(2x + x + 2)$ _____

$14(3x + 2)$ _____

$42x + 28$ _____

13. $11(13 - 13 + x - 9)$

$11(0 + x - 9)$ _____

$11(x - 9)$ _____

$11x - 99$ _____

14. $7(x - 4) + 28$

$7x - 28 + 28$ _____

$7x - 0$ _____

$7x$ _____

15. $3(5 + 7x - 5)$

$3(7x + 5 - 5)$ _____

$3(7x + 0)$ _____

$3(7x)$ _____

$21x$ _____

16. $4(10x + 2) - 40x$

$40x + 8 - 40x$ _____

$8 + 40x - 40x$ _____

$8 + 0$ _____

8 _____

Name _____ Date _____

Each equation has been solved one step at a time. Next to each step, identify the property, transformation, or simplification used in the step.

17. $x + 19 = 23$

$x + 19 + (-19) = 23 + (-19)$ Addition Property of Equality

$x + 0 = 23 + (-19)$ Combine like terms

$x = 23 + (-19)$ Additive Identity

$x = 4$ Combine like terms

18. $x - 7 = 34$

$x - 7 + 7 = 34 + 7$ _____

$x + 0 = 34 + 7$ _____

$x = 34 + 7$ _____

$x = 41$ _____

19. $13x = 52$

$13x \cdot \dfrac{1}{13} = 52 \cdot \dfrac{1}{13}$ _____

$x(13) \cdot \dfrac{1}{13} = 52 \cdot \dfrac{1}{13}$ _____

$x(1) = 52 \cdot \dfrac{1}{13}$ _____

$x = 52 \cdot \dfrac{1}{13}$ _____

$x = 4$ _____

20. $\dfrac{1}{7}x = 9$

$x\left(\dfrac{1}{7}\right) = 9$ _____

$x\left(\dfrac{1}{7}\right) \cdot 7 = 9 \cdot 7$ _____

$x \cdot 1 = 9 \cdot 7$ _____

$x = 9 \cdot 7$ _____

$x = 63$ _____

21. $3(3x - 8) + 2 = 32$

$9x - 24 + 2 = 32$

$9x - 22 = 32$

$9x - 22 + 22 = 32 + 22$

$9x + 0 = 32 + 22$

$9x = 32 + 22$

$9x = 54$

$9x \cdot \dfrac{1}{9} = 54 \cdot \dfrac{1}{9}$

$x(9) \cdot \dfrac{1}{9} = 54 \cdot \dfrac{1}{9}$

$x(1) = 54 \cdot \dfrac{1}{9}$

$x = 54 \cdot \dfrac{1}{9}$

$x = 6$

22. $5(3 + 6x) - 25 = 20$

$15 + 30x - 25 = 20$

$30x + 15 - 25 = 20$

$30x - 10 = 20$

$30x - 10 + 10 = 20 + 10$

$30x + 0 = 20 + 10$

$30x = 20 + 10$

$30x = 30$

$30x \cdot \dfrac{1}{30} = 30 \cdot \dfrac{1}{30}$

$x(30) \cdot \dfrac{1}{30} = 30 \cdot \dfrac{1}{30}$

$x(1) = 1$

$x = 1$

Name _____ Date _____

23. $7x + 1 = \dfrac{12x + 6}{2}$

$7x + 1 = \dfrac{12x}{2} + \dfrac{6}{2}$ _____

$7x + 1 = 6x + 3$ _____

$7x + 1 - 1 = 6x + 3 - 1$ _____

$7x = 6x + 2$ _____

$7x - 6x = 6x + 2 - 6x$ _____

$7x - 6x = 2 + 6x - 6x$ _____

$x = 2$ _____

24. $\dfrac{4x - 8}{2} = 11 - 3x$

$\dfrac{4x}{2} - \dfrac{8}{2} = 11 - 3x$ _____

$2x - 4 = 11 - 3x$ _____

$2x - 4 + 4 = 11 - 3x + 4$ _____

$2x - 4 + 4 = 11 + 4 - 3x$ _____

$2x = 15 - 3x$ _____

$2x + 3x = 15 - 3x + 3x$ _____

$5x = 15$ _____

$\dfrac{1}{5} \cdot 5x = \dfrac{1}{5} \cdot 15$ _____

$x = 3$ _____

25. $\dfrac{2x-5}{3} = -2x + 17$

$3\left(\dfrac{2x-5}{3}\right) = 3(-2x + 17)$ _____

$2x - 5 = 3(-2x + 17)$ _____

$2x - 5 = -6x + 51$ _____

$2x - 5 + 5 = -6x + 51 + 5$ _____

$2x = -6x + 56$ _____

$2x + 6x = -6x + 56 + 6x$ _____

$2x + 6x = -6x + 6x + 56$ _____

$8x = 56$ _____

$\dfrac{1}{8} \cdot 8x = \dfrac{1}{8} \cdot 56$ _____

$x = 7$ _____

26. $2x - 3 = \dfrac{(4x + 9)}{5}$

$5(2x - 3) = 5\left(\dfrac{4x + 9}{5}\right)$ _____

$5(2x - 3) = 4x + 9$ _____

$10x - 15 = 4x + 9$ _____

$10x - 15 + 15 = 4x + 9 + 15$ _____

$10x = 4x + 24$ _____

$10x - 4x = 4x + 24 - 4x$ _____

$10x - 4x = 24 + 4x - 4x$ _____

$6x = 24$ _____

$\dfrac{1}{6} \cdot 6x = \dfrac{1}{6} \cdot 24$ _____

$x = 4$ _____

Name _____ Date _____

Imagine the Possibilities
Imaginary and Complex Numbers

Vocabulary

Match each definition to the corresponding term.

1. the set of all numbers written in the form $a + bi$, where a and b are real numbers

    a. exponentiation

2. the set of all numbers written in the form $a + bi$, where a and b are real numbers and b is not equal to 0

    b. the number i

3. the term bi in a complex number written as $a + bi$

    c. imaginary numbers

4. a number equal to $\sqrt{-1}$

    d. pure imaginary number

5. to raise a quantity to a power

    e. complex numbers

6. a number of the form bi where b is a real number and is not equal to 0

    f. real part of a complex number

7. the term a in a complex number written as $a + bi$

    g. imaginary part of a complex number

Problem Set

Calculate each power of i.

1. i^{12}

$$i^{12} = (i^4)^3$$
$$= (1)^3$$
$$= 1$$

2. i^{13}

3. i^{15}

4. i^{20}

5. i^{22}

6. i^{25}

7. i^{44}

8. i^{46}

9. i^{84}

10. i^{99}

Name _____ Date _____

Simplify each expression using *i*.

11. $\sqrt{-9}$

$\sqrt{-9} = \sqrt{9} \cdot \sqrt{-1}$

$\qquad = 3i$

12. $\sqrt{-36}$

13. $\sqrt{-20}$

14. $3 + \sqrt{-18}$

15. $9 - \sqrt{-64}$

16. $\dfrac{10 + \sqrt{-12}}{2}$

17. $\dfrac{8 - \sqrt{-32}}{4}$

18. $\dfrac{16 + \sqrt{-48}}{2}$

Simplify each algebraic expression.

19. $5xi - 2xi$

     $5xi - 2xi = 3xi$

20. $10xi + 8i - 6xi - i$

21. $5x + 10i - 2 + 3x - 2i - 7$

22. $(x - i)^2$

23. $(x - i)(x + 3i)$

24. $(4x + i)(2x - 2i)$

Name _____ Date _____

Determine the real part and the imaginary part of each complex number.

25. 24

The real part is 24. The imaginary part is 0*i*.

26. 8*i*

27. 7 + 3*i*

28. $\sqrt{8}$

29. −35*i*

30. 14 − $\sqrt{5}$*i*

31. 52

32. 2.5 + 3$\sqrt{2}$*i*

Identify each given number using words from the box.

natural number	whole number	integer
rational number	irrational number	real number
imaginary number	complex number	

33. -25

integer, rational number, real number, complex number

34. $\sqrt{3}$

35. 9

36. $6 + 7i$

37. $\dfrac{2}{5}$

38. $14i$

39. $0.\overline{18}$

40. $\sqrt{-4}$

Name _____ Date _____

Now It's Getting Complex . . . But It's Really Not Difficult!
Complex Number Operations

Vocabulary

Match each term to its corresponding definition.

1. the number i

A. a number in the form $a + bi$ where a and b are real numbers and b is not equal to 0

2. imaginary number

B. term a of a number written in the form $a + bi$

3. pure imaginary number

C. a polynomial with two terms

4. complex number

D. pairs of numbers of the form $a + bi$ and $a - bi$

5. real part of a complex number

E. a number such that its square equals -1

6. imaginary part of a complex number

F. a number in the form $a + bi$ where a and b are real numbers

7. complex conjugates

G. a polynomial with three terms

8. monomial

H. a number of the form bi where b is not equal to 0

9. binomial

I. term bi of a number written in the form $a + bi$

10. trinomial

J. a polynomial with one term

Problem Set

Calculate each power of i.

1. i^{48}

$i^{48} = (i^4)^{12}$

$\quad = 1^{12}$

$\quad = 1$

2. i^{361}

3. i^{55}

4. i^{1000}

5. i^{-22}

6. i^{-7}

Name _____ Date _____

Rewrite each expression using *i*.

7. $\sqrt{-72}$

$\sqrt{-72} = \sqrt{36(2)(-1)}$

$\qquad = 6\sqrt{2}i$

8. $\sqrt{-49} + \sqrt{-23}$

9. $38 - \sqrt{-200} + \sqrt{121}$

10. $\sqrt{-45} + 21$

11. $\dfrac{\sqrt{-48} - 12}{4}$

12. $\dfrac{1 + \sqrt{4} - \sqrt{-15}}{3}$

13. $-\sqrt{-28} + \dfrac{\sqrt{21}}{3} - \dfrac{\sqrt{12}}{6}$

14. $\dfrac{\sqrt{-75} + \sqrt{80}}{10}$

Simplify each expression.

15. $(2 + 5i) - (7 - 9i)$

$(2 + 5i) - (7 - 9i) = 2 + 5i - 7 + 9i$

$\qquad = (2 - 7) + (5i + 9i)$

$\qquad = -5 + 14i$

16. $-6 + 8i - 1 - 11i + 13$

17. $-(4i - 1 + 3i) + (6i - 10 + 17)$

18. $22i + 13 - (7i + 3 + 12i) + 16i - 25$

19. $9 + 3i(7 - 2i)$

20. $(4 - 5i)(8 + i)$

21. $-0.5(14i - 6) - 4i(0.75 - 3i)$

22. $\left(\frac{1}{2}i - \frac{3}{4}\right) + \left(\frac{1}{8} - \frac{3}{4}i\right)$

Name _____ Date _____

Determine each product.

23. $(3 + i)(3 - i)$

$$(3 + i)(3 - i) = 9 - 3i + 3i - i^2$$
$$= 9 - (-1)$$
$$= 10$$

24. $(4i - 5)(4i + 5)$

25. $(7 - 2i)(7 + 2i)$

26. $\left(\frac{1}{3} + 3i\right)\left(\frac{1}{3} - 3i\right)$

27. $(0.1 + 0.6i)(0.1 - 0.6i)$

28. $-2[(-i - 8)(-i + 8)]$

Identify each expression as a monomial, binomial, or trinomial. Explain your reasoning.

29. $4xi + 7x$

The expression is a monomial because it can be rewritten as $(4i + 7)x$, which shows one x term.

30. $-3x + 5 - 8xi + 1$

31. $6x^2i + 3x^2$

32. $8i - x^3 + 7x^2i$

33. $xi - x + i + 2 - 4i$

34. $-3x^3i - x^2 + 6x^3 + 9i - 1$

Simplify each expression, if possible.

35. $(x - 6i)^2$

$$(x - 6i)^2 = x^2 - 6xi - 6xi + 36i^2$$
$$= x^2 - 12xi + 36(-1)$$
$$= x^2 - 12xi - 36$$

36. $(2 + 5xi)(7 - xi)$

37. $3xi - 4yi$

38. $(2xi - 9)(3x + 5i)$

Name _____ Date _____

39. $(x + 4i)(x - 4i)(x + 4i)$

40. $(3i - 2xi)(3i - 2xi) + (2i - 3xi)(2 - 3xi)$

For each complex number, write its conjugate.

41. $7 + 2i$
  $7 - 2i$

42. $3 + 5i$

43. $8i$

44. $-7i$

45. $2 - 11i$

46. $9 - 4i$

47. $-13 - 6i$

48. $-21 + 4i$

Calculate each quotient.

49. $\dfrac{3 + 4i}{5 + 6i}$

$$\dfrac{3 + 4i}{5 + 6i} = \dfrac{3 + 4i}{5 + 6i} \cdot \dfrac{5 - 6i}{5 - 6i} = \dfrac{15 - 18i + 20i - 24i^2}{25 - 30i + 30i - 36i^2}$$

$$= \dfrac{15 + 2i + 24}{25 + 36} = \dfrac{39 + 2i}{61} = \dfrac{39}{61} + \dfrac{2}{61}i$$

50. $\dfrac{8 + 7i}{2 + i}$

51. $\dfrac{-6 + 2i}{2 - 3i}$

52. $\dfrac{-1 + 5i}{1 - 4i}$

53. $\dfrac{6 - 3i}{2 - i}$

54. $\dfrac{4 - 2i}{-1 + 2i}$

Name _____ Date _____

It's Not Complex—Just Its Solutions Are Complex!
Solving Quadratics with Complex Solutions

Vocabulary

Define the term in your own words.

1. imaginary roots (imaginary zeros)

Problem Set

For each given graph, determine the number of roots for the quadratic equation then determine whether the roots are real or imaginary.

1.

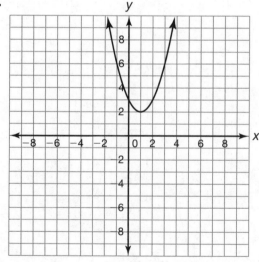

2.

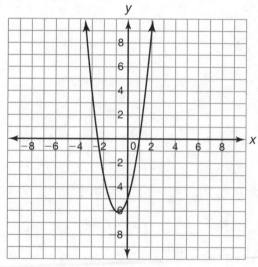

The equation has two imaginary roots.

3.

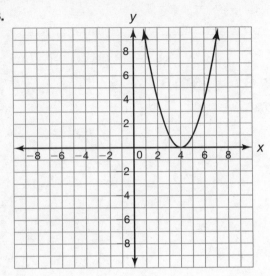

4.

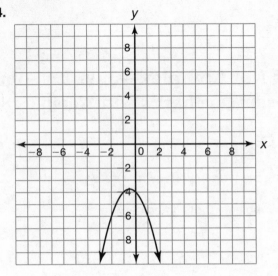

5.

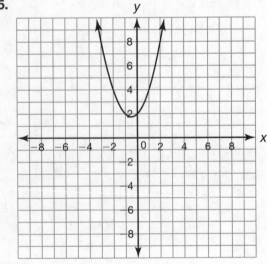

6.

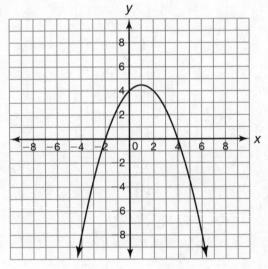

Name _____ Date _____

Determine the zeros of each given function.

7. $f(x) = 4x^2 + 1$

$x = \dfrac{-b \pm \sqrt{b^2 - 4ac}}{2a}$

$x = \dfrac{0 \pm \sqrt{0^2 - 4(4)(1)}}{2(4)}$

$x = \dfrac{0 \pm \sqrt{-16}}{8}$

$x = \dfrac{0 \pm 4i}{8}$

$x = \pm \dfrac{1}{2}i$

The zeros are $\dfrac{1}{2}i$ and $-\dfrac{1}{2}i$.

8. $f(x) = x^2 + 9$

9. $f(x) = x^2 + 2x + 5$

10. $f(x) = -x^2 + 4x - 6$

11. $f(x) = x^2 + 2x + 2$

12. $f(x) = -x^2 + 6x - 25$

13. $f(x) = x^2 - 4x + 9$

14. $f(x) = 2x^2 + 8x + 10$

Name _____ Date _____

I Graph in Pieces
Linear Piecewise Functions

Problem Set

Complete each table. Then, sketch a graph that represents the problem situation.

1. Rosa saved $100 to spend on vacation. For the first 3 days of her vacation she spent $20 each day. Then for the next 2 days, she spent nothing. After those 5 days, she spent $10 each day until her savings were depleted.

Time (days)	Savings (dollars)
0	100
1	80
2	60
3	40
4	40
5	40
6	30
7	20
8	10
9	0

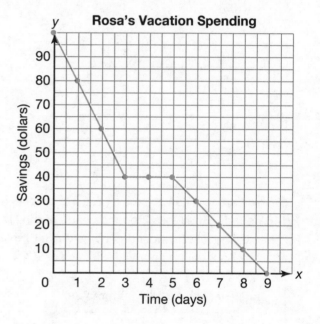

Rosa's Vacation Spending

2. Belinda is saving money for a new snowboard. She earns $30 every 5 days she tutors. After 30 days, she takes a break from tutoring and does not earn any money for 10 days. After those 10 days she begins tutoring again and earns $30 every 5 days until she reaches her goal of $300.

Time (days)	Savings (dollars)
0	
5	
10	
15	
20	
25	
30	
35	
40	
45	
50	
55	
60	

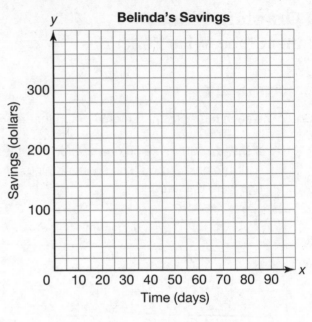

3. Shanise starts a new exercise program to lose weight. Before starting the program her weight is 146 pounds. She loses 2 pounds each of the first 4 weeks of her new program. Then, for the next 2 weeks she loses 1 pound per week. After those 2 weeks she adds swimming to her program and again loses 2 pounds per week for the next 2 weeks until she reaches her goal.

Time (weeks)	Weight (pounds)
0	
1	
2	
3	
4	
5	
6	
7	
8	

Name _____ Date _____

4. Carlos is training for a bike race in 30 days. For the first 5 days of his training he bikes 3 miles each day. For the next 10 days he bikes 5 miles each day. For the next 10 days of his training he bikes 8 miles each day. For the last 5 days of his training he bikes 10 miles a day.

Time (days)	Total Distance (miles)
0	
5	
10	
15	
20	
25	
30	

5. Maria earns money delivering newspapers each morning. For the first 3 days she earns $18 each day. For the next 2 days, she takes on an additional route to cover a coworker who is out sick and earns $36 each day. For the next 2 days she returns to her original route and earns $18 each day.

Time (days)	Earnings (dollars)
0	
1	
2	
3	
4	
5	
6	
7	

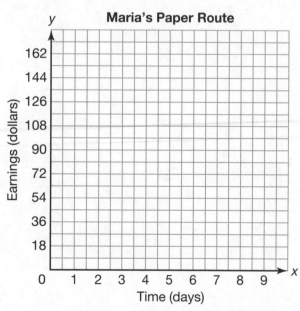

6. Franco saved $200 to spend at an amusement park while on vacation. For the first 2 days of his vacation he spent $36 each day. Then for the next 2 days, he spent nothing. After those 4 days, he stayed 3 more days and spent $40 each day.

Time (days)	Savings (dollars)
0	
1	
2	
3	
4	
5	
6	
7	

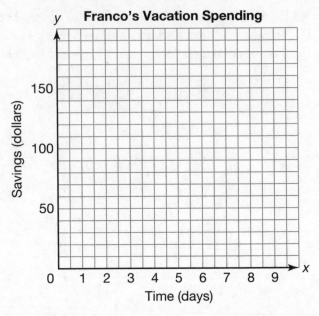

Franco's Vacation Spending

Write a piecewise function to represent the data shown in each table.

7.

x	f(x)
0	60
1	55
2	50
3	45
4	45
5	45
6	45
7	43
8	41
9	39

From 0 to 3:

The y-intercept is 60.

$$m = \frac{y_2 - y_1}{x_2 - x_1}$$

$$= \frac{55 - 60}{1 - 0} = -\frac{5}{1} = -5$$

$y = mx + b$
$y = -5x + 60$

From 3 to 6:

The slope is 0.

$y = 45$

From 6 to 9:

A point is (6, 45).

$$m = \frac{y_2 - y_1}{x_2 - x_1}$$

$$= \frac{41 - 43}{8 - 7} = \frac{-2}{1} = -2$$

$y - y_1 = m(x - x_1)$
$y - 45 = -2(x - 6)$
$y - 45 = -2x + 12$
$y = -2x + 57$

$$f(x) = \begin{cases} -5x + 60, & 0 \leq x \leq 3 \\ 45, & 3 < x \leq 6 \\ -2x + 57, & 6 < x \leq 9 \end{cases}$$

Name _____ Date _____

8.

x	f(x)
0	0
2	3
4	6
6	9
8	12
10	12
12	12
14	18
16	24
18	30

9.

x	f(x)
0	80
1	75
2	70
3	65
4	64
5	63
6	62
7	61
8	60
9	58

16

Name _____ Date _____

10.

x	f(x)
0	4
3	6
6	8
9	12
12	16
15	20
18	22
21	24
24	26
27	28

16

11.

x	f(x)
0	100
2	80
4	60
6	60
8	60
10	60
12	54
14	48
16	42
18	36

12.

x	f(x)
0	74
1	70
2	66
3	62
4	64
5	66
6	68
7	60
8	52
9	44

Name _____ Date _____

Sketch a graph that represents the data shown in each table. Write a function to represent the graph.

13.

x	f(x)
−3	2
−2	6
−1	10
0	14
1	10
2	6
3	2

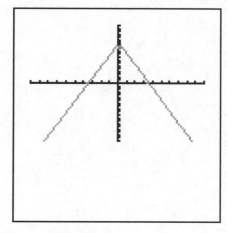

$$f(x) = -|4x| + 14$$

14.

x	f(x)
−3	−4
−2	−6
−1	−8
0	−10
1	−8
2	−6
3	−4

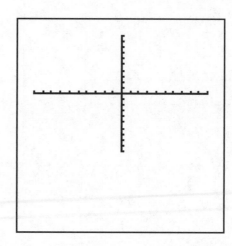

15.

x	f(x)
−6	−2
−4	−4
−2	−6
0	−8
2	−6
4	−4
6	−2

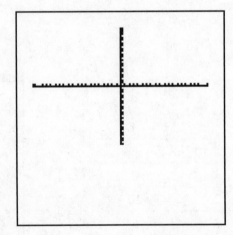

16.

x	f(x)
−15	5
−10	10
−5	15
0	20
5	15
10	10
15	5

Name _____ Date _____

17.

x	f(x)
−3	14
−2	11
−1	8
0	5
1	8
2	11
3	14

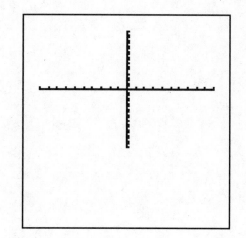

18.

x	f(x)
−3	−5
−2	−4
−1	−3
0	−2
1	−3
2	−4
3	−5

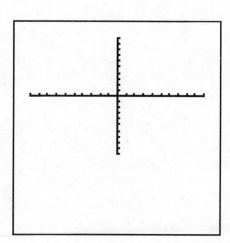

16

Name _____ Date _____

Step By Step
Step Functions

Vocabulary

For each function, write a definition and give an example.

1. step function

2. greatest integer (floor) function

3. least integer (ceiling) function

Problem Set

Write and graph a function to represent each problem situation.

1. An online mall assigns shipping charges based on the total value of merchandise purchased. The shipping charges are as follows:

   - 18% for purchases more than $0 and up to and including $50,

   - 16% for purchases more than $50 and up to and including $100,

   - 14% for purchases more than $100 and up to and including $150,

   - 12% for purchases more than $150 and up to and including $200, and

   - 10% for purchases more than $200.

$$f(x) = \begin{cases} 0.18x, & 0 < x \le 50 \\ 0.16x, & 50 < x \le 100 \\ 0.14x, & 100 < x \le 150 \\ 0.12x, & 150 < x \le 200 \\ 0.10x, & 200 < x \end{cases}$$

Name _____ Date _____

2. A fundraising company bases the profit returned to organizations on the total value of products sold. The profit returned is calculated as follows:

   • 40% for sales more than $0 and up to and including $250,

   • 45% for sales more than $250 and up to and including $500,

   • 50% for sales more than $500 and up to and including $750,

   • 55% for sales more than $750 and up to and including $1000, and

   • 60% for sales more than $1000.

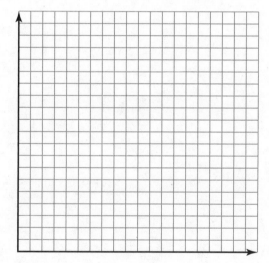

3. A theater company offers discounts based on the value of tickets purchased. The discounts are as follows:

- 5% for purchases more than $0 and up to and including $20,

- 10% for purchases more than $20 and up to and including $40,

- 15% for purchases more than $40 and up to and including $60, and

- 20% for purchases more than $60.

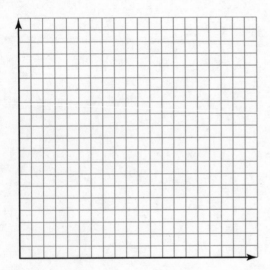

Name _____ Date _____

4. A small clothing company pays its employees a commission based on the total value of clothing sold. The commission for each sale is calculated as follows:

- 6% for sales more than $0 and up to and including $30,

- 9% for sales more than $30 and up to and including $60,

- 12% for sales more than $60 and up to and including $90, and

- 15% for sales more than $90.

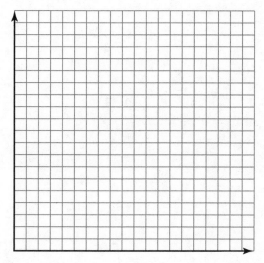

5. A small town calculates its local sales tax rate based on the total value of the goods sold. The local sales tax is calculated as follows:

- 9% for sales more than $0 and up to and including $100,

- 8% for sales more than $100 and up to and including $200,

- 7% for sales more than $200 and up to and including $300, and

- 6% for sales more than $300.

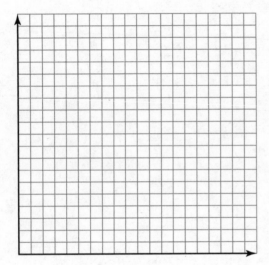

Name _____ Date _____

6. An electronics store rewards customers with in-store reward vouchers. The value of the reward vouchers are based on the total value of merchandise purchased. The rewards are calculated as follows:

- 4% for purchases more than $0 and up to and including $50,

- 8% for purchases more than $50 and up to and including $100,

- 14% for purchases more than $100 and up to and including $150,

- 16% for purchases more than $150 and up to and including $200, and

- 18% for purchases more than $200.

16

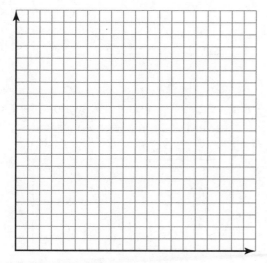

16

Write a function to represent each problem situation. Then use your graphing calculator to graph the function.

7. To encourage quality and minimize defects, a manufacturer pays his employees a bonus based on the value of defective merchandise produced. The fewer defective merchandise produced, the greater the employee's bonus. The bonuses are calculated as follows:

- $50 for more than $0 and up to and including $100 of defective merchandise,

- $30 for more than $100 and up to and including $200 of defective merchandise,

- $10 for more than $200 and up to and including $300 of defective merchandise, and

- $0 for more than $300 of defective merchandise.

$$f(x) = \begin{cases} 50, & 0 < x \le 100 \\ 30, & 100 < x \le 200 \\ 10, & 200 < x \le 300 \\ 0, & 300 < x \end{cases}$$

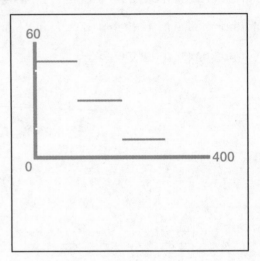

8. A jewelry store offers reward coupons to its customers. A $2 reward coupon is awarded for each $20 spent. Write a function that represents the value of reward coupons awarded for up to $100 spent.

Name _____ Date _____

9. A kids bounce house charges $8 for the first hour and $2 for each additional hour of playtime. Write a function that represents the charges for up to 5 hours of playtime.

10. A fundraising company bases the profit returned to organizations on the total value of products sold. The profit returned is calculated as follows:

- $100 for sales more than $0 and up to and including $250,

- $225 for sales more than $250 and up to and including $500,

- $350 for sales more than $500 and up to and including $750, and

- $475 for sales more than $750 and up to and including $1000.

16

11. An ice rink charges hockey teams for ice time to practice. The ice rink charges $10 for the first hour and $12 for each additional hour. Write a function that represents the charges for up to 5 hours.

12. Ava is participating in a walk for charity. Her sponsors agree to donate $2.50 plus $2.50 for each whole mile that she walks. Write a function that represents the donation amount for up to 5 miles.

Name _____ Date _____

Evaluate.

13. $\lfloor 4.5 \rfloor$

    $\lfloor 4.5 \rfloor = 4$

14. $\lceil 5.1 \rceil$

15. $\lceil -8.3 \rceil$

16. $\lfloor -3.2 \rfloor$

17. $\lfloor 7.3 \rfloor$

18. $\lfloor 0.6 \rfloor$

19. $\lceil 7.9 \rceil$

20. $\lceil 0.03 \rceil$

Name _____ Date _____

The Inverse Undoes What a Function Does
Inverses of Linear Functions

Vocabulary

Match each definition with the corresponding term.

1. inverse operation

    a. the combination of functions such that the output from one function becomes the input for the next function

2. inverse function

    b. working backwards or retracing steps to return to an original value or position

3. composition of functions

    c. a function which takes an output value, performs some operation(s) on the value, and arrives back at the original function's input value

Problem Set

Identify the domain and range of each relationship and the reverse relationship. Determine if the relationship and the reverse relationship are functions.

1. Each student in your school chooses his or her favorite sport.

Relationship domain: students in your school

Relationship range: all of the sports chosen

The relationship is a function because for each student there is exactly one favorite sport.

Reverse relationship domain: all of the sports chosen

Reverse range: students in your school

The reverse relationship is not a function because for each sport there may be more than one student who chose it as their favorite.

2. Each student in your school is assigned a unique student ID number.

3. Each of the 24 students in your class chooses a red, blue, orange, green, or yellow marble from a bag of assorted marbles.

4. Every member of the basketball team is assigned a jersey number.

5. Each member of your family chooses their favorite game for game night.

Name _____ Date _____

6. Each student in your class is assigned a letter grade for their final exam.

Write a phrase, expression, or sentence to describe the inverse of each situation.

7. Close a dresser drawer.

   Open the dresser drawer.

8. Light a candle.

9. Jog 3 blocks north and 5 blocks east.

10. Open the garage door and drive out of the garage.

11. Divide a number by 2 then add 7.

12. Multiply a number by 3 then add 1.

Complete each table. Write an equation to represent the relationship. Write an equation for the inverse of the problem situation.

13. One foot is equivalent to 12 inches.

Feet	Inches
1	12
2	24
3	36
4	48
5	60

Let i = the number of inches.

Let f = the number of feet.

$i = 12f$

Inverse: $f = \dfrac{i}{12}$

14. One meter is equivalent to 100 centimeters.

Meters	Centimeters
1	
2	
3	
4	
5	

15. One pint is equivalent to 2 cups.

Pints	Cups
2	
4	
6	
8	
10	

Name _____ Date _____

16. Four quarters is equivalent to 1 dollar.

Quarters	Dollars
4	
16	
32	
64	
128	

17. Three feet is equivalent to 1 yard.

Feet	Yards
3	
9	
12	
18	
24	

18. One US dollar is equivalent to 13 Mexican pesos.

Dollars	Pesos
1	
2	
3	
4	
5	

Determine the inverse of each function. Graph the original function and its inverse.

19. $f(x) = 4x$

$f(x) = 4x$

$y = 4x$

$x = 4y$

$\dfrac{x}{4} = y$

$f^{-1}(x) = \dfrac{x}{4}$

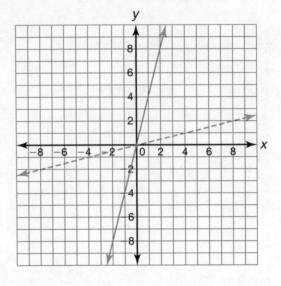

20. $f(x) = \dfrac{1}{3}x$

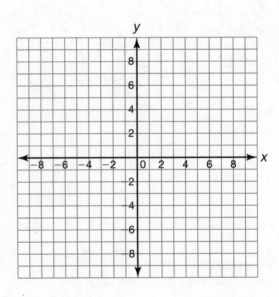

Name _____ Date _____

21. $f(x) = 2x + 1$

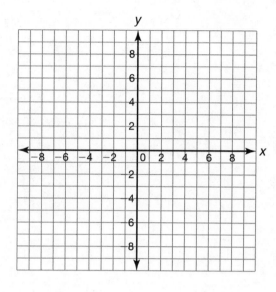

22. $f(x) = -6x - 2$

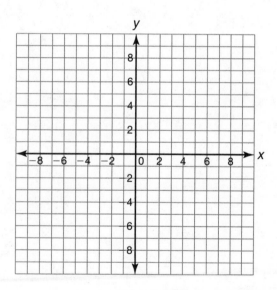

23. $f(x) = \dfrac{2}{3}x - 8$

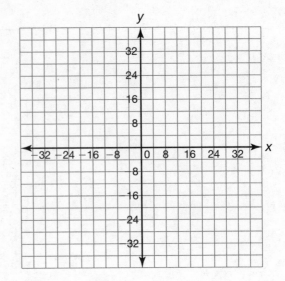

24. $f(x) = -0.5x + 9$

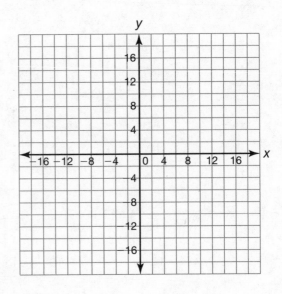

Name _____ Date _____

Determine the corresponding point on the graph of each inverse function.

25. Given that (2, 5) is a point on the graph of $f(x)$, what is the corresponding point on the graph of $f^{-1}(x)$?

The corresponding point on the graph of $f^{-1}(x)$ is (5, 2).

26. Given that (−3, 1) is a point on the graph of $f(x)$, what is the corresponding point on the graph of $f^{-1}(x)$?

27. Given that (−4, −1) is a point on the graph of $f(x)$, what is the corresponding point on the graph of $f^{-1}(x)$?

28. Given that (0, 8) is a point on the graph of $f(x)$, what is the corresponding point on the graph of $f^{-1}(x)$?

29. Given that (1, −7) is a point on the graph of $f(x)$, what is the corresponding point on the graph of $f^{-1}(x)$?

30. Given that (−6, 0) is a point on the graph of $f(x)$, what is the corresponding point on the graph of $f^{-1}(x)$?

Determine if the functions in each pair are inverses.

31. $f(x) = 5x + 1$ and $g(x) = \frac{1}{5}x - \frac{1}{5}$

$f(x) = 5x + 1$

$f(g(x)) = f\left(\frac{1}{5}x - \frac{1}{5}\right)$

$f(g(x)) = 5\left(\frac{1}{5}x - \frac{1}{5}\right) + 1$

$= (x - 1) + 1$

$= x$

$g(x) = \frac{1}{5}x - \frac{1}{5}$

$g(f(x)) = g(5x + 1)$

$g(f(x)) = \frac{1}{5}(5x + 1) - \frac{1}{5}$

$= \left(x + \frac{1}{5}\right) - \frac{1}{5}$

$= x$

The functions are inverses because $f(g(x)) = g(f(x)) = x$.

32. $f(x) = 8x - 2$ and $g(x) = \frac{1}{8}x - \frac{1}{4}$

33. $f(x) = -\frac{1}{2}x + 5$ and $g(x) = -2x + 10$

Name _____ Date _____

34. $f(x) = -\dfrac{2}{3}x - 2$ and $g(x) = -\dfrac{3}{2}x - 3$

35. $f(x) = 0.4x - 8$ and $g(x) = 2.5x + 20$

36. $f(x) = -0.2x + 6$ and $g(x) = 5x - 30$

Name _____ Date _____

Taking the Egg Plunge!
Inverses of Non-Linear Functions

Vocabulary

Write a definition for each term in your own words.

1. one-to-one function

2. restrict the domain

Problem Set

Complete each table of values for the function and its inverse. Determine whether the function is a one-to-one function.

1. $f(x) = 2x + 5$

x	f(x)
−2	1
−1	3
0	5
1	7
2	9

x	$f^{-1}(x)$
1	−2
3	−1
5	0
7	1
9	2

The function is one-to-one because both the original function and its inverse are functions.

2. $f(x) = -6x + 1$

x	f(x)
-2	
-1	
0	
1	
2	

x	$f^{-1}(x)$
	-2
	-1
	0
	1
	2

3. $f(x) = 5x^2 - 8$

x	f(x)
-2	
-1	
0	
1	
2	

x	$f^{-1}(x)$
	-2
	-1
	0
	1
	2

4. $f(x) = 4^x$

x	f(x)
-2	
-1	
0	
1	
2	

x	$f^{-1}(x)$
	-2
	-1
	0
	1
	2

Name _____ Date _____

5. $f(x) = -3$

x	f(x)
−2	
−1	
0	
1	
2	

x	f⁻¹(x)
	−2
	−1
	0
	1
	2

6. $f(x) = |4x|$

x	f(x)
−2	
−1	
0	
1	
2	

x	f⁻¹(x)
	−2
	−1
	0
	1
	2

Determine whether each function is a one-to-one function by examining the graph of the function and its inverse.

7. $f(x) = -4x + 7$

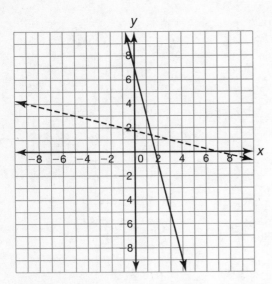

The function is one-to-one because both the original function and its inverse are functions.

8. $f(x) = 5$

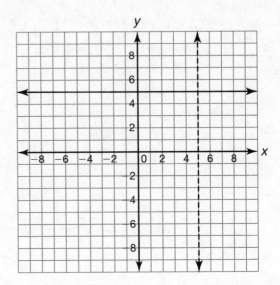

9. $f(x) = |3x|$

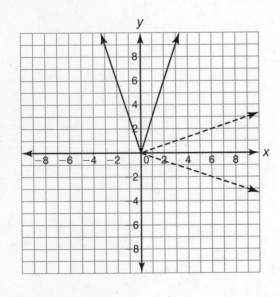

10. $f(x) = -x^2 - 3$

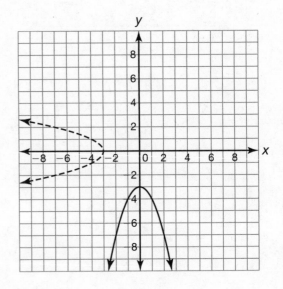

Name _____ Date _____

11. $f(x) = 6x - 3$

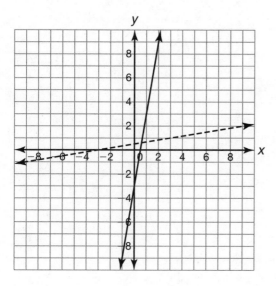

12. $f(x) = 3^x$

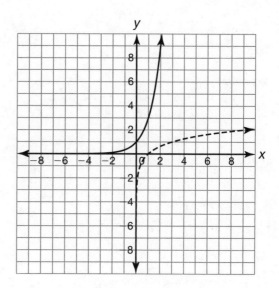

Identify each equation as linear, exponential, quadratic, or linear absolute value. Determine whether the function is a one-to-one function.

13. $f(x) = 2x - 9$

The function is a linear function. A linear function that is not a constant function is a one-to-one function. So, the function is one-to-one.

14. $f(x) = -6$

15. $f(x) = -3x + 10$

16. $f(x) = 5^x$

17. $f(x) = -|6x|$

18. $f(x) = 9x^2 + 3$

Determine the equation of the inverse for each quadratic function.

19. $f(x) = 7x^2$

$$f(x) = 7x^2$$
$$y = 7x^2$$
$$x = 7y^2$$
$$\frac{x}{7} = y^2$$
$$\pm\sqrt{\frac{x}{7}} = y$$
$$f^{-1}(x) = \pm\sqrt{\frac{x}{7}}$$

20. $f(x) = -x^2$

21. $f(x) = 6x^2 + 11$

22. $f(x) = 2x^2 - 12$

Name _____ Date _____

23. $f(x) = -4x^2 - 6$　　　　　　　　　**24.** $f(x) = -3x^2 + 20$

Determine the equation of the inverse for each given function. Graph the function and its inverse. Restrict the domain of the original function and the inverse so that the inverse is also a function.

25. $f(x) = 2x^2$

$f(x) = 2x^2$

$y = 2x^2$

$x = 2y^2$

$\dfrac{x}{2} = y^2$

$\pm\sqrt{\dfrac{x}{2}} = y$

$f^{-1}(x) = \pm\sqrt{\dfrac{x}{2}}$

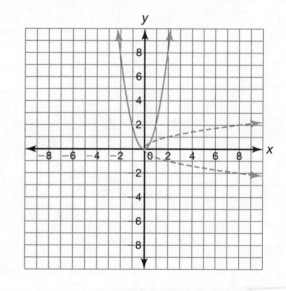

$f(x) = \begin{cases} 2x^2, & \text{domain: } x \geq 0, \text{ range: } y \geq 0, \\ 2x^2, & \text{domain: } x \leq 0, \text{ range: } y \geq 0, \end{cases}$

$f^{-1}(x) = \begin{cases} \sqrt{\dfrac{x}{2}}, & \text{domain: } x \geq 0, \text{ range: } y \geq 0, \\ -\sqrt{\dfrac{x}{2}}, & \text{domain: } x \geq 0, \text{ range: } y \leq 0, \end{cases}$

For the function $y = 2x^2$ with $x \geq 0$, the inverse is $y = \sqrt{\dfrac{x}{2}}$.

For the function $y = 2x^2$ with $x \leq 0$, the inverse is $y = -\sqrt{\dfrac{x}{2}}$.

16

26. $f(x) = x^2 + 3$

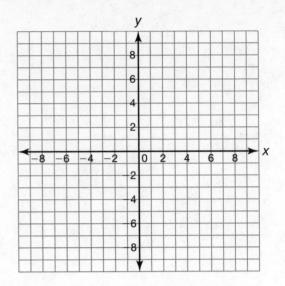

Name _____ Date _____

27. $f(x) = -4x^2 - 2$

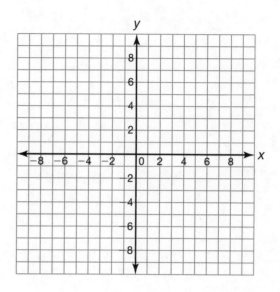

28. $f(x) = |2x|$

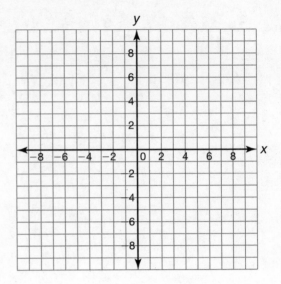

Name _____ Date _____

29. $f(x) = -|x|$

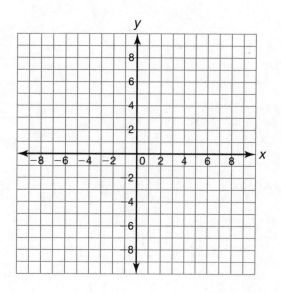

30. $f(x) = -|5x|$

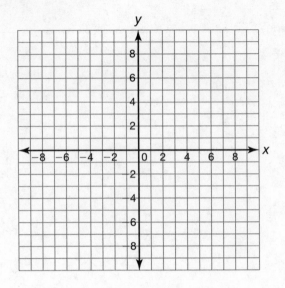

Name _____ Date _____

It's All About the Slope
Parallel and Perpendicular Lines on the Coordinate Plane

Vocabulary

Complete the sentence.

1. The point-slope form of the equation of the line that passes through (x_1, y_1) and has slope m is _____.

Problem Set

Determine whether each pair of lines are parallel, perpendicular, or neither. Explain your reasoning.

1. line n: $y = -2x - 4$

   line m: $y = -2x + 8$

   Parallel. The slope of line n is -2, which is equal to the slope of line m, so the lines are parallel.

2. line p: $y = 3x + 5$

   line q: $y = \frac{1}{3}x + 5$

3. line r: $y = -5x + 12$

   line s: $y = \frac{1}{5}x - 6$

4. line n: $y = 6x + 2$

   line m: $y = -6x - 2$

5. line p: $y - x = 4$

line q: $2x + y = 8$

6. line r: $2y + x = 6$

line s: $3x + 6y = 12$

17

Determine whether the lines shown on each coordinate plane are parallel, perpendicular, or neither. Explain your reasoning.

7.

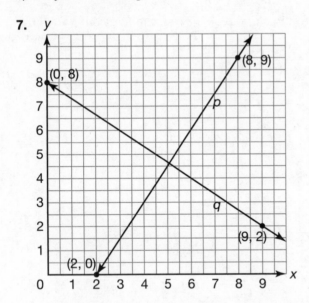

The lines are perpendicular. The slope of line p is $\frac{3}{2}$ and the slope of line q is $-\frac{2}{3}$.

Because $\frac{3}{2}\left(-\frac{2}{3}\right) = -1$, the lines are perpendicular.

Name _____ Date _____

8.

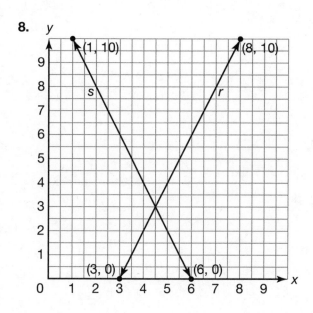

9.

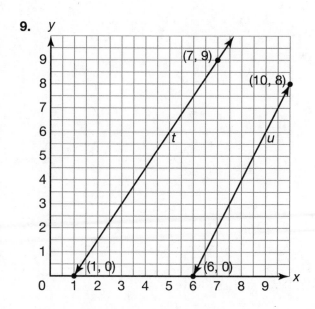

10.

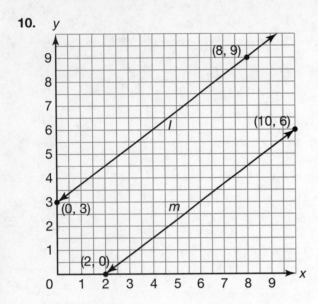

11.

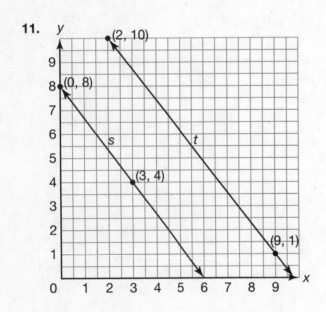

Name _____ Date _____

12.

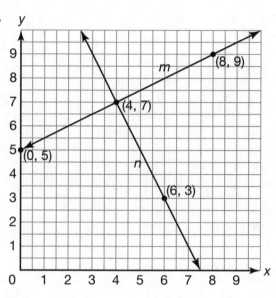

Determine an equation for each parallel line described. Write your answer in both point-slope form and slope-intercept form.

13. What is the equation of a line parallel to $y = \frac{4}{5}x + 2$ that passes through (1, 2)?

Point-slope form: $(y - 2) = \frac{4}{5}(x - 1)$

Slope-intercept form:

$y - 2 = \frac{4}{5}x - \frac{4}{5}$

$y = \frac{4}{5}x - \frac{4}{5} + 2$

$y = \frac{4}{5}x + \frac{6}{5}$

14. What is the equation of a line parallel to $y = -5x + 3$ that passes through (3, 1)?

15. What is the equation of a line parallel to $y = 7x - 8$ that passes through $(5, -2)$?

17

16. What is the equation of a line parallel to $y = -\frac{1}{2}x + 6$ that passes through $(-4, 1)$?

17. What is the equation of a line parallel to $y = \frac{1}{3}x - 4$ that passes through $(9, 8)$?

Name _____ Date _____

18. What is the equation of a line parallel to $y = -4x - 7$ that passes through $(2, -9)$?

Determine an equation for each perpendicular line described. Write your answer in both point-slope form and slope-intercept form.

19. What is the equation of a line perpendicular to $y = 2x - 6$ that passes through $(5, 4)$?

The slope of the new line must be $-\dfrac{1}{2}$.

Point-slope form: $(y - 4) = -\dfrac{1}{2}(x - 5)$

Slope-intercept form:
$$y - 4 = -\dfrac{1}{2}x + \dfrac{5}{2}$$
$$y = -\dfrac{1}{2}x + \dfrac{5}{2} + 4$$
$$y = -\dfrac{1}{2}x + \dfrac{13}{2}$$

20. What is the equation of a line perpendicular to $y = -3x + 4$ that passes through $(-1, 6)$?

21. What is the equation of a line perpendicular to $y = -\dfrac{2}{5}x - 1$ that passes through $(2, -8)$?

22. What is the equation of a line perpendicular to $y = \dfrac{3}{4}x + 12$ that passes through $(12, 3)$?

23. What is the equation of a line perpendicular to $y = 6x - 5$ that passes through $(6, -3)$?

24. What is the equation of a line perpendicular to $y = \dfrac{5}{2}x - 1$ that passes through $(-1, -4)$?

Name _____ Date _____

Determine the equation of a vertical line that passes through each given point.

25. (−2, 1)

x = −2

26. (3, 15)

27. (9, −7)

28. (−11, −8)

29. (−5, −10)

30. (0, −4)

Determine the equation of a horizontal line that passes through each given point.

31. (4, 7)

y = 7

32. (−6, 5)

33. (−8, −3)

34. (2, −9)

35. (−7, 8)

36. (6, −2)

Calculate the distance from each given point to the given line.

37. Point: (0, 4); Line: $f(x) = 2x - 3$

Write the equation for the line perpendicular to the given line that goes through the given point.

Since the slope of f is 2, the slope of the perpendicular segment is $-\frac{1}{2}$.

$y = mx + b$

$4 = -\frac{1}{2}(0) + b$

$4 = b$

The equation of the line containing the perpendicular segment is $y = -\frac{1}{2}x + 4$.

Calculate the point of intersection of the segment and the line $f(x) = 2x - 3$.

$-\frac{1}{2}x + 4 = 2x - 3$

$-x + 8 = 4x - 6$

$-5x = -14$

$x = \frac{-14}{-5} = 2.8$

$y = -\frac{1}{2}(2.8) + 4 = 2.6$

The point of intersection is (2.8, 2.6).

Calculate the distance.

$d = \sqrt{(0 - 2.8)^2 + (4 - 2.6)^2}$

$d = \sqrt{(-2.8)^2 + (1.4)^2}$

$d = \sqrt{7.84 + 1.96}$

$d = \sqrt{9.8} \approx 3.13$

The distance from the point (0, 4) to the line $f(x) = 2x - 3$ is approximately 3.13 units.

Name _____ Date _____

38. Point: $(-1, 3)$; Line: $f(x) = -\dfrac{1}{2}x - 4$

Write the equation for the line perpendicular to the given line that goes through the given point.

39. Point: $(-2, 5)$; Line: $f(x) = \dfrac{2}{3}x - \dfrac{1}{6}$

Write the equation for the line perpendicular to the given line that goes through the given point.

Name _____ Date _____

40. Point: $(-1, -2)$; Line: $f(x) = -4x + 11$

Write the equation for the line perpendicular to the given line that goes through the given point.

41. Point: $(3, -1)$; Line: $f(x) = \frac{1}{3}x - 6$

Write the equation for the line perpendicular to the given line that goes through the given point.

Name _____ Date _____

42. Point: $(-4, -2)$; Line: $f(x) = -\dfrac{1}{2}x + 4$

Write the equation for the line perpendicular to the given line that goes through the given point.

Name _____ Date _____

Hey, I Know That Triangle!
Classifying Triangles on the Coordinate Plane

Problem Set

Determine the location of point *C* such that triangle *ABC* has each given characteristic. The graph shows line segment *AB* and circles *A* and *B*.

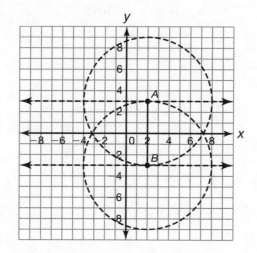

1. Triangle *ABC* is a right triangle.

   Point *C* can have an infinite number of locations as long as the location satisfies one of the following conditions:
   - Point *C* could be located anywhere on line $y = 3$ except where $x = 2$.
   - Point *C* could be located anywhere on line $y = -3$ except where $x = 2$.

2. Triangle *ABC* is an acute triangle.

3. Triangle *ABC* is an obtuse triangle.

4. Triangle *ABC* is an equilateral triangle.

5. Triangle *ABC* is an isosceles triangle.

6. Triangle *ABC* is a scalene triangle.

Name _____ Date _____

Graph triangle *ABC* using each set of given points. Determine if triangle *ABC* is scalene, isosceles, or equilateral.

7. $A\,(-3, 1)$, $B\,(-3, -3)$, $C\,(1, 0)$

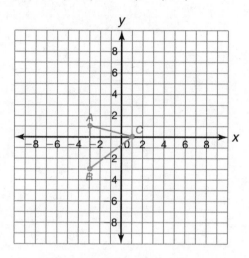

Triangle *ABC* is scalene because all of the side lengths are different.

$AB = 1 - (-3)$

$\quad = 4$

$BC = \sqrt{(x_2 - x_1)^2 + (y_2 - y_1)^2}$

$\quad = \sqrt{(1 - (-3))^2 + (0 - (-3))^2}$

$\quad = \sqrt{(4)^2 + (3)^2}$

$\quad = \sqrt{16 + 9}$

$\quad = \sqrt{25}$

$\quad = 5$

$AC = \sqrt{(x_2 - x_1)^2 + (y_2 - y_1)^2}$

$\quad = \sqrt{(-3 - 1)^2 + (1 - 0)^2}$

$\quad = \sqrt{(-4)^2 + (1)^2}$

$\quad = \sqrt{16 + 1}$

$\quad = \sqrt{17}$

8. $A(8, 5)$, $B(8, 1)$, $C(4, 3)$

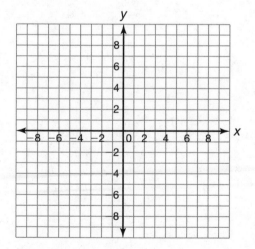

9. *A* (5, 8), *B* (5, 2), *C* (−3, 5)

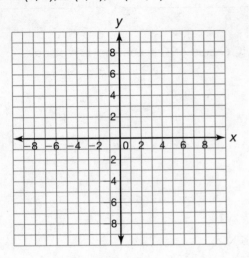

10. *A* (−2, −6), *B* (6, −6), *C* (2, −3)

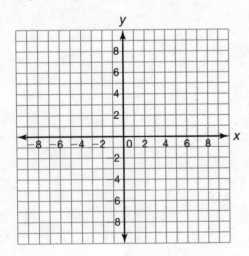

Name _____ Date _____

11. *A* (0, 0), *B* (4, 0), *C* (3, 7)

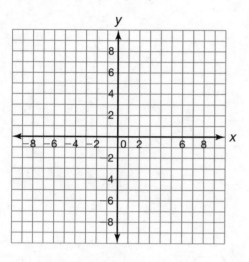

12. *A* (−6, 4), *B* (0, 4), *C* (−2, −2)

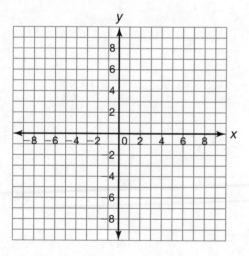

Graph triangle *ABC* using each set of given points. Determine if triangle *ABC* is a right triangle, an acute triangle, or an obtuse triangle.

13. *A* (0, 4), *B* (4, 5), *C* (1, 0)

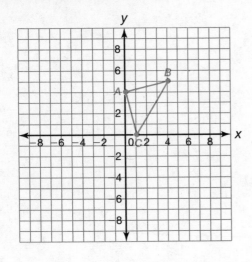

Slope of line segment *AB*:

$$m = \frac{y_2 - y_1}{x_2 - x_1}$$

$$= \frac{5 - 4}{4 - 0}$$

$$= \frac{1}{4}$$

Slope of line segment *BC*:

$$m = \frac{y_2 - y_1}{x_2 - x_1}$$

$$= \frac{0 - 5}{1 - 4}$$

$$= \frac{-5}{-3} = \frac{5}{3}$$

Slope of line segment *AC*:

$$m = \frac{y_2 - y_1}{x_2 - x_1}$$

$$= \frac{0 - 4}{1 - 0}$$

$$= \frac{-4}{1} = -4$$

Triangle *ABC* is a right triangle because segments *AB* and *AC* have negative reciprocal slopes.

14. *A* (−6, 1), *B* (−6, −4), *C* (4, 0)

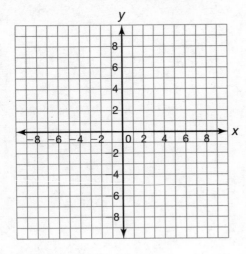

Name _____ Date _____

15. *A* (−5, 7), *B* (7, 7), *C* (1, 4)

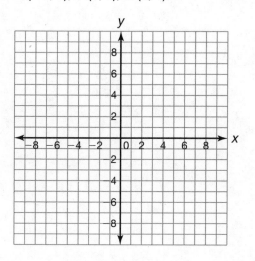

16. *A* (−4, −1), *B* (1, 3), *C* (3, −4)

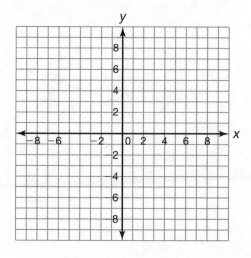

17. _A_ (2, 6), _B_ (8, −3), _C_ (2, −7)

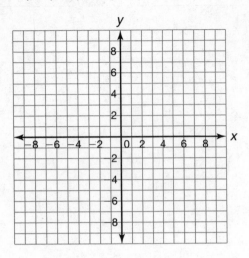

18. _A_ (−2, 6), _B_ (6, −3), _C_ (0, 0)

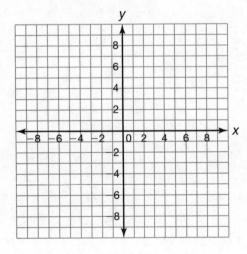

Name _____ Date _____

And I Know That Quadrilateral Too!
Classifying Quadrilaterals on the Coordinate Plane

Problem Set

Determine the distance between the two points.

1. $A(-2, 5)$ $B(3, 2)$

$AB = \sqrt{(-2 - 3)^2 + (5 - 2)^2}$

$= \sqrt{(-5)^2 + 3^2}$

$= \sqrt{25 + 9}$

$= \sqrt{34}$

2. $C(-3, -1)$ $D(4, 0)$

3. $R(5, 1)$ $S(-6, 4)$

4. $T(-1, 0)$ $W(-5, -1)$

5. $M(0, 0)$ $N(5, 1)$

6. $P(0, -8)$ $Q(2, 6)$

Determine the slope of $\overline{AB}$ and $\overline{CD}$. Then state if the segments are *parallel*, *perpendicular* or *neither*. Explain your reasoning.

7. $A(-4, 2)$, $B(4, 4)$, $C(0, 0)$, $D(4, 1)$

Slope of $\overline{AB}$

$m = \dfrac{4 - 2}{4 - (-4)}$

$= \dfrac{2}{8}$

$= \dfrac{1}{4}$

Slope of $\overline{CD}$

$m = \dfrac{1 - 0}{4 - 0}$

$= \dfrac{1}{4}$

The slopes of the segments are the same. The segments are parallel.

8. $A(-1, -3), B(1, 2), C(-1, 7), D(5, 1)$

9. $A(-2, 1), B(0, -4), C(-5, -4), D(0, -2)$

10. $A(-2, -1), B(10, 2), C(3, 6), D(5, -2)$

11. $A(1, 2), B(-1, -6), C(0, -5), D(2, 3)$

Name _____ Date _____

12. $A(-3, 0)$, $B(1, 2)$, $C(1, 2)$, $D(3, -2)$

Determine the equation of the line with the given slope and passing through the given point.

13. $m = \frac{2}{3}$ passing through $(9, 1)$

$$(y - 1) = \frac{2}{3}(x - 9)$$
$$y - 1 = \frac{2}{3}x - 6$$
$$y = \frac{2}{3}x - 5$$

14. $m = -\frac{1}{4}$ passing through $(-4, 2)$

15. $m = 0$ passing through $(3, 5)$

16. $m = \frac{3}{5}$ passing through $(-8, 2)$

17. $m = -5$ passing through $(6, -3)$

18. $m = \dfrac{6}{5}$ passing through $(0, -10)$

17

Determine the coordinates of point D, the solution to the system of linear equations.

19. $y = -\dfrac{3}{2}x + 8$ and $y = -x + 10$

$-\dfrac{3}{2}x + 8 = -x + 10$ $y = -\dfrac{3}{2}x + 8$

$\qquad -\dfrac{3}{2}x = -x + 2$ $y = -\dfrac{3}{2}(-4) + 8$

$\qquad -\dfrac{1}{2}x = 2$ $y = 6 + 8$

$\qquad\quad x = -4$ $y = 14$

The coordinates of point D are $(-4, 14)$.

20. $y = \dfrac{3}{2}x - 2$ and $y = -2x + 5$

21. $y = 4x - 2$ and $y = -\dfrac{3}{2}x + \dfrac{7}{2}$

Name _____ Date _____

22. $y = -2x + 5$ and $y = \frac{3}{2}x - 2$

23. $y = \frac{5}{3}x + 2$ and $y = x - 4$

24. $y = -\frac{1}{5}x + \frac{4}{5}$ and $y = \frac{3}{7}x + \frac{10}{7}$

Use the given information to determine if quadrilateral *ABCD* can best be described as a trapezoid, a rhombus, a rectangle, a square, or none of these. Explain your reasoning.

25. Side lengths: $AB = \sqrt{20}$, $BC = \sqrt{45}$, $CD = \sqrt{20}$, $DA = \sqrt{45}$

Slope of $\overline{AB}$ is -2 Slope of $\overline{BC}$ is $\frac{1}{2}$

Slope of $\overline{CD}$ is -2 Slope of $\overline{DA}$ is $\frac{1}{2}$

The slopes of the line segments have a negative reciprocal relationship. This means the line segments are perpendicular which means the angles must be right angles. Also, the opposite sides have the same slope, so I know the opposite sides are parallel. Finally, opposite sides are congruent. Quadrilateral *ABCD* can best be described as a rectangle.

26. Side lengths: $AB = \sqrt{13}$, $BC = \sqrt{13}$, $CD = \sqrt{13}$, $DA = \sqrt{13}$

Slope of $\overline{AB}$ is $-\frac{3}{2}$ Slope of $\overline{BC}$ is 1

Slope of $\overline{CD}$ is $-\frac{3}{2}$ Slope of $\overline{DA}$ is 1

27. Side lengths: $AB = \sqrt{13}$, $BC = \sqrt{17}$, $CD = \sqrt{52}$, $DA = \sqrt{10}$

Slope of $\overline{AB}$ is $\frac{2}{3}$ Slope of $\overline{BC}$ is $-\frac{1}{4}$

Slope of $\overline{CD}$ is $\frac{2}{3}$ Slope of $\overline{DA}$ is -3

Name _____ Date _____

28. Side lengths: $AB = \sqrt{8}$, $BC = \sqrt{32}$, $CD = \sqrt{8}$, $DA = \sqrt{32}$

Slope of $\overline{AB}$ is -1 Slope of $\overline{BC}$ is 1

Slope of $\overline{CD}$ is -1 Slope of $\overline{DA}$ is 1

29. Side lengths: $AB = \sqrt{14}$, $BC = \sqrt{14}$, $CD = \sqrt{14}$, $DA = \sqrt{14}$

Slope of $\overline{AB}$ is $\frac{1}{8}$ Slope of $\overline{BC}$ is -8

Slope of $\overline{CD}$ is $\frac{1}{8}$ Slope of $\overline{DA}$ is -8

30. Side lengths: $AB = \sqrt{17}$, $BC = \sqrt{26}$, $CD = \sqrt{50}$, $DA = \sqrt{34}$

Slope of $\overline{AB}$ is 4 Slope of $\overline{BC}$ is $\frac{1}{5}$

Slope of $\overline{CD}$ is $\frac{1}{7}$ Slope of $\overline{DA}$ is $\frac{4}{5}$

Name _____ Date _____

The Coordinate Plane
Circles and Polygons on the Coordinate Plane

Problem Set

Use the given information to show that each statement is true. Justify your answers by using theorems and by using algebra.

1. The center of circle O is at the origin. The coordinates of the given points are $A(-4, 0)$, $B(4, 0)$, and $C(0, 4)$. Show that $\triangle ABC$ is a right triangle.

   $\triangle ABC$ is an inscribed triangle in circle O with the hypotenuse as the diameter of the circle, therefore the triangle is a right triangle by the Right Triangle Diameter Theorem.

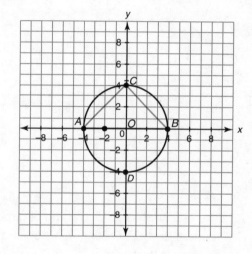

   $AB = \sqrt{(-4 - 4)^2 + (0 - 0)^2}$

   $\quad = \sqrt{(-8)^2} = \sqrt{64} = 8$

   $AC = \sqrt{(-4 - 0)^2 + (0 - 4)^2}$

   $\quad = \sqrt{(-4)^2 + (-4)^2}$

   $\quad = \sqrt{32} = 4\sqrt{2}$

   $BC = \sqrt{(4 - 0)^2 + (0 - 4)^2}$

   $\quad = \sqrt{4^2 + (-4)^2}$

   $\quad = \sqrt{32} = 4\sqrt{2}$

   $(4\sqrt{2})^2 + (4\sqrt{2})^2 \overset{?}{=} 8^2$

   $\qquad 32 + 32 = 64$

   Therefore, by the Converse of the Pythagorean Theorem, $\triangle ABC$ is a right triangle.

18

2. The center of circle O is at the origin. $\overleftrightarrow{AZ}$ and $\overleftrightarrow{AT}$ are tangent to circle O. The coordinates of the given points are A(−10, 30), T(8, 6), and Z(−10, 0). Show that the lengths of $\overline{AT}$ and $\overline{AZ}$ are equal.

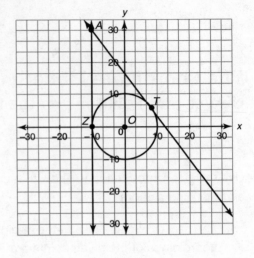

3. The center of circle C is at the origin. $\overleftrightarrow{AB}$ is tangent to circle C at (3, 4). Show that the tangent line is perpendicular to $\overline{CA}$.

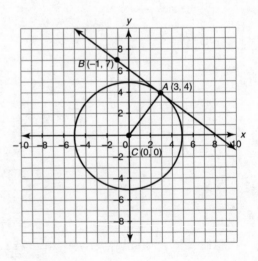

Name _____ Date _____

4. The center of circle *O* is at the origin. The coordinates
of the given points are *A*(3, 4), *B*(−4, −3), *D*(0, −5), *E*(−3, 4),
and *F*(−1.5, −0.5). Show that *EF* · *FD* = *AF* · *FB*.

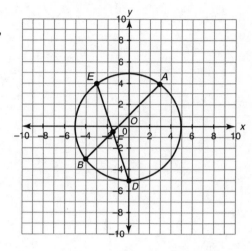

18

5. The center of circle O is at the origin. The coordinates of the given points are $A(-5, 5)$, $B(-4, 3)$, $C(0, -5)$, and $D(0, 5)$. Show that $AD^2 = AB \cdot AC$.

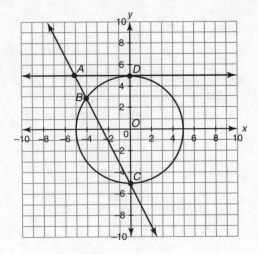

Name _____ Date _____

6. The center of circle O is at the origin. $\overline{BD}$ is perpendicular to $\overline{OA}$ at point C. The coordinates of the given points are A(−5, 0), B(−4, 3), C(−4, 0), and D(−4, −3). Show that $\overline{OA}$ bisects $\overline{BD}$.

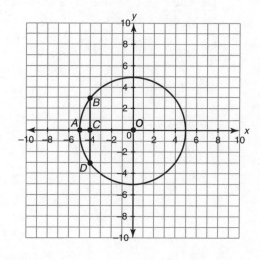

18

Classify the polygon formed by connecting the midpoints of the sides of each quadrilateral. Show all your work.

7. The rectangle shown has vertices $A(0, 0)$, $B(x, 0)$, $C(x, y)$, and $D(0, y)$.

Midpoint $\overline{AB}$: $U\left(\dfrac{x}{2}, 0\right)$

Midpoint $\overline{BC}$: $S\left(x, \dfrac{y}{2}\right)$

Midpoint $\overline{CD}$: $T\left(\dfrac{x}{2}, y\right)$

Midpoint $\overline{DA}$: $R\left(0, \dfrac{y}{2}\right)$

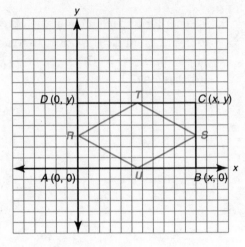

Slope $\overline{RT} = \dfrac{y - \frac{y}{2}}{\frac{x}{2} - 0} = \dfrac{\frac{y}{2}}{\frac{x}{2}} = \dfrac{y}{x}$

Slope $\overline{TS} = \dfrac{\frac{y}{2} - y}{x - \frac{x}{2}} = \dfrac{-\frac{y}{2}}{\frac{x}{2}} = -\dfrac{y}{x}$

Slope $\overline{US} = \dfrac{0 - \frac{y}{2}}{\frac{x}{2} - x} = \dfrac{-\frac{y}{2}}{-\frac{x}{2}} = \dfrac{y}{x}$

Slope $\overline{RU} = \dfrac{\frac{y}{2} - 0}{0 - \frac{x}{2}} = \dfrac{\frac{y}{2}}{-\frac{x}{2}} = -\dfrac{y}{x}$

$\overline{RT}$ and $\overline{US}$ are parallel since they have the same slope of $\dfrac{y}{x}$.

$\overline{TS}$ and $\overline{RU}$ are parallel since they have the same slope of $-\dfrac{y}{x}$.

There are no perpendicular sides. The slopes are not opposite reciprocals.

$RT = \sqrt{\left(0 - \frac{x}{2}\right)^2 + \left(\frac{y}{2} - y\right)^2}$

$\quad = \sqrt{\left(-\frac{x}{2}\right)^2 + \left(-\frac{y}{2}\right)^2}$

$\quad = \sqrt{\dfrac{x^2}{4} + \dfrac{y^2}{4}}$

$TS = \sqrt{\left(\frac{x}{2} - x\right)^2 + \left(y - \frac{y}{2}\right)^2}$

$\quad = \sqrt{\left(-\frac{x}{2}\right)^2 + \left(\frac{y}{2}\right)^2}$

$\quad = \sqrt{\dfrac{x^2}{4} + \dfrac{y^2}{4}}$

$US = \sqrt{\left(x - \frac{x}{2}\right)^2 + \left(\frac{y}{2} - 0\right)^2}$

$\quad = \sqrt{\left(\frac{x}{2}\right)^2 + \left(\frac{y}{2}\right)^2}$

$\quad = \sqrt{\dfrac{x^2}{4} + \dfrac{y^2}{4}}$

$RU = \sqrt{\left(0 - \frac{x}{2}\right)^2 + \left(\frac{y}{2} - 0\right)^2}$

$\quad = \sqrt{\left(-\frac{x}{2}\right)^2 + \left(\frac{y}{2}\right)^2}$

$\quad = \sqrt{\dfrac{x^2}{4} + \dfrac{y^2}{4}}$

All four sides of $RTSU$ are congruent.

Opposite sides are parallel and all sides are congruent, so the quadrilateral formed by connecting the midpoints of the rectangle is a rhombus.

Name _____ Date _____

8. The isosceles trapezoid shown has vertices
   A(0, 0), *B*(6, 0), *C*(4, 3), and *D*(2, 3).

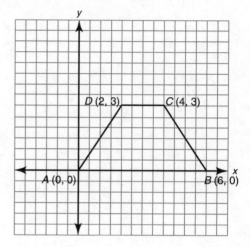

9. The parallelogram shown has vertices $A(4, 5)$, $B(7, 5)$, $C(3, 0)$, and $D(0, 0)$.

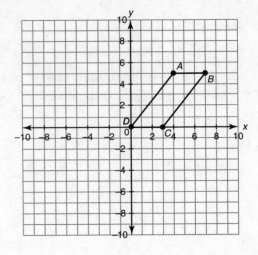

Name _____ Date _____

10. The rhombus shown has vertices $A(4, 10)$, $B(8, 5)$, $C(4, 0)$, and $D(0, 5)$.

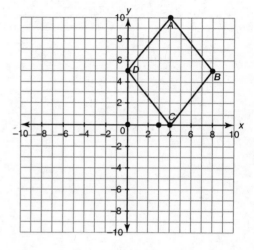

11. The square shown has vertices $A(0, 0)$, $B(4, 0)$, $C(4, 4)$, and $D(0, 4)$.

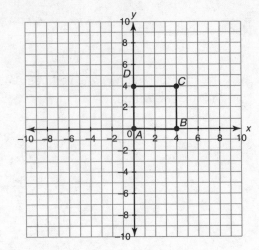

Name _____ Date _____

12. The kite shown has vertices $A(0, 2)$, $B(2, 0)$,
    $C(0, -3)$, and $D(-2, 0)$.

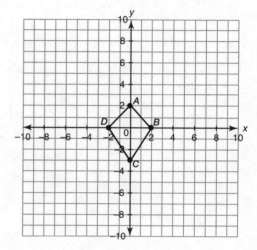

18

Name _____ Date _____

Bring On the Algebra
Deriving the Equation for a Circle

Problem Set

Write an equation in standard form of each circle.

1. a circle with center point at the origin when $r = 4$

   $x^2 + y^2 = r^2$

   $x^2 + y^2 = 4^2$

   $x^2 + y^2 = 16$

2. a circle with center point at the origin when $r = \dfrac{2}{3}$

3. a circle with center point (6, 5) when $r = 1$

4. a circle with center point $(-8, -12)$ when $r = 7$

5.

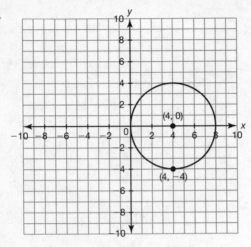

6.

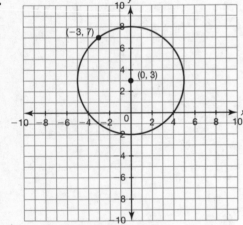

Write the equation of each circle in standard form. Then identify the center point and radius of the circle.

7. $x^2 + y^2 + 6x - 2y + 1 = 0$

$$x^2 + y^2 + 6x - 2y + 1 = 0$$
$$x^2 + 6x + y^2 - 2y = -1$$
$$(x^2 + 6x + 9) + (y^2 - 2y + 1) = -1 + 9 + 1$$
$$(x + 3)^2 + (y - 1)^2 = 9$$

center: $(-3, 1)$, radius: 3

Name _____ Date _____

8. $x^2 + y^2 - 14x + 4y + 49 = 0$

9. $x^2 + y^2 - 2x - 2y + 1 = 0$

10. $81x^2 + 81y^2 + 36x - 324y + 327 = 0$

11. $9x^2 + 9y^2 + 72x - 12y + 147 = 0$

12. $36x^2 + 36y^2 - 36x + 72y + 29 = 0$

Determine if each equation represents a circle. If so, describe the location of the center and radius.

13. $x^2 + y^2 + 4x + 4y - 17 = 0$

$$x^2 + y^2 + 4x + 4y - 17 = 0$$
$$x^2 + 4x + y^2 + 4y = 17$$
$$(x^2 + 4x + 4) + (y^2 + 4y + 4) = 17 + 4 + 4$$
$$(x + 2)^2 + (y + 2)^2 = 25$$

center: $(-2, -2)$, radius: 5

14. $2x^2 + y^2 + 2x - 6y + 6 = 0$

15. $x^2 + 4y^2 - 3x + 3y - 9 = 0$

16. $x^2 + y^2 - 8x - 10y + 5 = 0$

Name _____ Date _____

Determine an equation of the circle that meets the given conditions.

17. Same center as circle A, $(x + 3)^2 + (y + 5)^2 = 9$, but with a circumference that is twice that of circle A

The radius of circle A is $\sqrt{9}$, or 3. To determine the circumference of A, substitute 3 for r in the formula for the circumference of a circle.

$C = 2\pi r$

$\quad = 2\pi(3)$

$C = 6\pi$

A circle with twice the circumference of circle A has circumference $2(6\pi)$, or 12π units. To determine its radius, substitute 12π for C in the formula for the circumference of a circle, and then solve for r.

$\quad C = 2\pi r$

$12\pi = 2\pi r$

$\quad 6 = r$

The radius of the circle is 6. So an equation of the circle with the same center as circle A but with a circumference that is twice that of circle A is

$(x + 3)^2 + (y + 5)^2 = 6^2$, or $(x + 3)^2 + (y + 5)^2 = 36$.

18. Same center as circle B, $(x - 6)^2 + (y + 4)^2 = 49$, but with a circumference that is three times that of circle B

18

Name _____ Date _____

Is That Point on the Circle?
Determining Points on a Circle

Problem Set

For each circle A, determine whether the given point P lies on the circle. Explain your reasoning.

1.

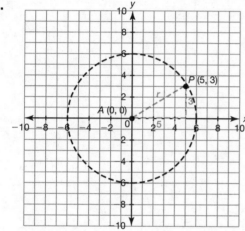

$a^2 + b^2 = c^2$

$5^2 + 3^2 = r^2$

$25 + 9 = r^2$

$34 = r^2$

$r = \sqrt{34} \approx 5.8$

Because the length of line segment AP is approximately 5.8 units instead of 6 units, line segment AP is not a radius of circle A; therefore, point P does not lie on circle A.

2.

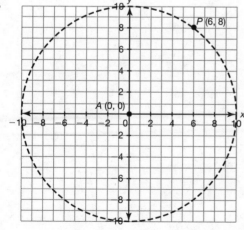

3.

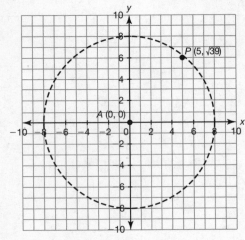

4.

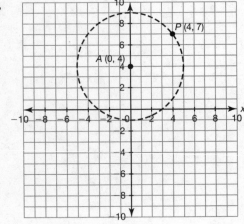

Name _____ Date _____

5.

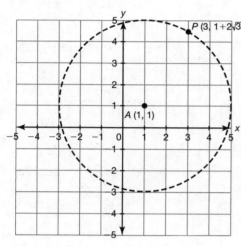

6.

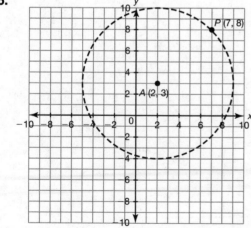

Use symmetry to determine the coordinates of each labeled point on the circle. Give exact values, not approximations.

7.

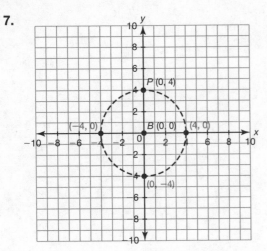

8.

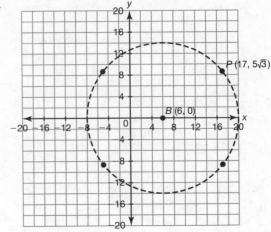

9.

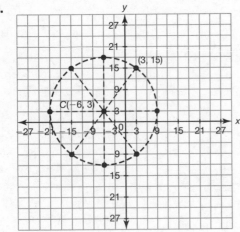

10.

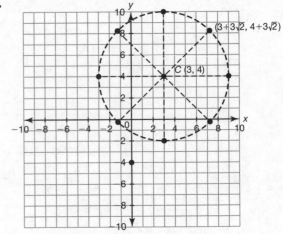

11.

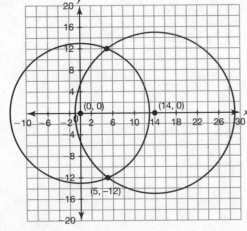

12.

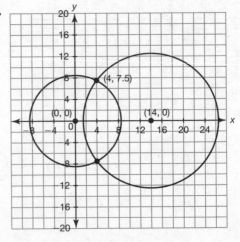

Name _____ Date _____

The Parabola
Equation of a Parabola

Vocabulary

1. locus of points

   a. $Ax^2 + Dy = 0$ or $By^2 + Cx = 0$

2. parabola

   b. $x^2 = 4py$ or $y^2 = 4px$

3. focus of a parabola

   c. describes the orientation of the curvature of the parabola

4. directrix of a parabola

   d. a set of points in a plane that are equidistant from a fixed point and a fixed line

5. general form of a parabola

   e. the maximum or minimum point of a parabola

6. standard form of a parabola

   f. a set of points that share a property

7. axis of symmetry

   g. a line that passes through the parabola and divides the parabola into two symmetrical parts that are mirror images of each other

8. vertex of a parabola

   h. the fixed point from which all points of a parabola are equidistant

9. concavity

   i. the fixed line from which all points of a parabola are equidistant

18

Problem Set

Determine the equation of the parabola.

1.

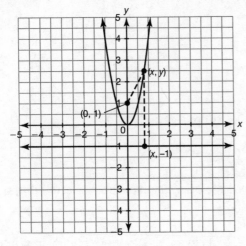

$$\sqrt{(0-x)^2 + (1-y)^2} = \sqrt{(x-x)^2 + (-1-y)^2}$$
$$\sqrt{x^2 + (1-y)^2} = \sqrt{(-1-y)^2}$$
$$x^2 + (1-y)^2 = (-1-y)^2$$
$$x^2 + 1 - 2y + y^2 = 1 + 2y + y^2$$
$$x^2 = 4y$$

2.

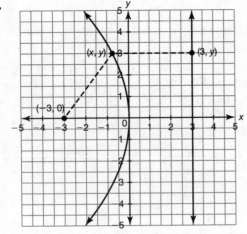

Name _____ Date _____

3.

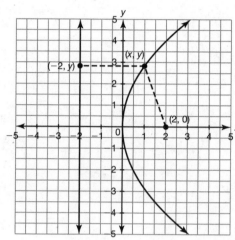

4.

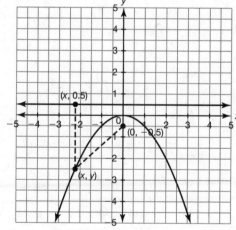

Identify the vertex, axis of symmetry, value of *p*, focus and directrix for each parabola.

5.

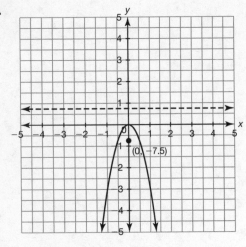

Vertex: (0, 0)

Axis of symmetry: $x = 0$

Value of *p*: -0.75

Focus: (0, -0.75)

Directrix: $y = 0.75$

6.

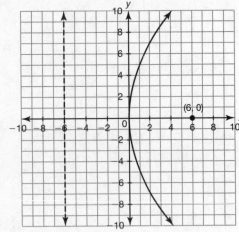

Name _____ Date _____

7.

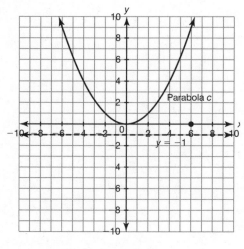

8.

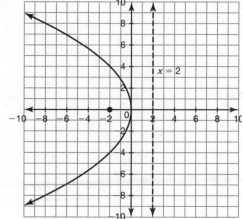

Sketch each parabola.

9. $x^2 = -4y$

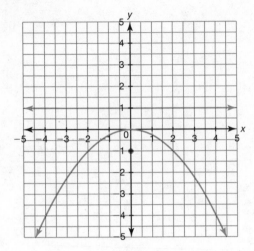

10. $y^2 = 16x$

Name _____   Date _____

11. $y^2 = -20x$

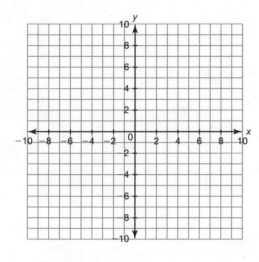

12. $x^2 = 6y$

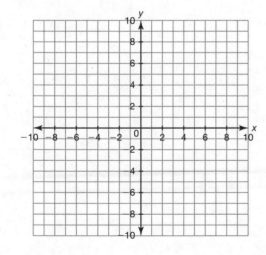

18

Name _____ Date _____

Simply Parabolic
More with Parabolas

Problem Set

Determine the equation of the parabola.

1.

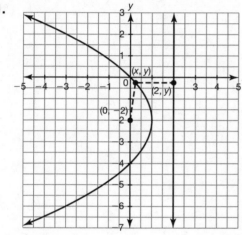

$$\sqrt{(0 - x)^2 + (-2 - y)^2} = \sqrt{(x - 2)^2 + (y - y)^2}$$
$$\sqrt{x^2 + (-2 - y)^2} = \sqrt{(x - 2)^2}$$
$$x^2 + (-2 - y)^2 = (x - 2)^2$$
$$x^2 + 4 + 4y + y^2 = x^2 - 4x + 4$$
$$y^2 - 4x + 4y = 0$$

2.

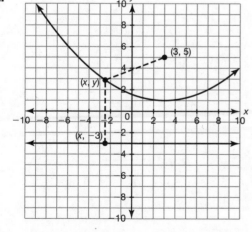

3.

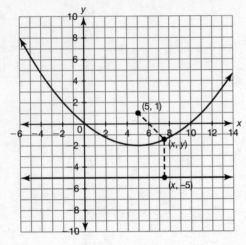

4.

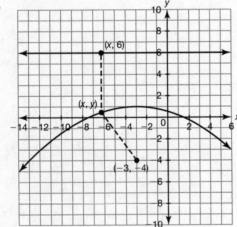

Name _____ Date _____

Identify the vertex, axis of symmetry, value of *p*, focus and directrix for each parabola.

5.

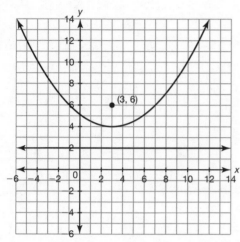

Vertex: (3, 4)

Axis of symmetry: $x = 3$

Value of *p*: 2

Focus: (3, 6)

Directrix: $y = 2$

6.

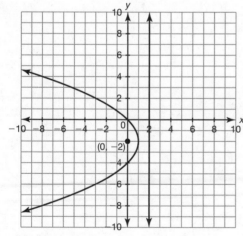

7.

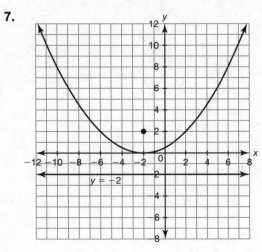

8.

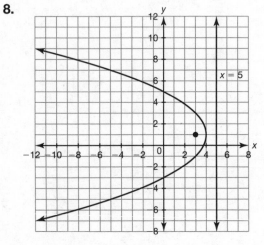

Name _____   Date _____

Complete the table for each equation. Then, plot the points and graph the curve on the coordinate plane.

9. $x^2 - 6x - y + 11 = 0$

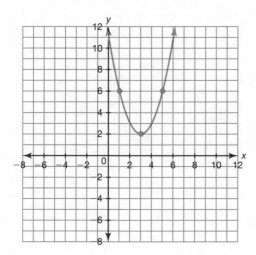

x	y
1	6
3	2
5	6

10. $y^2 - x + 6y + 8 = 0$

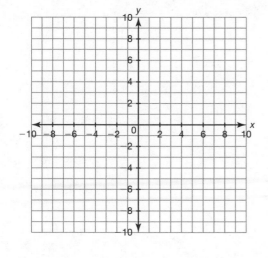

x	y
−1	
3	
3	

11. $x^2 + 4x + y + 5 = 0$

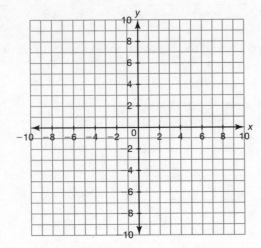

x	y
−4	
−2	
0	

12. $y^2 - 6x - y + 11 = 0$

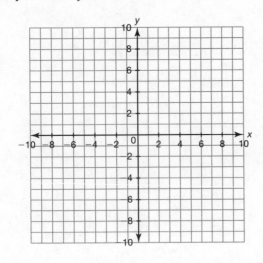

x	y
−1	
1	
1	

Name _____ Date _____

Rewrite the equations in standard form.

13. $x^2 - 4x + 3y + 10 = 0$

$x^2 - 4x + 3y + 10 = 0$

$x^2 - 4x = -3y - 10$

$x^2 - 4x + 4 = -3y - 10 + 4$

$(x - 2)^2 = -3(y + 2)$

14. $y^2 - 6x - 6y + 15 = 0$

15. $x^2 + 2x + 2y + 1 = 0$

16. $y^2 - 2x + 6y + 3 = 0$

18

Name _____ Date _____

These Are a Few of My Favorite Things
Modeling Probability

Vocabulary

Match each term to its corresponding definition.

1. event

2. outcome

3. probability model

4. sample space

5. probability

6. complement of an event

a. all of the possible outcomes in a probability experiment

b. a list of the possible outcomes and each outcome's probability

c. one of the possible results of a probability experiment

d. an outcome or set of outcomes in a sample space

e. contains all the outcomes in the sample space that are not outcomes of the event

f. the ratio of the number of desired outcomes to the total number of possible outcomes

Identify the similarities and differences between the terms.

7. uniform probability model and non-uniform probability model

19

Problem Set

Identify the sample space for each situation.

1. A number cube with sides labeled with 1 to 6 dots is rolled once.
The sample space is 1, 2, 3, 4, 5, 6.

2. An ice cream shop has a sale for its most popular ice cream flavors. Customers can have one scoop of ice cream in a cup or a cone, and the flavors on sale are chocolate, vanilla, and strawberry. It can be served with or without sprinkles.

3. You spin the spinner one time.

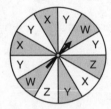

4. A jar contains 3 red marbles, 4 blue marbles, 2 green marbles, and 1 yellow marble.

5. An even number between 1 and 15 is chosen at random.

6. A ball is chosen at random from the box.

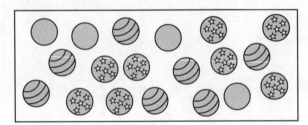

Name _____ Date _____

Construct a probability model for each situation. Then state whether it is a uniform probability model or a non-uniform probability model.

7. A box contains 4 plain bagels, 2 blueberry bagels, 1 sesame seed bagel, and 2 cheese bagels. A bagel is chosen at random from the box.

Outcomes	Plain Bagel	Blueberry Bagel	Sesame Seed Bagel	Cheese Bagel
Probability	$\frac{1}{3}$, or 0.33	$\frac{1}{6}$, or 0.17	$\frac{1}{12}$, or 0.08	$\frac{5}{12}$, or 0.42

This is a non-uniform probability model.

8. Janet has 3 pairs of blue socks, 2 pairs of white socks, 4 pairs of green socks, and 1 pair of brown socks. She chooses a pair of socks at random from a drawer.

9. A shape is chosen at random from the set.

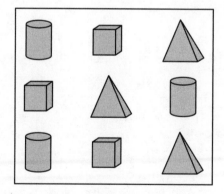

10. There are 6 oranges, 4 apples, 3 kiwis, and 9 pears in your refrigerator. You randomly choose a piece of fruit to eat.

11. You randomly choose a block from the set.

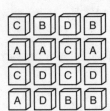

12. A choral group consists of 5 sopranos, 3 altos, 4 tenors, and 3 bases. A group member is chosen at random to sing a solo at a concert.

Determine the probability of each event, $P(E)$, and its complement, $P(E^c)$.

13. You spin the spinner one time.

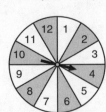

$P(\text{greater than } 7) = \dfrac{5}{12}$

$P(\text{not greater than } 7) = \dfrac{7}{12}$

14. You write the letters A to K on separate index cards. Then you choose a card at random.

$P(\text{vowel}) =$

$P(\text{not a vowel}) =$

15. You choose a ball at random from the box.

$P(5) =$

$P(\text{not a 5}) =$

Name _____ Date _____

16. You have 5 quarters, 3 nickels, 2 dimes, and 6 pennies. You choose a coin at random.

P(a coin worth more than 5 cents) =

P(not a coin worth more than 5 cents) =

17. You choose a ball at random from the bag.

P(shaded) =

P(not shaded) =

18. Among the students in a class, 10 ride the bus, 3 walk, and 5 ride a car to school. A student is chosen at random.

P(walk) =

P(not walk) =

Name _____ Date _____

It's in the Cards
Compound Sample Spaces

Vocabulary

Write the term that best completes each statement.

1. A _____ is a collection or group of items.

2. Each item in a set is called an _____.

3. Sets that do not have common elements are called _____.

4. Sets that do have common elements are called _____.

5. _____ and _____ are two types
of visual models that display sample space.

6. Events for which the occurrence of one event has no impact on the occurrence of the other event are
_____.

7. Events for which the occurrence of one event has an impact on the following events are
_____.

8. The _____ states that if an action A can occur in m ways and for
each of these m ways, an action B can occur in n ways, then Actions A and B can occur in $m \cdot n$ ways.

19

Problem Set

For each situation, identify the following.

- What are the actions?
- What are the outcomes of each action?
- Do the outcomes of each action belong to disjoint sets or intersecting sets?
- What events are described?
- Are the events independent or dependent?

1. You randomly choose one shaded block and one unshaded block.

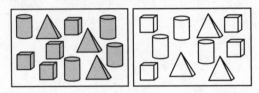

- The actions are choosing a shaded block from the first set and choosing an unshaded block from the second set.
- The outcomes of choosing a shaded block are cylinder, pyramid, and cube. The outcomes of choosing an unshaded block are cylinder, pyramid, and cube.
- The outcomes of each action form disjoint sets because one set had shaded blocks and the other has unshaded blocks.
- The events are choosing a shaded block and choosing an unshaded block.
- The events are independent because the outcome of the first event does not affect the outcome of the second event.

2. A teacher randomly chooses 2 students from a class, Matt and Mia, to solve a math problem on the board.

Name _____ Date _____

3. You spin the spinner and flip a coin, resulting in a 3 and tails up.

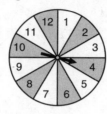

4. You randomly choose a number between 1 and 50. Your friend chooses a number between 51 and 100. Your choice is 6 and your friend's choice is 77.

19

5. A bowl contains numbered cubes. You randomly withdraw a cube from the bowl, and then your friend randomly withdraws a cube from the remaining ones. Your choice is a 3 and your friend's choice is a 5.

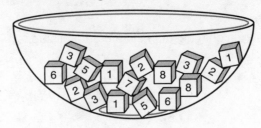

6. The school lunchroom offers a choice of 5 different vegetable wraps. You randomly choose a different one each day. On the first day of the week your choice was a mixed vegetable wrap and on the second day your choice was a spinach and mushroom wrap.

Name _____ Date _____

7. You randomly choose one numbered ping pong ball and then choose another numbered ping pong ball. Your first choice is an even-numbered ping pong ball and your second choice is an odd-numbered ping pong ball.

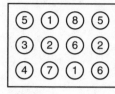

8. At the local deli, you can have your choice of bread and cheese on every sandwich. Your randomly choose rye bread and Swiss cheese.

Sketch a tree diagram and write an organized list to represent each sample space.

9. Show all of the different 3-digit numbers using the numbers 4, 5, and 6.

Tree Diagram:

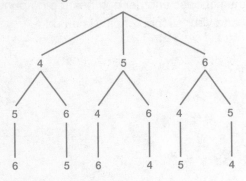

Organized List:

456	546	645
465	564	654

10. Zack, Rick, Salim, and Sean race to the end of the field. Show all of the different ways of finishing in the top two spots.

Name _____ Date _____

11. Lunch includes a drink of your choice. The options are orange juice, apple juice, or cranberry juice. What are the possible outcomes for your choice of drink on two days.

12. What are the possible outcomes for flipping a coin 3 times?

13. The pizza shop offers a weekly special that includes one free vegetable topping and one free meat topping with every large pizza. The vegetable toppings are peppers, mushrooms, onions, and olives. The meat toppings are sausage and pepperoni.

14. You just made it to the ice cream store before closing. The only remaining frozen yogurt flavors are strawberry, peach, and lemon. You can choose one scoop in a cup or one scoop in a cone.

Name _____ Date _____

Use the Counting Principle to determine the number of possible outcomes for each situation.
Show your calculations.

15. There are 5 students scheduled to read their essays aloud in an English class one day. The teacher
will randomly choose the order of the students. In how many different orders can the students read
their essays?

There are 120 different orders of the students possible.

$5 \cdot 4 \cdot 3 \cdot 2 \cdot 1 = 120$

16. A restaurant offers a special price for customers who order a sandwich, soup, and a drink for lunch.
The diagram shows the restaurant's menu. How many different lunches are possible?

Lunch Menu		
Sandwiches	Soup	Drinks
Cheese	Minestrone	Cola
Chicken	Chicken Noodle	Tea
Ham and Egg	Vegetable	Coffee
Turkey Club		

17. A website requires users to make up a password that consists of three letters (A to Z) followed
by three numbers (0 to 9). Neither letters nor digits can be repeated. How many different passwords
are possible?

18. Letter blocks are arranged in a row from A to H, as shown.

How many different arrangements in a row could you make with blocks?

19. Gina has 12 favorite songs. She sets her audio player to continuously play songs, randomly selecting
a song each time. How many different ways can Gina listen to 5 of her 12 favorite songs?

20. You spin the spinner shown in the diagram 5 times. How many different outcomes are possible?

21. A photographer arranges 12 members of a soccer team in a row to take a group picture. How many different arrangements are possible?

22. The travel lock shown in the figure requires users to move the spinners to a 4-digit code that will open the lock. Each spinner includes the digits 0 to 9. How many different codes are possible with the lock?

Name _____ Date _____

And?
Compound Probability with "And"

Vocabulary

Define each term in your own words.

1. compound event

2. Rule of Compound Probability involving "and"

Problem Set

Determine the probability of each individual event. Then, determine the probability of each compound event. Show your calculations.

1. The "shell game" consists of placing three opaque cups, representing shells, upside down on a table and hiding a ball under one of the cups, as shown in the diagram. A player, who has not seen where the ball is hidden, has to choose one of the cups. If the ball is hidden under it, the player wins. What is the probability that a player will win 5 times in a row?

The probability that a player wins 5 times in a row is $\frac{1}{243}$.

I calculated the answer by using the Rule of Compound Probability involving "and."

The probability of winning the shell game 1 time is $\frac{1}{3}$.

Let W represent the probability of winning the shell game 1 time.

$P(W) = \frac{1}{3}$

$P(W, W, W, W, \text{ and } W) = P(W) \cdot P(W) \cdot P(W) \cdot P(W) \cdot P(W)$

$$= \frac{1}{3} \cdot \frac{1}{3} \cdot \frac{1}{3} \cdot \frac{1}{3} \cdot \frac{1}{3}$$

$$= \frac{1}{243}$$

19

2. There are 24 students in a math class. Each day, the teacher randomly chooses 1 students to show a homework problem solution on the board. What is the probability that the same student will be chosen 5 days in a row?

3. You spin each spinner in the diagram one time. What is the probability that the first two spinners land on a 1?

Name _____ Date _____

4. You randomly choose a block from each set below. What is the probability of choosing a block labeled *W* from the second set?

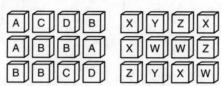

5. You randomly choose a marble from each set. What is the probability that both marbles with have stripes on it?

 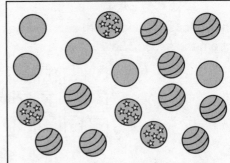

Name _____ Date _____

6. A store is having a grand opening sale. To attract customers, the manager plans to randomly choose one of the first 50 customers each day for a prize. The prize giveaway will occur each day for 5 days. If you and a friend are among the first 50 customers each day, what is the probability that one of you will win the prize every day?

Determine the probability that each event will occur. Then determine the probability that both or all of the dependent events will occur. Show your calculations.

7. A common deck of playing cards includes 4 aces. Altogether there are 52 cards. If you randomly choose 4 cards from the deck, what is the probability of choosing 4 aces?

The probability of choosing all 4 aces is $\frac{1}{270,725}$.

I calculated the answer by using the Rule of Compound Probability involving "and."

The probability of choosing an ace first is $\frac{4}{52}$, or $\frac{1}{13}$.

The probability of choosing an ace second is $\frac{3}{51}$, or $\frac{1}{17}$.

The probability of choosing an ace third is $\frac{2}{50}$, or $\frac{1}{25}$.

The probability of choosing an ace fourth is $\frac{1}{49}$.

P(ace 1st, ace 2nd, ace 3rd, and ace 4th) = P(ace 1st) · P(ace 2nd) · P(ace 3rd) · P(ace 4th)

$$= \frac{1}{13} \cdot \frac{1}{17} \cdot \frac{1}{25} \cdot \frac{1}{49}$$

$$= \frac{1}{270,725}$$

8. A bag contains 8 red ribbons, 7 green ribbons, and 3 yellow ribbons. If you randomly remove 3 of the ribbons from the bag, what is the probability that the first two ribbons will be yellow?

Name _____ Date _____

9. A box contains discs with letters on them, as shown in the diagram. You randomly remove four of the discs, one at a time, and set them in a row on a table. What is the probability that the discs you remove will be, in order, A B C D?

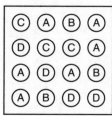

10. Evan has 6 quarters, 4 dimes, 3 nickels, and 8 pennies in his pocket. If he randomly removes 3 coins from his pocket, what is the probability of choosing a quarter first?

19

Name _____ Date _____

11. The table shows the birth months of students in a class. If 4 students in the class are chosen at random, what is the probability that they will all have birthdays in June, July, or August?

Month	January	February	March	April	May	June
Number of Students	2	3	1	0	3	2

Month	July	August	September	October	November	December
Number of Students	6	1	3	5	2	0

19

12. Alicia writes the numbers 1 to 45 on separate cards. She then randomly chooses three of the cards. What is the probability that the 2nd and 3rd cards will include the digit 9 in the number?

Name _____ Date _____

Or?
Compound Probability with "Or"

Vocabulary

Answer each question.

1. In symbols, what is the Addition Rule for Probability?

2. When should you use the Addition Rule for Probability?

Problem Set

Use the Addition Rule for Probability to determine the probability that one or the other of the independent events described will occur.

1. You randomly choose a block from each set in the diagram. What is the probability that you will choose a block labeled with a T or a block labeled with a 6?

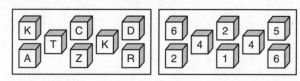

The probability of choosing a block labeled with a T or a block labeled with a 6 is $\frac{11}{32}$.

I used the Addition Rule for Probability to determine the answer.

Let T represent choosing a block labeled with a T.

Let 6 represent choosing a block labeled with a 6.

$P(T \text{ or } 6) = P(T) + P(6) - P(T \text{ and } 6)$

$$= \frac{1}{8} + \frac{2}{8} - \left(\frac{1}{8}\right)\left(\frac{2}{8}\right)$$

$$= \frac{1}{8} + \frac{2}{8} - \frac{2}{64}$$

$$= \frac{8}{64} + \frac{16}{64} - \frac{2}{64}$$

$$= \frac{22}{64}$$

$$= \frac{11}{32}$$

19

2. The vegetable display at a market has exactly 48 apples and 36 oranges. Of these, 2 of the apples are rotten and 2 of the oranges are rotten. You randomly choose an apple and an orange from the display. What is the probability that the apple or the orange is rotten?

3. The sides of a 6-sided number cube are labeled from 1 to 6. You roll the cube 2 times. What is the probability that it will land with a 1 facing up the first roll or the second roll?

19

Name _____ Date _____

4. You spin the spinner 2 times. What is the probability that it will land on a number greater than 9 the first spin or a number less than 6 the second spin?

5. There are 28 students in a math class and 24 students in a history class. In each of the classes, 7 of the students are members of the school band. A student is chosen at random from each class. What is the probability that the student chosen in the math class or the student chosen in the history class is in the band?

6. You randomly choose a block from each set of shapes. What is the probability of choosing a pyramid from the shaded set or a cylinder from the unshaded set?

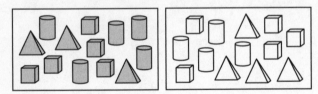

Name _____ Date _____

Use the Addition Rule for Probability to determine the probability that one or the other of the dependent events will occur.

7. You decide to randomly choose two days this week to go jogging. What is the probability that the first day you choose will be Monday or the second day you choose will be Tuesday?

The probability of choosing Monday or Tuesday is $\frac{11}{42}$.

I used the Addition Rule for Probability to determine the answer.

$P(\text{Monday or Tuesday}) = P(\text{Monday}) \cdot P(\text{Tuesday}) - P(\text{Monday and Tuesday})$

$$= \frac{1}{7} + \frac{1}{7} - \left(\frac{1}{7}\right)\left(\frac{1}{6}\right)$$

$$= \frac{1}{7} + \frac{1}{7} - \frac{1}{42}$$

$$= \frac{6}{42} + \frac{6}{42} - \frac{1}{42}$$

$$= \frac{11}{42}$$

8. You have 6 blue socks, 8 white socks, 4 green socks, and 2 brown socks in a drawer. You randomly remove 2 socks from the drawer. What is the probability that the first sock will be blue or the second sock will be green?

19

9. The figure shows number cubes in a jar. Without looking, you randomly remove two cubes from the jar. What is the probability that the first cube you remove will have a 2 on it or the second cube you remove will have a 3 on it?

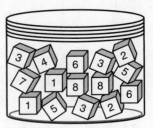

10. You and a friend decide to sign up for soccer tryouts. Altogether, there are 42 people trying out. What is the probability that you will be chosen to try out first or your friend will be chosen to try out second?

19

Name _____ Date _____

11. You choose two balls from the set in the figure and place both balls on a table. What is the probability that the first ball you choose will have stars on it or the second ball you choose will have stripes on it?

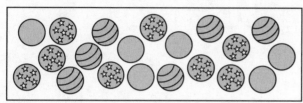

12. A standard deck of cards has 4 aces, 4 Kings, and 4 Queens. There are 52 cards altogether in the deck. One at a time, you randomly choose 2 cards from the deck and lay them on a table. What is the probability that the first card you choose is an ace or the second card you choose is a King?

19

13. You randomly choose two different numbers in the box below. What is the probability that the first number you choose will be in a shaded box or the second number you choose will be in a shaded box?

1	2	3	4	5	6	7	8	9
10	11	12	13	14	15	16	17	18
19	20	21	22	23	24	25	26	27
28	29	30	31	32	33	34	35	36

14. You have 26 songs on your music player. Of these, 4 are your favorite songs. Your player is set to randomly play different songs until all 26 are played. If you listen to 2 songs, what is the probability that the first song played or the second song played will be one of your favorites?

Name _____ Date _____

And, Or, and More!
Calculating Compound Probability

Problem Set

Determine the probability that each compound event will occur with replacement.

1. You randomly choose a number from the set, replace it, and then randomly choose another number. What is the probability of choosing a 2 first and a 3 second?

The probability of choosing a 2 first and a 3 second is $\frac{1}{9}$.

$P(2 \text{ 1st and } 3 \text{ 2nd}) = P(2 \text{ 1st}) \cdot P(3 \text{ 2nd})$

$$= \frac{1}{3} \cdot \frac{1}{3}$$

$$= \frac{1}{9}$$

2. A box contains 25 marbles. There are 6 blue, 2 green, 8 red, 1 yellow, and 3 orange marbles. You randomly choose 3 marbles, one after the other. Each time, you replace the marble back in the box before choosing the next one. What is the probability that the first marble is green, the second marble is red, and the third marble is blue?

3. You choose a shape at random from the box, replace it, and then choose another shape at random. What is the probability that the first shape is a triangle or the second is a square?

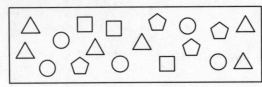

4. You choose a blocks at random from the set, replace it, and then choose another block. What is the probability that you will choose an A block the first time or a D block the second time?

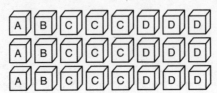

19

Name _____ Date _____

5. You have 4 quarters, 6 dimes, 3 nickels, and 9 pennies in your pocket. You randomly draw a coin out of your pocket, replace it, and then draw out another coin. What is the probability that the first coin is a quarter or the second coin is a dime?

6. A box contains 6 blue blocks, 4 green blocks, 8 orange blocks, 12 yellow blocks, and 14 red blocks. You randomly choose 3 blocks from the box. Each time you choose a block, you replace it before choosing the next one. What is the probability of choosing a green block first, a yellow block second, and a blue block third?

19

Determine the probability that each compound event will occur without replacement.

7. You randomly choose three shapes from the set, one after the other, without replacement. What is the probability that the first shape is a triangle, the second shape is a cube, and the third shape is a cylinder?

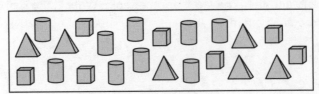

The probability of choosing a triangle first, a cube second, and a cylinder third is $\frac{9}{220}$.

P(triangle 1st , cube 2nd, or cylinder 3rd) = P(triangle 1st) · P(cube 2nd) · P(cylinder 3rd)

$$= \frac{6}{22} \cdot \frac{7}{21} \cdot \frac{9}{20}$$

$$= \frac{3}{11} \cdot \frac{1}{3} \cdot \frac{9}{20}$$

$$= \frac{27}{660}$$

$$= \frac{9}{220}$$

8. A fruit bowl contains 6 apples, 2 pears, and 4 oranges. You randomly choose one fruit, and then without replacement, you choose another fruit. What is the probability that you choose a pear first or an orange second?

Name _____ Date _____

9. You randomly choose one ball from the bag without replacement, and then choose another ball. What is the probability that you will choose a white ball first or a shaded ball second?

10. A teacher is dividing the 24 members of a class into groups to work on different projects. The letter A, B, or C is written on each of 24 cards, and the cards are placed in a box. There are eight A cards, six B cards, and ten C cards. Each student randomly draws a card from the box, without replacement, to determine the student's group assignment. What is the probability that the first student will draw out an A or the second student will draw out a B?

19

11. You have 8 black socks, 6 blue socks, 2 green socks, and 4 white socks in a drawer. You randomly draw out two socks, one after the other, without replacement. What is the probability that you will draw out a black sock first and a black sock second?

12. You draw a block at random from the set. Then, without replacing it, you draw another block at random from the set. What is the probability that the first block has a J on it or the second block has a K on it?

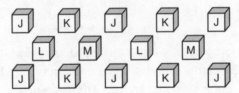

Name _____ Date _____

13. A standard deck of 52 playing cards is composed of four cards each of aces, Kings, Queens, and Jacks, as well as four cards of each number from 2 to 10. You randomly draw out a card and, without replacement, then draw out another card. What is the probability that the first card is a numbered card or the second card is a King?

14. The diagram shows the tee-shirts that you have in a drawer. You randomly remove two tee-shirts from the drawer, one after the other, without replacement. What is the probability that the first tee-shirt will be blue and the second tee-shirt will be blue?

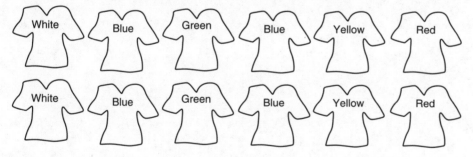

19

Name _____ Date _____

Do You Have a Better Chance of Winning the Lottery or Getting Struck By Lightning?
Investigate Magnitude through Theoretical Probability and Experimental Probability

Vocabulary

Write the term that best completes each statement.

1. A(n) _____ is the number of times an outcome occurs divided by the total number of trials performed.

2. An experiment that models a real-life situation is a(n) _____.

3. A(n) _____ is the number of desired outcomes divided by the total number of possible outcomes.

Problem Set

Solve each problem using the multiplication rule of probability for compound independent events.

1. You spin each spinner once. What is the probability of spinning a number less than 7 followed by spinning either A or B?

The probability of a spin resulting in a number less than 7 and an A or B is $\frac{1}{6}$.

Let <7 represent of a spin resulting in a number less than 7.
Let L represent a spin resulting in the letters A or B.

$P(<7 \text{ 1st and } L \text{ 2nd}) = P(<7 \text{ 1st}) \cdot P(L \text{ 2nd})$

$\qquad = \frac{6}{12} \cdot \frac{2}{6}$

$\qquad = \frac{1}{2} \cdot \frac{1}{3}$

$\qquad = \frac{1}{6}$

2. A 6-sided number cube is rolled three times. What is the probability that the first time the number will be greater than 4, the second time it will be an even number, and the third time it will be a multiple of 2?

3. An amusement park has job openings for high school students. Jake, Terrance, and Mia are each offered a job. They are allowed to choose two of the available types of jobs, and each will be randomly assigned one of the two types of jobs they have chosen. Jake chooses food service and custodial. Terrance chooses food service and operations. Mia chooses food service and merchandise. What is the probability that all three of the friends will be assigned the same type of job?

Types of Jobs	Number of Openings
Food service	64
Games	76
Custodial	16
Operations	24
Merchandise	32
Warehouse	44

19

Name _____ Date _____

4. A website assigns a 5-digit password to you. Each digit is randomly chosen from 0 to 9. What is the probability that each digit in the password is less than 2?

5. You randomly choose a ball from each group. What is the probability that you will choose a red ball from each group?

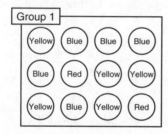 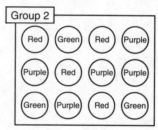

6. You flip a coin 10 times. What is the probability that it will land heads up all 10 times?

Solve each problem by determining the experimental probability using a random number generator on a graphing calculator.

7. Using the random number generator on a calculator, you press **ENTER** 40 times to simulate 200 trials. A number that represents a successful outcome appears 12 times. What is the experimental probability of a successful outcome?

   experimental probability $= \dfrac{12}{200} = \dfrac{3}{50}$

8. Using the random number generator on a calculator, you press **ENTER** 60 times to simulate 300 trials. A number that represents a successful outcome appears 6 times. What is the experimental probability of a successful outcome?

9. Using the random number generator on a calculator, you press **ENTER** 35 times to simulate 175 trials. A number that represents a successful outcome appears 15 times. What is the experimental probability of a successful outcome?

10. Using the random number generator on a calculator, you press **ENTER** 65 times to simulate 325 trials. A number that represents a successful outcome appears 10 times. What is the experimental probability of a successful outcome?

11. Using the random number generator on a calculator, you press **ENTER** 50 times to simulate 250 trials. A number that represents a successful outcome appears 22 times. What is the experimental probability of a successful outcome?

12. Using the random number generator on a calculator, you press **ENTER** 30 times to simulate 150 trials. A number that represents a successful outcome appears 25 times. What is the experimental probability of a successful outcome?

Name _____ Date _____

Compare the theoretical probability and the experimental probability in each situation.

13. A bag contains 36 red balls, 17 green balls, and 28 white balls. You randomly choose 25 balls and 4 of them are red. Compare the theoretical and experimental probabilities of drawing a red ball out of the bag.

The theoretical probability is greater.

theoretical probability $= \dfrac{36}{81} \approx 0.44$

experimental probability $= \dfrac{4}{25} = 0.16$

14. You randomly choose a letter of the alphabet 30 times, and 5 of them are vowels (a, e, i, o, or u). Compare the theoretical and experimental probabilities of choosing a vowel.

15. You flip a coin 30 times and it lands on tails 18 times. Compare the theoretical and experimental probabilities of the coin landing on tails.

19

16. You roll a 6-sided number cube 25 times, and 15 of the rolls land on a number greater than 2. Compare the theoretical and experimental probabilities the cube landing on a number greater than 2.

17. You spin the spinner 50 times, and 32 of those times it lands on a number greater than 5. Compare the theoretical and experimental probabilities of the spinner landing on a number greater than 5.

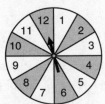

18. A jar contains 12 silver marbles, 8 gold marbles, and 6 purple marbles. You randomly choose 10 of the marbles and 4 are purple. Compare the theoretical and experimental probabilities of choosing a purple marble.

19

Name _____ Date _____

Left, Left, Left, Right, Left
Compound Probability for Data Displayed in Two-Way Tables

Vocabulary

Write the term that best completes each statement.

1. A two-way table is a table that shows the relationship between two data sets, one organized in _____ and one organized in _____.

2. A _____ table is a table that shows how often each item, number, or event appears in a sample space.

3. A _____, also called a _____, shows the number of data points and their frequencies for two variables.

4. Data that can be grouped into categories, such as eye color and gender, are called _____ or _____ data.

5. A relative frequency is the ratio of occurrences within a category to the _____ of occurrences.

6. A two-way relative frequency table displays the _____ for two categories of data.

Problem Set

Of the students in Molly's homeroom, 11 students have brown hair, 7 have black hair, 5 have auburn hair, 4 have blonde hair, and 3 have red hair. Calculate each relative frequency. Round to the nearest thousandth if necessary.

1. brown hair
   $\frac{11}{30} \approx 0.367$

2. black hair

3. auburn hair

4. blonde hair

5. red hair

6. brown or black hair

7. auburn or red hair

8. not brown hair

20

The two-way frequency table shows the number of students from each grade who plan to attend this year's homecoming football game.

Grade

Are you going to the homecoming game?		Freshmen	Sophomores	Juniors	Seniors	Total
	Attending Homecoming Game	31	28	25	32	116
	Not Attending Homecoming Game	17	24	11	6	58
	Total	48	52	36	38	174

Calculate the relative frequency of the entries in the two-way table. Round each relative frequency to the nearest tenth of a percent if necessary.

9. a freshman going to the homecoming game

$\frac{31}{174} \approx 17.8\%$

10. a sophomore going to the homecoming game

11. a junior going to the homecoming game

12. a senior going to the homecoming game

13. a freshman not going to the homecoming game

14. a sophomore not going to the homecoming game

15. a junior not going to the homecoming game

16. a senior not going to the homecoming game

17. freshmen students

Name _____ Date _____

18. sophomore students

19. junior students

20. senior students

21. students from all grades going to the homecoming game

22. students from all grades not going to the homecoming game

The two-way frequency table shows the current inventory of hardwood that a lumberyard carries. Suppose a board is selected at random from the lumberyard's inventory. Use the table to calculate each probability. Round to the nearest tenth of a percent if necessary.

		Size				
		1 × 2	**1 × 3**	**1 × 4**	**1 × 6**	**Total**
Type of Hardwood	**Oak**	20	13	17	12	62
	Maple	14	28	9	19	70
	Cherry	8	17	28	25	78
	Total	42	58	54	56	210

23. $P(oak)$

$\frac{62}{210} \approx 0.295 = 29.5\%$

24. $P(maple)$

25. $P(cherry)$

26. $P(1 \times 2)$

27. $P(1 \times 3)$

28. $P(1 \times 4)$

20

29. $P(1 \times 6)$

30. $P(\text{maple and } 1 \times 3)$

31. $P(\text{oak and } 1 \times 2)$

32. $P(\text{maple or cherry})$

33. $P(\text{cherry or } 1 \times 4)$

34. $P(\text{maple or } 1 \times 6)$

The two-way relative frequency table shows the results of a survey on the mayor's job approval. Suppose a member of the sample population is selected at random. Use the table of relative frequencies to calculate each probability. Express each probability as a decimal.

Party Affiliation

Do You Approve of the Mayor's Job Performance?		Republican	Democrat	Independent	Total
	Approve	0.14	0.25	0.03	0.42
	Disapprove	0.22	0.1	0.12	0.44
	No Opinion	0.03	0.07	0.04	0.14
	Total	0.39	0.42	0.19	1

35. $P(\text{approve})$

0.42

36. $P(\text{disapprove})$

37. $P(\text{no opinion})$

38. $P(\text{republican})$

39. $P(\text{democrat})$

40. $P(\text{independent})$

41. $P(\text{republican and disapprove})$

42. $P(\text{democrat and no opinion})$

43. $P(\text{independent and approve})$

44. $P(\text{disapprove or no opinion})$

Name _____ Date _____

45. *P*(democrat or independent)

46. *P*(democrat or disapprove)

47. *P*(republican or approve)

48. *P*(independent or disapprove)

Name _____ Date _____

It All Depends
Conditional Probability

Vocabulary

Define the term in your own words.

1. conditional probability

Problem Set

A five-sided letter die with faces labeled A, B, C, D, and E is rolled twice. The table shows the sample space of possible outcomes. Use the table to determine each probability. Express your answers as fractions in simplest form.

Second Roll

First Roll		A	B	C	D	E
	A	A, A	A, B	A, C	A, D	A, E
	B	B, A	B, B	B, C	B, D	B, E
	C	C, A	C, B	C, C	C, D	C, E
	D	D, A	D, B	D, C	D, D	D, E
	E	E, A	E, B	E, C	E, D	E, E

1. P(B on the first roll)

P(B on the first roll) $= \dfrac{1}{5}$

There are 25 possible outcomes and the 5 cells in row B represent getting a B on the first roll. So, P(B on the first roll) $= \dfrac{15}{25}$, or $\dfrac{1}{5}$.

2. P(vowel on the second roll)

20

3. *P*(consonant on the second roll)

4. *P*(A or B on the first roll)

5. *P*(A on the first roll and consonant on the second roll)

6. *P*(vowel on the first roll and vowel or D on the second roll)

7. *P*(B or D on the second roll, given that the first roll was a consonant)

20

Name _____ Date _____

8. *P*(consonant on the second roll, given that the first roll was a vowel)

9. *P*(A on the second roll, given that the first roll was a vowel)

10. *P*(vowel on the second roll, given that the first roll was not an A)

Determine each conditional probability.

11. Given $P(A) = 0.25$, $P(B) = 0.3$, and $P(A \text{ and } B) = 0.1$, determine $P(B \mid A)$.

$P(B|A) = 0.4$

$$P(B|A) = \frac{P(A \text{ and } B)}{P(A)}$$

$$= \frac{0.1}{0.25}$$

$$= 0.4$$

20

12. Given $P(A) = \frac{2}{9}$, $P(B) = \frac{3}{10}$, and $P(A \text{ and } B) = \frac{2}{15}$, determine $P(A \mid B)$.

13. Given $P(A) = \frac{5}{6}$, $P(B) = \frac{1}{2}$, and $P(A \text{ and } B) = \frac{1}{12}$, determine $P(B \mid A)$.

14. Given $P(A) = 0.12$, $P(B) = 0.2$, and $P(A \text{ and } B) = 0.05$, determine $P(A \mid B)$.

Name _____ Date _____

The jar on Mrs. Wilson's desk contains 20 green paper clips, 30 red paper clips, 15 white paper clips, and 10 black paper clips. She selects a paper clip without looking, does not replace it, and selects another. Determine each probability. Round each answer to the nearest tenth of a percent if necessary.

15. P(both paper clips are red)

The probability of choosing two red paper clips is approximately 15.7%.

P(red 1st and red 2nd) = P(red 1st) $\cdot$ P(red 2nd)

$$= \frac{30}{75} \cdot \frac{29}{74}$$
$$= \frac{2}{5} \cdot \frac{29}{74}$$
$$= \frac{58}{370}$$
$$\approx 0.157$$

16. P(both paper clips are white)

17. P(second paper clip is green | first paper clip is black)

20

18. *P*(second paper clip is white | first paper clip is red)

19. *P*(second paper clip is green | first paper clip is not green)

20. *P*(second paper clip is not red | first paper clip is red)

20

Name _____ Date _____

The two-way frequency table shows the results of a study in which a new topical medicine cream was tested for its effectiveness in treating poison ivy. Half of the study participants applied the cream to their poison ivy for 3 days and noted any changes in their symptoms. The other half applied a placebo and noted any changes.

Results

Treatment	Significant improvement	Moderate Improvement	No Improvement	Total
Medicine Cream	21	10	4	35
Placebo	9	14	12	35
Total	30	24	16	70

21. Use the table to determine each probability. Round each answer to the nearest tenth of a percent if necessary.

   a. P(significant improvement | medicine cream)

   P(significant improvement | medicine cream) = 60%

   $$P(\text{significant improvement given medicine cream}) = \frac{P(\text{medicine cream and significant improvement})}{P(\text{medicine cream})}$$

   $$= \frac{\frac{21}{70}}{\frac{35}{70}}$$

   $$= \frac{\frac{21}{70}}{\frac{35}{70}} \times \frac{\frac{70}{35}}{\frac{70}{35}}$$

   $$= \frac{21}{70} \times \frac{70}{35}$$

   $$= \frac{21}{35}$$

   $$= 0.6$$

   b. Are significant improvement and medicine cream treatment independent or dependent events? Explain your reasoning.

   Significant improvement, S, and medicine cream treatment, M, are dependent events because the value of $P(S \mid T)$ is not equal to the value of $P(S)$.

   $$P(S \mid M) = \frac{21}{35} = \frac{3}{5}$$

   $$P(S) = \frac{30}{70} = \frac{3}{7}$$

20

22. Use the table to determine each probability. Round each answer to the nearest tenth of a percent if necessary.

    a. *P*(placebo | no improvement)

    b. Are no improvement and placebo treatment independent or dependent events? Explain your reasoning.

Name _____ Date _____

23. Use the table to determine each probability. Round each answer to the nearest tenth of a percent if necessary.

   a. *P*(medicine cream | moderate improvement)

   b. Are medicine cream treatment and moderate improvement independent or dependent events? Explain your reasoning.

24. Use the table to determine each probability. Round each answer to the nearest tenth of a percent if necessary.

    a. *P*(placebo | significant improvement)

    b. Are placebo treatment and significant improvement independent or dependent events? Explain your reasoning.

Name _____ Date _____

Counting
Permutations and Combinations

Vocabulary

Define each term in your own words.

1. factorial

2. permutation

3. combination

4. circular permutation

Problem Set

Evaluate each expression.

1. $_8P_3$

$$_8P_3 = \frac{8!}{(8-3)!} = \frac{8!}{5!} = 8 \times 7 \times 6 = 336$$

2. $_5P_5$

20

3. $_{10}P_4$

4. $_7P_5$

5. $_6P_6$

6. $_9P_6$

Calculate the number of possible outcomes in each of the following situations.

7. A computer code uses 4 randomly selected letters of the alphabet. If no letters are repeated, how many possible codes are there?

There are 358,800 possible codes.

$_{26}P_4 = 26 \times 25 \times 24 \times 23 = 358,800$

8. Twelve students are competing in the finals of a spelling bee. The top 3 finishers are awarded a gold, silver, and bronze medal. In how many ways can the medals be won?

9. A summer camp offers 12 different afternoon activities. Caleb selects 2 of the activities to do today. How many possible outcomes are there if the order of the activities is important?

10. There are 15 different seminars at a teacher's convention. Mrs. Alvarez will choose 3 of the seminars to attend today. How many possible outcomes are there if the order of the seminars is important?

20

Name _____ Date _____

Evaluate each expression.

11. $_{11}C_4$

$_{11}C_4 = \dfrac{11!}{(11-4)!4!} = \dfrac{11!}{7!4!} = 330$

12. $_6C_5$

13. $_5C_3$

14. $_{12}C_{10}$

15. $_8C_4$

16. $_7C_2$

Calculate the number of possible outcomes in each of the following situations.

17. A committee of 4 students is to be formed from a homeroom of 25 students. How many different committees are possible?

$_{25}C_4 = \dfrac{25!}{21!4!} = 12{,}650$

18. A pizzeria offers 8 different toppings on their pizzas. If a customer wants to order a 3-topping pizza, how many possible options are there?

19. Seven friends are playing musical chairs. In the first round there are 5 chairs, so only 5 of the friends will move on to the second round. How many different groups of friends are possible for the second round of the game?

20. Fran has 4 pennies, 3 nickels, 5 dimes, and 2 quarters in her pocket. In how many ways can she pull 3 coins out of her pocket if the order of the coins is not important?

20

A website requires users to enter a 6-digit personal identification number (PIN) for security. A user's PIN must use the digits 1, 2, 3, 4, 5, and 6, and no digit can be used more than once. Determine each probability. Express your answers as fractions in simplest form.

21. Suppose a user is unable to remember his PIN and enters the digits randomly. What is the probability that he will guess correctly?

The probability of guessing correctly is $\frac{1}{720}$.

There is 1 correct PIN and I determined the total possible number of PINs by calculating $_6P_6$, which equals 720.

So, the probability of guessing correctly is $\frac{1}{720}$.

22. Suppose a user randomly selects a PIN. What is the probability that the user's PIN is an even number?

23. Suppose a user randomly selects a PIN. What is the probability that the user's PIN begins with 3 even digits and ends with 3 odd digits?

20

Name _____ Date _____

24. Suppose a user randomly selects a PIN. What is the probability that the user's PIN begins with the digits 123?

A group of 6 seniors, 5 juniors, and 4 sophomores are running for student council. The council is made up of 6 members. Assume that each student has an equal chance of being elected to student council. Determine each probability and express your answers as fractions in simplest form.

25. What is the probability that 2 seniors, 2 juniors, and 2 sophomores are elected?

The probability of choosing 2 seniors, 2 juniors, and 2 sophomores is $\frac{180}{1001}$.

There are 15 ways to choose 2 seniors: $_6C_2 = 15$.
There are 10 ways to choose 2 juniors: $_5C_2 = 10$.
There are 6 ways to choose 2 sophomores: $_4C_2 = 6$.
So, there are 900 ways to choose 2 seniors, 2 juniors, and 2 sophomores: $15 \times 10 \times 6 = 900$.

There are 5005 ways to choose 6 student council members from a pool of 15 candidates: $_{15}C_6 = 5005$.

So, the probability of choosing 2 seniors, 2 juniors, and 2 sophomores is $\frac{900}{5005}$, or $\frac{180}{1001}$

26. What is the probability that the student council is made up of all seniors?

20

27. What is the probability that 3 seniors, 2 juniors, and 1 sophomore are elected?

28. What is the probability that 3 juniors and 3 sophomores are elected?

Calculate the number of ways the letters of each word can be arranged.

29. SUNNY

The letters in the word SUNNY can be arranged 60 different ways.

$$\frac{5!}{2!} = 60$$

30. FACTORIAL

31. ARRANGE

32. PROBABILITY

33. PARALLEL

34. MISSISSIPPI

Name _____ Date _____

Calculate the number of ways each arrangement can be made.

35. 12 flowers planted around the base of a tree

The flowers can be arranged around the base of the tree in 39,916,800 different ways.

$(12 - 1)! = 11! = 39,916,800$

36. 7 dinner guests seated around a table

37. 10 candles arranged around the outside of a circulate birthday cake

38. 3 baseball players standing in a circle under a fly ball

39. 6 teachers seated around a circular table at a conference

20

40. 5 kittens arranged around a ball of yarn

20

Name _____ Date _____

Trials
Independent Trials

Problem Set

Determine the probability in each situation. Express your answers as fractions in simplest form.

1. On average, Malcolm makes a par on $\frac{2}{3}$ of the golf holes that he plays. What is the probability that he will make a par on each of the next 2 holes that he plays?

    The probability that Malcolm makes a par on the next 2 holes is $\frac{4}{9}$.

    Let PAR represent making par on one hole.

    $P(\text{PAR 1st and PAR 2nd}) = P(\text{PAR 1st}) \cdot P(\text{PAR 2nd})$

    $$= \frac{2}{3} \cdot \frac{2}{3}$$
    $$= \frac{4}{9}$$

2. Clarence rolls 2 number cubes. What is the probability that he will roll a number greater than 4 on both rolls?

3. For every 5 penalty kicks that Missy attempts, she scores on average 3 goals. What is the probability that Missy will score 2 goals in her next 2 penalty kick attempts?

20

4. On average 3 out of 4 students order spaghetti at the cafeteria when it is offered. What is the probability that the first 2 students in line for lunch will have spaghetti if it is offered?

5. A spinner has 8 equal size spaces with the colors: red, green, yellow, red, blue, white, green, red. If the spinner is spun twice, what is the probability of spinning red on both spins?

6. The table shows the results of a survey of likely voters. Suppose 2 likely voters are selected at random. Based on the results of the survey, what is the probability that both likely voters support Issue #1?

Do You Support Issue #1?	
Response	Frequency
Strongly Oppose	40
Somewhat Oppose	16
No Opinion	19
Somewhat Support	10
Strongly Support	25

20

Name _____ Date _____

According to a recent survey, 80% of high school students have their own cell phone. Suppose 10 high school students are selected at random. Determine each probability. Round your answers to the nearest tenth of a percent if necessary.

7. $P(8$ of the students have cell phones)

   $_{10}C_8(0.8)^8(0.2)^2 \approx 0.302 = 30.2\%$

8. $P(5$ of the students have cell phones)

9. $P(3$ of the students do not have cell phones)

10. $P(\text{all of the students have cell phones})$

11. $P(9$ of the students have cell phones)

12. $P(\text{none of the student shave cell phones})$

Based on past results, a batter knows that the opposing pitcher throws a fastball 75% of the time and a curveball 25% of the time. Suppose the batter sees 8 pitches during a particular at-bat. Determine each probability. Round your answers to the nearest tenth of a percent if necessary.

13. $P(4$ fastballs and 4 curveballs)

   $_8C_4(0.75)^4(0.25)^4 \approx 0.087 = 8.7\%$

14. $P(\text{all fastballs})$

15. $P(5$ fastballs and 3 curveballs)

16. *P*(5 curveballs and 3 fastballs)

17. *P*(7 fastballs and 1 curveball)

18. *P*(no fastballs)

Name _____ Date _____

To Spin or Not to Spin
Expected Value

Vocabulary

Write the term that best completes each statement.

1. Geometric probability is a _____ of measures such as length, area, and volume.

2. The expected value is the _____ value when the number of trials is large.

Problem Set

Determine the probability that a dart that lands on a random part of each target will land in the shaded scoring section. Assume that all squares in a figure and all circles in a figure are congruent unless otherwise marked. Round each answer to the nearest tenth of a percent if necessary.

1.

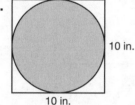

10 in.

10 in.

2.

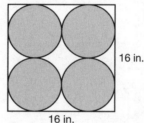

16 in.

16 in.

The probability of a dart landing in the shaded area is approximately 78.5%.

Area of Entire Board: 10(10) = 100 in.²

Area of Shaded Section:

$5^2\pi \approx 78.54$ in.²

Probability of Landing in Shaded Section:

$\frac{78.54}{100} \approx 78.5\%$

20

3.

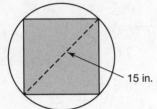

15 in.

4.

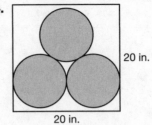

20 in.

20 in.

5.

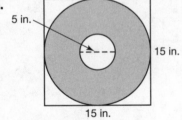

5 in.

15 in.

15 in.

6.

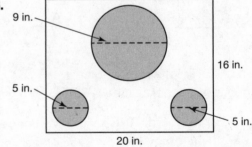

9 in.

5 in.

5 in.

16 in.

20 in.

Name _____ Date _____

7.

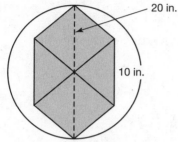

20 in.

10 in.

8.

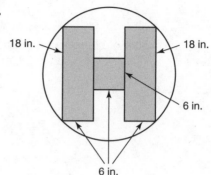

18 in.   18 in.

6 in.

6 in.

Benjamin rolls a six-sided number cube 12 times. Determine each expected value and explain your solution method.

9. How many of the outcomes do you expect to result in a 1?

I would expect 2 out of the 12 outcomes to result in a 1.

$\frac{1}{6}(12) = 2$

10. How many of the outcomes do you expect to result in a 1 or a 6?

11. How many of the outcomes do you expect to result in number greater than 2?

20

12. How many of the outcomes do you expect to result in an even number?

Calculate the expected value of spinning each spinner one time. Round to the nearest hundredth if necessary.

13.

$$4\left(\frac{1}{3}\right) + 6\left(\frac{1}{3}\right) + 8\left(\frac{1}{3}\right) = 6$$

14.

15.

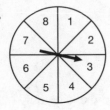

16.

17.

18.

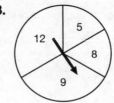

Odd-Numbered Answers

Chapter 1

LESSON 1.1

1. Points: A, B, and C
   Lines: $\overleftrightarrow{AB}$ and $\overleftrightarrow{BC}$
   Plane: m

3. Points: R, S, and Q
   Lines: $\overleftrightarrow{QR}$ and $\overleftrightarrow{QS}$
   Plane: p

5.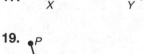

7.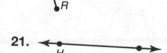

9. Lines m and p are coplanar.
   Lines n and q are coplanar.

11. Lines x and z are coplanar.
    Lines w and y are coplanar.

13. Lines f and g are skew.
    Lines f and h are skew.

15. Lines w and y are skew.
    Lines x and y are skew.

17.

19.

21.

23. $\overline{RT}$

25. $\overleftrightarrow{XY}$

27. $\overrightarrow{CD}$

29. $AB = 4$ centimeters or $m\,\overline{AB} = 4$ centimeters

31. $AB = 3.5$ centimeters or $m\,\overline{AB} = 3.5$ centimeters

LESSON 1.2

1. $d = 5$

3. $d \approx 12.1$

5. $d = 10$

7. $d \approx 7.1$

9. $d \approx 9.2$

11. $d \approx 12.8$

13.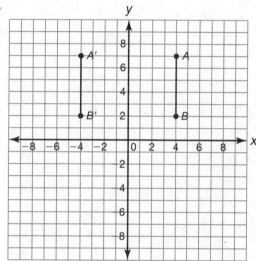

15.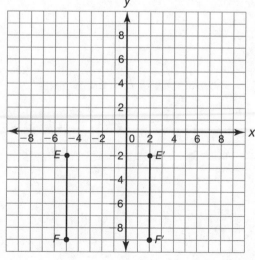

17.

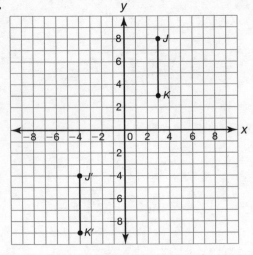

15.

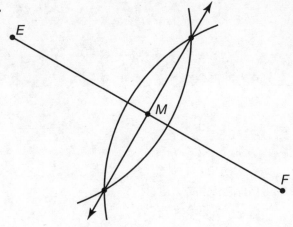

19.

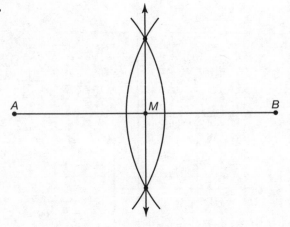

21.

23.

$\overline{J'L'}$ is twice the length of $\overline{JK}$.

17.

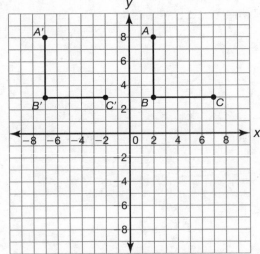

LESSON 1.3

1. (6, 3)
3. (−2, 4)
5. (−5, 1.5)
7. (5, 5)
9. (−1, 6)
11. (−4, −5.5)
13.

LESSON 1.4

1.

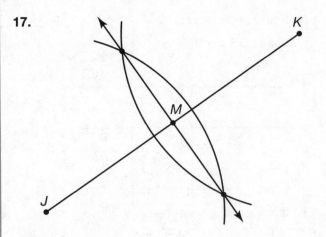

3.

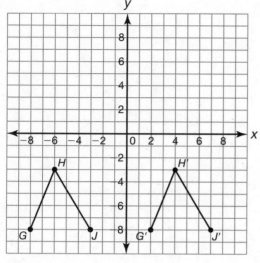

5.

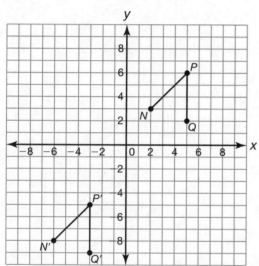

7.

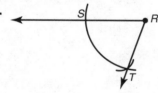

9.

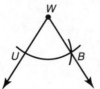

11.

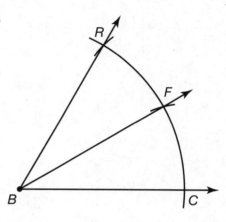

13.

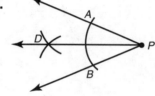

15.

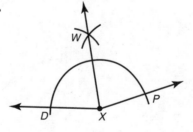

17.

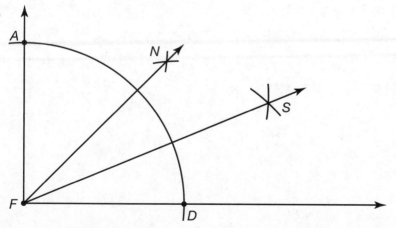

1.

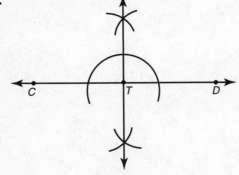

5.

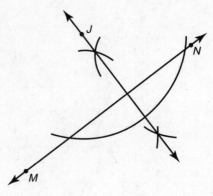

3.

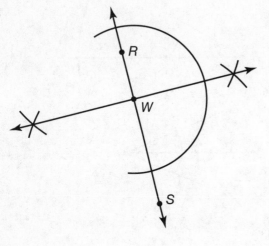

7.

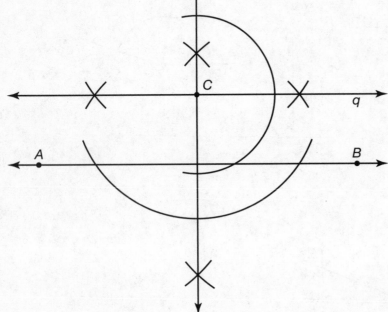

9.

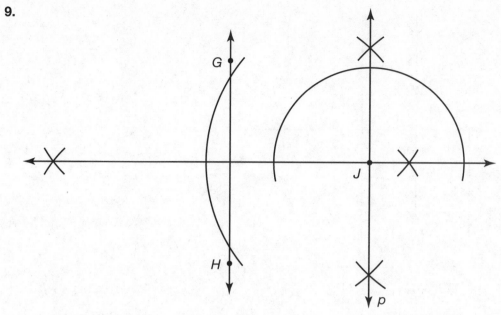

11.

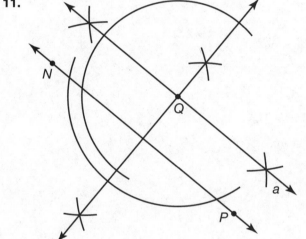

13.

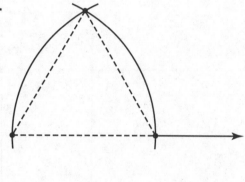

15.

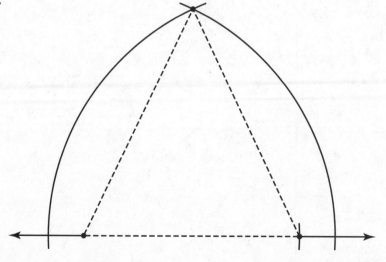

17.

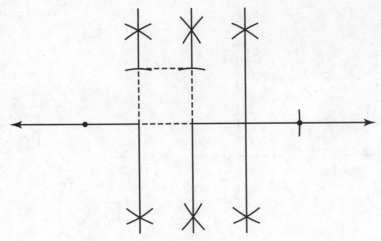

19.

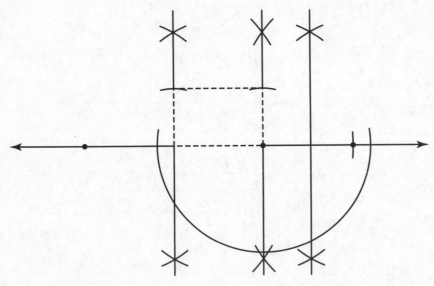

LESSON 1.6

1.

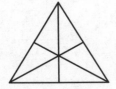

3.

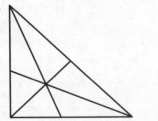

5.

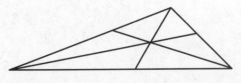

7.

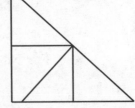

9.

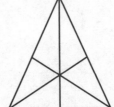

11.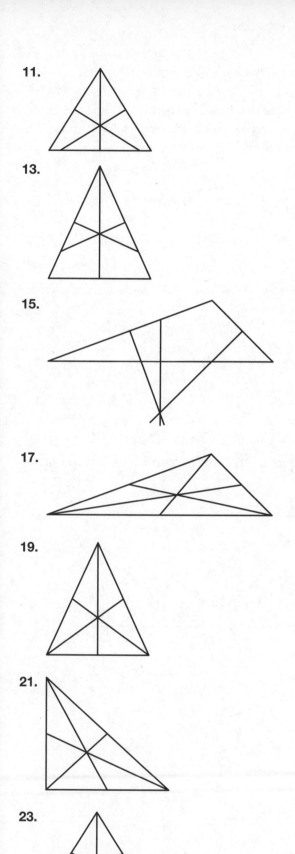

13.

15.

17.

19.

21.

23.

25.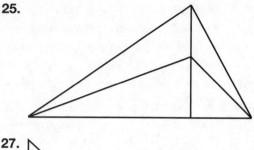

27.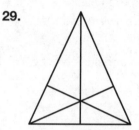

29.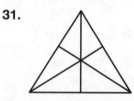

31.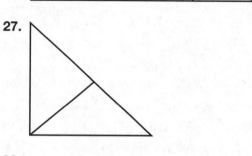

33. equilateral triangles

35. right triangles

37. all types of triangles

39. isosceles

41. scalene

43. scalene

Chapter 2

LESSON 2.1

1. Specific information: Your father has a lot of fat in his diet.
General information: High-fat diets increase the risk of heart disease.
Conclusion: Your father is at higher risk of heart disease.

3. Specific information: There have been a lot of people at the mall when Janice has been there.
General information: The problem does not include any general information.
Conclusion: It's always crowded at the mall.

5. Specific information: Mario watched 3 parades this summer with each having a fire truck in the lead.
General information: The problem does not have any general information.
Conclusion: A fire truck always leads a parade.

7. inductive reasoning. The conclusion is not necessarily true.

9. deductive reasoning. Her conclusion is not correct because she was given incorrect information.

11. inductive reasoning. The conclusion is not necessarily true.

13. inductive reasoning

15. inductive reasoning

17. inductive reasoning

19. If the measure of an angle is 90°, then the angle is a right angle.

21. If two lines are not on the same plane, then they are skew.

23. If two angles share a common vertex and a common side, then they are adjacent angles.

25. The hypothesis is "Two lines intersect at right angles."
The conclusion is "The lines are perpendicular."

27. The hypothesis is that the sum of two adjacent angles is 180°.
The conclusion is that the angles form a linear pair.

29. The hypothesis is "Two lines are located in the same plane."
The conclusion is "The lines are coplanar lines."

31. If the hypothesis is false and the conclusion is true, then the measure of angle *ABC* is not 45 degrees and the measure of angle *XYZ* is not 45 degrees, and angles *ABC* and *XYZ* are congruent. The truth value of the conditional statement is true, because the angles could have measures that are equal, but different than 45 degrees.

33. If the hypothesis is true and the conclusion is true, then angles 1 and 2 are nonadjacent angles formed by two intersecting lines, and the angles are vertical angles. The truth value of the conditional statement is true.

35.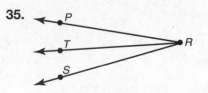

Given: $\overrightarrow{RT}$ bisects $\angle PRS$
Prove: $\angle PRT$ and $\angle SRT$ are adjacent angles

37.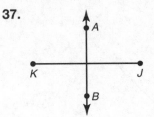

Given: $\overleftrightarrow{AB} \perp \overline{KJ}$ and $\overleftrightarrow{AB}$ bisects $\overline{KJ}$
Prove: $\overleftrightarrow{AB}$ is the perpendicular bisector of $\overline{KJ}$

LESSON 2.2

1.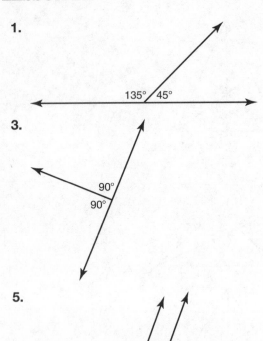

3.

5.

7.

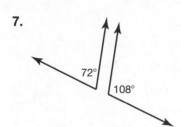

9.

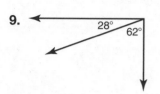

11.

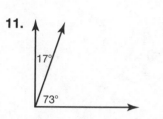

13.

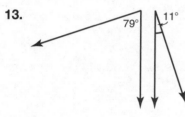

15.

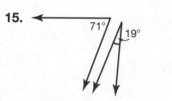

17. $x = 73°$

19. $x = 32°$

21. $x = 84°$

23. The measure of the angle is 22.5° and the measure of the complement is 67.5°.

25. The measure of the angle is 60° and the measure of the supplement is 120°.

27. The angles are not adjacent.

29. The angles are adjacent.

31. The angles do not form a linear pair.

33. The angles do not form a linear pair.

35. ∠1 and ∠6, ∠2 and ∠5, ∠3 and ∠8, ∠4 and ∠7, ∠9 and ∠11, ∠10 and ∠12

37. ∠1 and ∠10, ∠2 and ∠9, ∠3 and ∠12, ∠4 and ∠11, ∠6 and ∠8, ∠5 and ∠7

39. Linear Pair Postulate

41. Angle Addition Postulate

43. Segment Addition Postulate

45. $m\overline{LM} + m\overline{MN} = m\overline{LN}$
Segment Addition Postulate

47. $m\angle YVZ + m\angle ZVW = 180°$
Linear Pair Postulate

49. $m\overline{FG} + m\overline{GI} = m\overline{FI}$
Segment Addition Postulate

LESSON 2.3

1. Subtraction Property of Equality

3. Reflexive Property

5. Substitution Property

7. Subtraction Property of Equality

9. Addition Property of Equality

11. Substitution Property

13. Sample Answer: $\overline{XY} \cong \overline{XY}$

15. Sample Answer: $m\angle P = 10°$
$m\angle Q = 10°$
$m\angle P = m\angle Q$

17. Sample Answer: $m\overline{CD} = m\overline{GH}$
$m\overline{CD} - m\overline{JK} = m\overline{GH} - m\overline{JK}$

19. Given: ∠2 ≅ ∠1
Prove: ∠2 ≅ ∠3

21. Given: $m\angle ABC = m\angle LMN$
Prove: $m\angle ABC = m\angle XYZ$

23.

Statements	Reasons
1. $m\overline{AX} = m\overline{CX}$	1. Given
2. $m\overline{BX} = m\overline{DX}$	2. Given
3. $m\overline{AX} + m\overline{BX} = m\overline{CX} + m\overline{BX}$	3. Addition Property of Equality
4. $m\overline{AX} + m\overline{BX} = m\overline{CX} + m\overline{DX}$	4. Substitution Property
5. $m\overline{AX} + m\overline{BX} = m\overline{AB}$	5. Segment Addition Property
6. $m\overline{CX} + m\overline{DX} = m\overline{CD}$	6. Segment Addition Postulate
7. $m\overline{AB} = m\overline{CD}$	7. Substitution Property

25. If $m\angle VZW \cong \angle XZY$ then $m\angle VZW = m\angle XZY$ by the definition of congruent angles. Add the same angle measure, $m\angle WZX$ to both angles. By the Addition Property of Equality, $m\angle VZW + m\angle WZX = m\angle XZY + m\angle WZX$. By the Angle Addition Postulate, the angles can be renamed such that $m\angle VZW + m\angle WZX = m\angle VZX$ and $m\angle XZY + m\angle WZX = m\angle WZY$. Then $m\angle VZX = m\angle WZY$ because if you add the same angle to two angles of equal measure, the resulting angles remain equal in measure. Therefore, $\angle VZX \cong \angle WZY$.

27. If $\angle A$ is supplementary to $\angle B$, $\angle C$ is supplementary to $\angle D$, and $\angle A \cong \angle D$, then $m\angle A = m\angle D$ by the definition of congruent angles. By the definition of supplementary angles, $m\angle A + m\angle B = 180°$ and $m\angle C + m\angle D = 180°$. $m\angle A + m\angle B = m\angle C + m\angle D$ by the Substitution Property. Then $m\angle B = m\angle C$ by the Subtraction Property of Equality. So, $\angle B \cong \angle C$ by the definition of congruent angles.

29.

Statements	Reasons
1. $\angle PQT \cong \angle RQS$	1. Given
2. $m\angle PQT = m\angle RQS$	2. Definition of congruent angles
3. $m\angle PQT = m\angle PQS + m\angle SQT$	3. Angle Addition Postulate
4. $m\angle RQS = m\angle RQT + m\angle SQT$	4. Angle Addition Postulate
5. $m\angle PQS + m\angle SQT = m\angle RQT + m\angle SQT$	5. Substitution
6. $m\angle SQT = m\angle SQT$	6. Identity
7. $m\angle PQS = m\angle RQT$	7. Subtraction Property of Equality
8. $\angle PQS \cong m\angle RQT$	8. Definition of congruent angles

31. If angles 1 and 2 are supplementary, then $m\angle 1 + m\angle 2 = 180°$ by the definition of supplementary angles. Likewise, if angles 3 and 4 are supplementary, then $m\angle 3 + m\angle 4 = 180°$ by the definition of supplementary angles. You can use the Substitution Property to write $m\angle 1 + m\angle 2 = m\angle 3 + m\angle 4$. You are given that $\angle 2 \cong \angle 4$, so $m\angle 2 = m\angle 4$ by the definition of congruent angles. Then, you can use the Substitution Property to substitute $\angle 2$ for $\angle 4$ into the equation $m\angle 1 + m\angle 2 = m\angle 3 + m\angle 4$ to get $m\angle 1 + m\angle 2 = m\angle 3 1 m\angle 2$. By the Subtraction Property of Equality $m\angle 1 = m\angle 3$. So, $\angle 1 \cong \angle 3$ by the definition of congruent angles.

33.

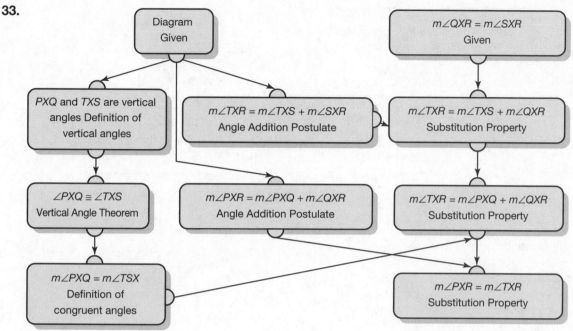

LESSON 2.4

1. ∠1 ≅ ∠5, ∠2 ≅ ∠6,
∠3 ≅ ∠7, ∠4 ≅ ∠8

3. ∠1 ≅ ∠3, ∠5 ≅ ∠7,
∠2 ≅ ∠4, ∠6 ≅ ∠8

5. Alternate interior angles are congruent.

7. Alternate exterior angles are congruent.

9. Same-side interior angles are congruent.

11. Corresponding angles are congruent.

13. ∠1 and ∠3 are supplementary or ∠2 and ∠4 are supplementary

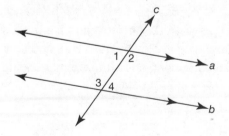

15. ∠1 ≅ ∠4 or ∠2 ≅ ∠3

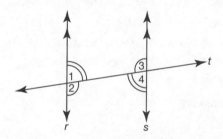

17. Given: r ∥ c, n is a transversal

Prove: ∠1 and ∠7 are supplementary or
∠2 and ∠8 are supplementary

19. Given: a ∥ z, d is a transversal

Prove: ∠2 ≅ ∠7 or ∠6 ≅ ∠3

21. You are given that lines a and b are parallel and line c is a transversal, as shown in the diagram. Angles 2 and 6 are corresponding angles by definition, and corresponding angles are congruent by the Corresponding Angles Postulate. So, ∠2 ≅ ∠6. Angles 6 and 8 are vertical angles by definition, and vertical angles are congruent by the Vertical Angles Congruence Theorem. So, ∠6 ≅ ∠8. Since ∠2 ≅ ∠6 and ∠2 ≅ ∠8, by the Transitive Property, ∠2 ≅ ∠8.

23.

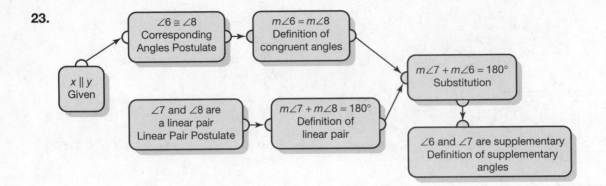

25. Same-Side Exterior Angles Theorem

27. Alternate Exterior Angles Theorem

LESSON 2.5

1. If alternate interior angles formed by two lines and a transversal are congruent, then the two lines are parallel.

3. If same-side interior angles formed by two lines and a transversal are supplementary, then the two lines are parallel.

5. Converse: If a triangle is an equilateral triangle, then the triangle has three congruent sides.

7. Converse: If a figure has four sides, then it is a rectangle.

9. Converse: If a triangle is isosceles, then two angles in the triangle are congruent.

11. Given: $\angle 1$ and $\angle 3$ are supplementary or $\angle 2$ and $\angle 4$ are supplementary

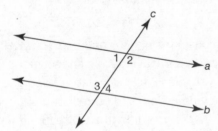

Conclusion: Lines a and b are parallel.

13. Given: $\angle 1 \cong \angle 4$ or $\angle 2 \cong \angle 3$

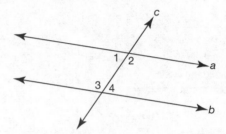

Conclusion: Lines a and b are parallel.

15. Given: s is a transversal; $\angle 1$ and $\angle 8$ are supplementary or $\angle 2$ and $\angle 7$ are supplementary

Prove: $w \parallel k$

17. Given: a is a transversal; $\angle 3 \cong \angle 6$ or $\angle 4 \cong \angle 5$

Prove: $b \parallel c$

19. You are given that $\angle 4 \cong \angle 5$ and line j is a transversal, as shown in the diagram. Angles 5 and 2 are vertical angles by definition, and vertical angles are congruent by the Vertical Angles Congruence Theorem. So, $\angle 5 \cong \angle 2$. Since $\angle 4 \cong \angle 5$ and $\angle 5 \cong \angle 2$, by the Transitive Property, $\angle 4 \cong \angle 2$. Angles 4 and 2 are corresponding angles by definition, and they are also congruent, so by the Corresponding Angles Converse Postulate, $p \parallel x$.

21.

Statements	Reasons
1. $\angle 1$ and $\angle 4$ are supplementary and line u is a transversal	1. Given
2. $\angle 1$ and $\angle 2$ are a linear pair	2. Definition of linear pair
3. $\angle 1$ and $\angle 2$ are supplementary	3. Linear Pair Postulate
4. $\angle 2 \cong \angle 4$	4. Supplements of the same angle are congruent
5. Angles 2 and 4 are corresponding angles	5. Definition of corresponding angles
6. $t \parallel v$	6. Corresponding Angles Converse Postulate

Chapter 3

LESSON 3.1

1. $m\angle B = 65°$

3. $m\angle L = 117°$

5. $m\angle Y = 60°$

7. The side lengths from shortest to longest are a, b, c.

9. The side lengths from shortest to longest are l, m, k.

11. The side lengths from shortest to longest are b, a, c, d, e.

13. Interior angles: $\angle XYZ$, $\angle YZX$, $\angle ZXY$
Exterior angle: $\angle WXZ$
Remote interior angles: $\angle XYZ$, $\angle YZX$

15. Interior angles: $\angle EFG$, $\angle EGF$, $\angle FEG$
Exterior angle: $\angle FGH$
Remote interior angles: $\angle EFG$, $\angle FEG$

17. Interior angles: $\angle JKL$, $\angle JLK$, $\angle KJL$
Exterior angle: $\angle LKM$
Remote interior angles: $\angle JLK$, $\angle KJL$

19. $49° = x$

21. $33° = x$

23. $30° = x$

25. $m\angle TRQ > m\angle S$ and $m\angle TRQ > m\angle T$

27. $m\angle TUV > m\angle V$ and $m\angle TUV > m\angle W$

29. $m\angle KLN > m\angle M$ and $m\angle KLN > m\angle N$

LESSON 3.2

1. The angles from least to greatest are $\angle H$, $\angle F$, $\angle G$.

3. The angles from least to greatest are $\angle P$, $\angle Q$, $\angle R$.

5. The angles from least to greatest are $\angle G$, $\angle F$, $\angle E$.

7. Yes.

9. No.

11. No.

13. Yes.

15. No.

17. $AB < 18$ meters

19. $HI < 34$ inches

21. $MN < 14$ centimeters

LESSON 3.3

1. The length of the hypotenuse is $2\sqrt{2}$ inches.

3. The length of the hypotenuse is $9\sqrt{2}$ feet.

5. The length of each leg is $8\sqrt{2}$ centimeters.

7. The length of each leg is 6 feet.

9. The kite is approximately 11.3 meters above the ground.

11. The support beam must be approximately 5.7 feet long.

13. The area of the triangle is 64 square millimeters.

15. The area of the triangle is 12.25 square feet.

17. The area of each tile is 42.25 square centimeters.

19. The area of the piece of fabric needed for the kite is 196 square inches.

21.

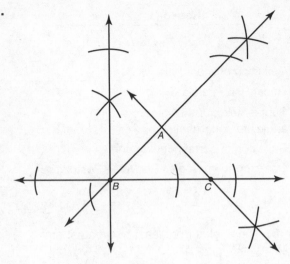

23.

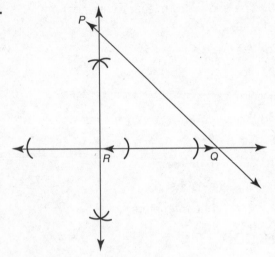

LESSON 3.4

1. $m\angle ABC = 60°$

3. $m\angle HAK = 90°$

5. $b = 3\sqrt{3}$ feet
   $c = 2(3) = 6$ feet

7. $b = 3\sqrt{2}$ millimeters
   $c = 2\sqrt{6}$ millimeters

9. $a = 10$ meters
   $b = 10\sqrt{3}$ meters

11. $a = 3\sqrt{3}$ yard
    $b = 9$ yard

13. $a = 8$ inches
    $c = 16$ inches

15. $a = 4\sqrt{3}$ miles
    $c = 8\sqrt{3}$ miles

17. The area of the triangle is approximately 7.8 square centimeters.

19. The area of the pennant is approximately 55.4 square inches.

21.

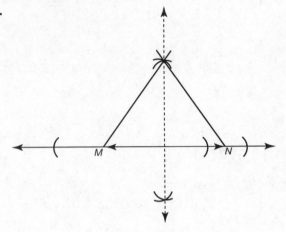

23.

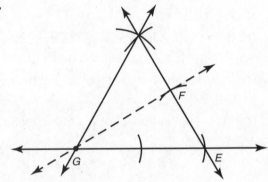

Chapter 4
LESSON 4.1

1. $ZL = 2$, $ZN = 3$, $ZM = 3$, $ZP = 2$, $ZL' = 5$,
   $ZN' = 7.5$, $ZM' = 7.5$, $ZP' = 5$

   $\dfrac{ZL'}{ZL} = \dfrac{5}{2} = 2.5$, $\dfrac{ZN'}{ZN} = \dfrac{7.5}{3} = 2.5$, $\dfrac{ZM'}{ZM} =$
   $\dfrac{7.5}{3} = 2.5$, $\dfrac{ZP'}{ZP} = \dfrac{5}{2} = 2.5$

3. $ZL = 1$, $ZN = 1.7$, $ZM = 1.7$, $ZP = 1$, $ZL' = 4$,
   $ZN' = 6.8$, $ZM' = 6.8$, $ZP' = 4$

   $\dfrac{ZL'}{ZL} = \dfrac{4}{1} = 4$, $\dfrac{ZN'}{ZN} = \dfrac{6.8}{1.7} = 4$, $\dfrac{ZM'}{ZM} = \dfrac{6.8}{1.7} = 4$,
   $\dfrac{ZP'}{ZP} = \dfrac{4}{1} = 4$

5. The scale factor is 2.

7. The scale factor is $\dfrac{1}{3}$.

9.

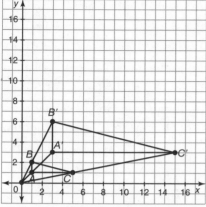

11.

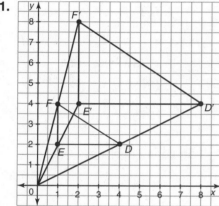

13. $A'(4, 8)$, $B'(12, 24)$, $C'(36, 28)$

15. $G'(0, 45)$, $H'(36, 18)$, $I'(27, 27)$

17. $A'(4, 2)$, $B'(7, 8)$, $C'(3, 5)$

19. $G'(0, 15)$, $H'(12, 18)$, $I'(9, 9)$

LESSON 4.2

1. The triangles are congruent by the Angle-Angle Similarity Theorem. Two corresponding angles are congruent.

3. The triangles are congruent by the Side-Side-Side Similarity Theorem. All corresponding sides are proportional.

5. The triangles are congruent by the Side-Angle-Side Similarity Theorem. Two of the corresponding sides are proportional and the included angles are congruent.

7. To prove that the triangles are similar using the Angle-Angle Similarity Theorem, the first triangle should have a corresponding 60 degree angle and the second triangle should have a corresponding 35 degree angle.

9. To prove that the triangles are similar using the Side-Angle-Side Similarity Theorem, the triangles both pairs of corresponding legs must be proportional.

11. To prove that the triangles are similar using the Side-Side-Side Similarity Theorem, all corresponding side lengths between the two triangles should be proportional.

13. The triangles are similar by the Side-Angle-Side Similarity Theorem because the included angles in both triangles are congruent and the corresponding sides are proportional.

15. The triangles are not similar. The corresponding sides are proportional, but the included angles are not congruent. So, I cannot use the Side-Angle-Side Similarity Theorem.

17. The triangles are similar by the Side-Angle-Side Similarity Theorem. The corresponding sides are proportional and the included angles are congruent.

19. The triangles are similar by the Angle-Angle Similarity Theorem. Two pairs of corresponding angles are congruent.

LESSON 4.3

1. The length of segment HF is 17.5 centimeters.

3. The length of segment AD is 4 feet.

5. The length of segment YW is 4.5 centimeters.

7. The length of segment FD is 11 centimeters.

9. Rick's house is 7.5 miles from the school.

11. Central City is 9 miles from Minville.

13. $\dfrac{AD}{DB} = \dfrac{AE}{EC}$, Triangle Proportionality Theorem

15. $\overline{DE} \parallel \overline{CB}$, Converse of Triangle Proportionality Theorem

17. $\dfrac{BP}{PA} = \dfrac{CQ}{QA}$, Triangle Proportionality Theorem

19. $\overline{GH} \parallel \overline{FI}$, Converse of Triangle Proportionality Theorem

21. $x = 3$

23. $x = 20.16$

25. $\overline{DE} \parallel \overline{AC}$, $DE = \dfrac{1}{2}AC$

27. $\overline{XY} \parallel \overline{NP}$, $XY = \frac{1}{2}NP$

29. Segment LM is two times the length of segment OP.

LESSON 4.4

1.

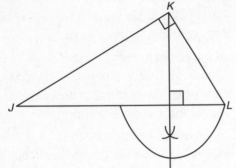

3.

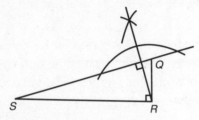

5. $\dfrac{CG}{MK} = \dfrac{GJ}{KP} = \dfrac{CJ}{MP}$

7. $\dfrac{AD}{GL} = \dfrac{DF}{LM} = \dfrac{AF}{GM}$

9. $\triangle HPG \sim \triangle PQG$, $\triangle HPG \sim \triangle HQP$, $\triangle PQG \sim \triangle HQP$

11. $\triangle NLT \sim \triangle NKL$, $\triangle NLT \sim \triangle LKT$, $\triangle NKL \sim \triangle LKT$

13. $x = 3.2$ cm

15. $x = 1.\overline{3}$ cm

17. $x = 2\sqrt{35}$ m

19. $x = 10 \qquad 5\sqrt{29} = y \qquad 2\sqrt{29} = z$

21. $x = 16 \qquad y = 8\sqrt{5} \qquad z = 4\sqrt{5}$

23. The river is 60.5 feet wide.

25. The parking lot is 420 feet from the clearing.

LESSON 4.5

1. Given: $\triangle ABC$ with right angle C
Prove: $AC^2 + BC^2 = AB^2$

3. Given: $\triangle VWX$ with right angle X
Prove: $v^2 + w^2 = x^2$

5. Given: $\triangle FGH$ with right angle H
Prove: $f^2 + g^2 = h^2$

7. Draw an altitude to the hypotenuse at point N.

According to the Right Triangle/Similarity Theorem, $\triangle KLM \sim \triangle LMN \sim \triangle MKN$.

According to the definition of similar triangles, the sides of similar triangles are proportional.

$\dfrac{KL}{KM} = \dfrac{KM}{KN}$

$KM^2 = KL \times KN$

$\dfrac{KL}{ML} = \dfrac{ML}{NL}$

$ML^2 = KL \times NL$

$KM^2 + ML^2 = KL \times KN + KL \times NL$

$KM^2 + ML^2 = KL(KN + NL)$

$KM^2 + ML^2 = KL(KL)$

$KM^2 + ML^2 = KL^2$

9. By the Pythagorean Theorem,

$t^2 = q^2 + r^2$

$t = \sqrt{q^2 + r^2}$

We are given the relationship for the original triangle:

$s^2 = q^2 + r^2$

$s = \sqrt{q^2 + r^2}$

By the transitive property, and since all distances are positive, then, $s = t$.

By the SSS Theorem, the triangles are congruent, $\triangle QRS \cong \triangle QRT$.

All corresponding angles of congruent triangles are congruent, so

$\angle S = T$

$\angle S = 90°$

By definition, a triangle with a 90 degree angle is a right triangle.

11. By the Pythagorean Theorem, $h^2 = w^2 + g^2$.

We are given the relationship for the original triangle:

$h^2 = f^2 + g^2$

By the transitive property, and since all distances are positive, then,

$w^2 + g^2 = f^2 + g^2$

$\qquad w^2 = g^2$

$\qquad\quad w = g$

By the SSS Theorem, the triangles are congruent.

All corresponding angles of congruent triangles are congruent, so $\angle H = 90°$

By definition, a triangle with a 90 degree angle is a right triangle.

LESSON 4.6

1. The angles where the vertices of the triangle intersect are vertical angles, so angles $\angle ACB$ and $\angle ECD$ are congruent. The angles formed by BD intersecting the two parallel lines are right angles, so they are also congruent. So by the Angle-Angle Similarity Theorem, the triangles formed are similar.

3. The known corresponding sides of the triangles are proportional: $\frac{6}{3} = \frac{2}{1}$ and $\frac{8}{4} = \frac{2}{1}$. The angle between the known sides is a right angle for both triangles, so those angles are congruent. Therefore, by the Side-Angle-Side Similarity Postulate, the triangles are similar.

5. The distance across the canyon is 140 feet.

7. The height of the statue is 35 feet.

9. The bog is 108 feet across at the widest point.

11. The sculpture is 8 feet in height.

Chapter 5

LESSON 5.1

1.

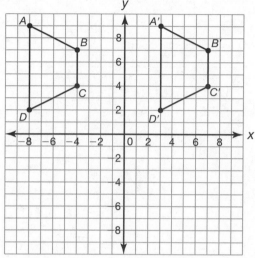

3.

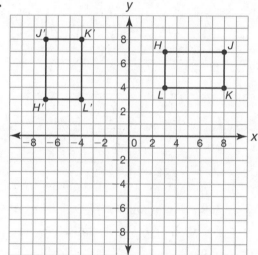

5.

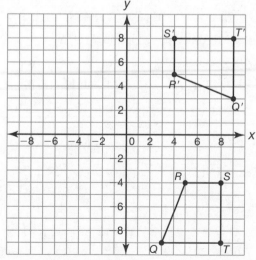

7.

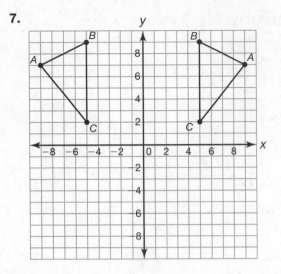

9.

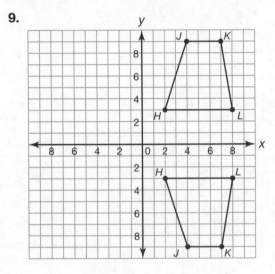

11. A' $(-1, 3)$, B' $(-4, 8)$, and C' $(-10, 5)$

13. H' $(2, 1)$, J' $(3, 6)$, K' $(7, 6)$, and L' $(6, 1)$

15. R' $(-5, 6)$, S' $(-3, 10)$, and T' $(-2, 2)$

17. A' $(-3, 5)$, B' $(-8, 2)$, and C' $(-5, -4)$

19. H' $(6, 2)$, J' $(1, 3)$, K' $(1, 7)$ and L' $(6, 6)$

21. R' $(-3, 0)$, S' $(-7, 2)$, and T' $(1, 3)$

23. A' $(5, -3)$, B' $(2, -8)$, and C' $(-4, -5)$

25. H' $(2, 6)$, J' $(3, 1)$, K' $(7, 1)$, and L' $(6, 6)$

27. R' $(0, -3)$, S' $(2, -7)$, and T' $(3, 1)$

LESSON 5.2

1. $BC \cong \overline{XY}$, $\overline{CA} \cong \overline{YZ}$, and $\overline{BA} \cong \overline{XZ}$; $\angle B \cong \angle X$, $\angle C \cong \angle Y$, and $\angle A \cong \angle Z$. $\triangle BCA \cong \triangle XYZ$

3. $\overline{MP} \cong \overline{XY}$, $\overline{PT} \cong \overline{YZ}$, and $\overline{MT} \cong \overline{XZ}$; $\angle M \cong \angle X$, $\angle P \cong \angle Y$, and $\angle T \cong \angle Z$. $\triangle MPT \cong \triangle XYZ$

5. $\overline{AW} \cong \overline{XY}$, $\overline{WF} \cong \overline{YZ}$, and $\overline{AF} \cong \overline{XZ}$; $\angle A \cong \angle X$, $\angle W \cong \angle Y$, and $\angle F \cong \angle Z$. $\triangle AWF \cong \triangle XYZ$

7. $\overline{GN} \cong \overline{XY}$, $\overline{NR} \cong \overline{YZ}$, and $\overline{GR} \cong \overline{XZ}$; $\angle G \cong \angle X$, $\angle N \cong \angle Y$, and $\angle R \cong \angle Z$. $\triangle GNR \cong \triangle XYZ$

9. $\overline{VT} \cong \overline{XY}$, $\overline{TA} \cong \overline{YZ}$, and $\overline{VA} \cong \overline{XZ}$; $\angle V \cong \angle X$, $\angle T \cong \angle Y$, and $\angle A \cong \angle Z$. $\triangle VTA \cong \triangle XYZ$

11. $\overline{JP} \cong \overline{TR}$, $\overline{PM} \cong \overline{RW}$, and $\overline{JM} \cong \overline{TW}$; $\angle J \cong \angle T$, $\angle P \cong \angle R$, and $\angle M \cong \angle W$.

13. $\overline{LU} \cong \overline{MT}$, $\overline{UV} \cong \overline{TH}$, and $\overline{LV} \cong \overline{HM}$; $\angle L \cong \angle M$, $\angle U \cong \angle T$, and $\angle V \cong \angle H$.

15. $\overline{TO} \cong \overline{BE}$, $\overline{OM} \cong \overline{EN}$, and $\overline{TM} \cong \overline{BN}$; $\angle T \cong \angle B$, $\angle O \cong \angle E$, and $\angle M \cong \angle N$.

17. $\overline{CA} \cong \overline{SU}$, $\overline{AT} \cong \overline{UP}$, and $\overline{CT} \cong \overline{SP}$; $\angle C \cong \angle S$, $\angle A \cong \angle U$, and $\angle T \cong \angle P$.

LESSON 5.3

1. The triangles are congruent by the SSS Congruence Theorem.

3. The triangles are not congruent.

5. The triangles are congruent by the SSS Congruence Theorem.

7. The triangles are congruent by the SSS Congruence Theorem.

9. The triangles are congruent by the SSS Congruence Theorem.

11. The triangles are congruent by the SSS Congruence Theorem.

LESSON 5.4

1. The triangles are congruent by the SAS Congruence Theorem.

3. The triangles are congruent by the SAS Congruence Theorem.

5. The triangles are congruent by the SAS Congruence Theorem.

7. The triangles are congruent by the SAS Congruence Theorem.

9. The triangles are congruent by the SAS Congruence Theorem.

11. The triangles are congruent by the SAS Congruence Theorem.

13. $SW = 8$

15. $MN = 2$

17. $m\angle D = 65°$

19. $m\angle T = 50°$

21. The triangles are congruent by SSS.

23. The triangles are congruent by SAS.

25. The triangles are congruent by SAS.

27. The triangles are congruent by SAS.

LESSON 5.5

1. The triangles are congruent by the ASA Congruence Theorem.

3. The triangles are not congruent.

5. The triangles are not congruent.

7. The triangles are congruent by the ASA Congruence Theorem.

9. The triangles are congruent by the ASA Congruence Theorem.

11. The triangles are congruent by the ASA Congruence Theorem.

13. $m\angle B = 20°$

15. $m\angle R = 60°$

17. $m\angle T = 40°$

19. $m\angle G = 60°$

LESSON 5.6

1. The triangles are congruent by the AAS Congruence Theorem.

3. The triangles are congruent by the AAS Congruence Theorem.

5. The triangles are congruent by the AAS Congruence Theorem.

7. The triangles are congruent by the AAS Congruence Theorem.

9. The triangles are congruent by the AAS Congruence Theorem.

11. The triangles are congruent by the AAS Congruence Theorem.

13. $m\angle B = 30°$

15. $m\angle G = 70°$

17. $m\angle Z = 70°$

19. $FR = 25$ m

21. The triangles are congruent by AAS.

23. The triangles are congruent by ASA.

25. There is not enough information to determine whether the triangles are congruent by ASA or AAS.

27. The triangles are congruent by AAS.

LESSON 5.7

1.

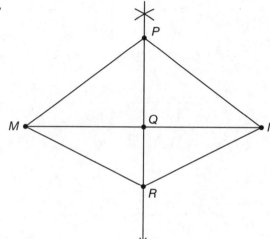

3.

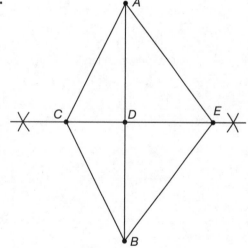

5.

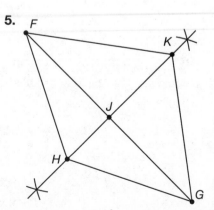

7.

1. $\overline{FG} \perp \overline{HK}$, $\overline{HK}$ bisects $\overline{FG}$	1. Definition of perpendicular bisector
2. $\angle FJH$ and $\angle GJH$ are right angles.	2. Definition of perpendicular lines
3. $\angle FJH \cong \angle GJH$	3. All right angles are congruent.
4. $\overline{FJ} \cong \overline{GJ}$	4. Definition of bisect
5. $\overline{HJ} \cong \overline{HJ}$	5. Reflexive Property
6. $\triangle FJH \cong \triangle GJH$	6. SAS Congruence Theorem
7. $\overline{FH} \cong \overline{GH}$	7. Corresponding sides of congruent triangles are congruent
8. Point H is equidistant to points F and G	8. Definition of equidistant

9.

1. $\overline{UW} \perp \overline{CA}$, $\overline{CA}$ bisects $\overline{UW}$	1. Definition of perpendicular bisector
2. $\angle UBC$ and $\angle WBC$ are right angles.	2. Definition of perpendicular lines
3. $\angle UBC \cong \angle WBC$	3. All right angles are congruent.
4. $\overline{UB} \cong \overline{WB}$	4. Definition of bisect
5. $\overline{CB} \cong \overline{CB}$	5. Reflexive Property
6. $\triangle UBC \cong \triangle WBC$	6. SAS Congruence Theorem
7. $\overline{UC} \cong \overline{WC}$	7. Corresponding sides of congruent triangles are congruent
8. Point C is equidistant to points U and W	8. Definition of equidistant

11.

1. $\overline{UV} \perp \overline{HT}$, $\overline{HT}$ bisects $\overline{UV}$	1. Definition of perpendicular bisector
2. $\angle UPH$ and $\angle VPH$ are right angles.	2. Definition of perpendicular lines
3. $\angle UPH \cong \angle VPH$	3. All right angles are congruent.
4. $\overline{UP} \cong \overline{VP}$	4. Definition of bisect
5. $\overline{HP} \cong \overline{HP}$	5. Reflexive Property
6. $\triangle UPH \cong \triangle VPH$	6. SAS Congruence Theorem
7. $\overline{UH} \cong \overline{VH}$	7. Corresponding sides of congruent triangles are congruent
8. Point H is equidistant to points U and V	8. Definition of equidistant

Answers

13.

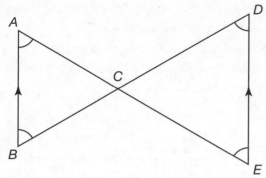

15.

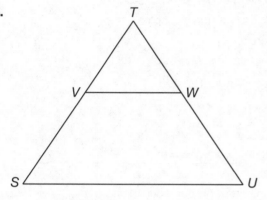

17.

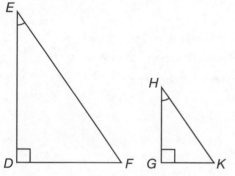

19. Not enough information is given.

21. ASA Triangle Congruence Theorem

23. SSS Triangle Congruence Theorem

Chapter 6

LESSON 6.1

1.

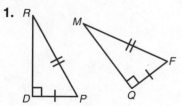

3.

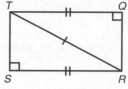

5.

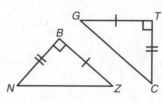

7.

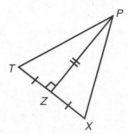

9.

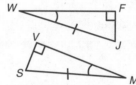

11.

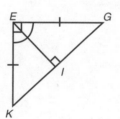

13.

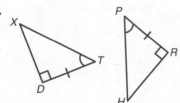

15.

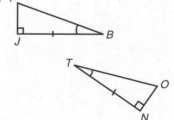

17. Yes. There is enough information to conclude that △*FRG* ≅ △*FSG* by HA.

19. Yes. There is enough information to conclude that △*NMD* ≅ △*EMO* by LL.

21. No. △*GEO* might not be congruent to △*MKI*. There is not enough information.

23. Yes. Maria's walking distance to the library is equal to Paula's walking distance.

25. No. There is not enough information to determine whether the guy wires have the same length.

27.

Statements	Reasons
1. $\overline{WV} \perp \overline{VY}$ and $\overline{YZ} \perp \overline{VY}$	1. Given
2. ∠*WVX* and ∠*ZYX* are right angles.	2. Definition of perpendicular angles
3. △*WVX* and △*ZYX* are right triangles.	3. Definition of right triangles
4. $\overline{WZ}$ bisects $\overline{VY}$.	4. Given
5. $\overline{VX} \cong \overline{YX}$	5. Definition of segment bisector
6. ∠*WXV* ≅ ∠*ZXY*	6. Vertical Angle Theorem
7. △*WVX* ≅ △*ZYX*	7. LA Congruence Theorem

29.

Statements	Reasons
1. $\overline{SU} \perp \overline{UP}$ and $\overline{TP} \perp \overline{UP}$	1. Given
2. ∠*U* and ∠*P* are right angles.	2. Definition of perpendicular lines
3. △*SUR* and △*TPR* are right triangles.	3. Definition of right triangles
4. $\overline{UR} \cong \overline{PR}$	4. Given
5. ∠*PRT* and ∠*URS* are vertical angles.	5. Definition of vertical angles
6. ∠*PRT* ≅ ∠*URS*	6. Vertical Angle Theorem
7. △*SUR* ≅ △*TPR*	7. LA Congruence Theorem

LESSON 6.2

1.

Statements	Reasons
1. $\overline{RS}$ is the ⊥ bisector of $\overline{PQ}$.	1. Given
2. $\overline{RS} \perp \overline{PQ}$	2. Definition of perpendicular bisector
3. ∠*PTS* and ∠*QTS* are right angles.	3. Definition of perpendicular lines
4. △*PTS* and △*QTS* are right triangles.	4. Definition of right triangles
5. $\overline{RS}$ bisects $\overline{PQ}$	5. Definition of perpendicular bisector
6. $\overline{PT} \cong \overline{QT}$	6. Definition of bisect
7. $\overline{TS} \cong \overline{TS}$	7. Reflexive Property of ≅
8. △*PTS* ≅ △*QTS*	8. Leg-Leg Congruence Theorem
9. ∠*SPT* ≅ ∠*SQT*	9. CPCTC

3.

Statements	Reasons
1. $\overline{AG}$ and $\overline{EK}$ intersect at C	1. Given
2. $\overline{AC} \cong \overline{EC}$	2. Given
3. $\overline{CK} \cong \overline{CG}$	3. Given
4. $\angle ACK \cong \angle ECG$	4. Vertical Angles Theorem
5. $\triangle ACK \cong \triangle ECG$	5. SAS Congruence Theorem
6. $\angle K \cong \angle G$	6. CPCTC

5.

Statements	Reasons
1. $\triangle UGT \cong \triangle SGB$	1. Given
2. $\overline{TU} \cong \overline{BS}$	2. CPCTC
3. $\overline{SG} \cong \overline{UG}$	3. CPCTC
4. $\overline{GT} \cong \overline{GB}$	4. CPCTC
5. $SG = UG$	5. Definition of congruent segments
6. $GT = GB$	6. Definition of congruent segments
7. $SG + GT = UG + GB$	7. Addition Property of Equality
8. $SG + GT = ST$	8. Segment Addition Postulate
9. $UG + GB = UB$	9. Segment Addition Postulate
10. $ST = UB$	10. Substitution Property
11. $\overline{ST} \cong \overline{UB}$	11. Definition of congruent segments
12. $\angle STU \cong \angle UBS$	12. CPCTC
13. $\triangle STU \cong \triangle UBS$	13. SAS Congruence Theorem
14. $\angle TUS \cong \angle BSU$	14. CPCTC

7.

Statements	Reasons
1. $\overline{AC} \perp \overline{DB}$	1. Given
2. $\angle DEA$ is a right angle.	2. Definition of perpendicular lines
3. $\angle BEA$ is a right angle.	3. Definition of perpendicular lines
4. $\triangle DEA$ is a right triangle.	4. Definition of right triangle
5. $\triangle BEA$ is a right triangle.	5. Definition of right triangle
6. $\overline{AC}$ bisects $\overline{DB}$	6. Given
7. $\overline{DE} \cong \overline{BE}$	7. Definition of bisect
8. $\overline{AE} \cong \overline{AE}$	8. Reflexive Property of $\cong$
9. $\triangle DEA \cong \triangle BEA$	9. Leg-Leg Congruence Theorem
10. $\overline{AD} \cong \overline{AB}$	10. CPCTC

9.

Statements	Reasons
1. $\overline{AT} \cong \overline{AQ}$	1. Given
2. $\angle T \cong \angle Q$	2. Base Angle Theorem
3. $\overline{AC}$ bisects $\angle TAQ$	3. Given
4. $\angle TAC \cong \angle QAC$	4. Definition of bisect
5. $\triangle TAC \cong \triangle QAC$	5. ASA Congruence Theorem
6. $\overline{TC} \cong \overline{QC}$	6. CPCTC
7. $\overline{AC}$ bisects $\overline{TQ}$	7. Definition of bisect

11.

Statements	Reasons
1. $\angle E \cong \angle EUV$	1. Given
2. $\overline{VU} \cong \overline{VE}$	2. Base Angle Converse Theorem
3. $\angle F \cong \angle FVU$	3. Given
4. $\overline{UF} \cong \overline{VU}$	4. Base Angle Converse Theorem
5. $\overline{UF} \cong \overline{VE}$	5. Transitive Property of $\cong$

13. The canyon is 80 feet wide.

15. $MR = 20$ cm.

17. Eight posts are needed to complete the fence.

LESSON 6.3

1. Isosceles Triangle Angle Bisector to Congruent Sides Theorem

3. Isosceles Triangle Base Theorem

5. Isosceles Triangle Altitude to Congruent Sides Theorem

7. $x = 32°$

9. $x = 13$ ft

11. $x = 10$ cm

13.

Statements	Reasons
1. $\overline{AB} \cong \overline{CB}$	1. Given
2. $\overline{BD} \perp \overline{AC}, \overline{DE} \perp \overline{AB}, \overline{DF} \perp \overline{CB}$	2. Given
3. $\angle AED$ and $\angle CFD$ are right angles.	3. Definition of perpendicular lines
4. $\triangle AED$ and $\triangle CFD$ are right triangles.	4. Definition of right triangle
5. $\angle A \cong \angle C$	5. Base Angle Theorem
6. $\overline{AD} \cong \overline{CD}$	6. Isosceles Triangle Base Theorem
7. $\triangle AED \cong \triangle CFD$	7. HA Congruence Theorem
8. $\overline{ED} \cong \overline{FD}$	8. CPCTC

15.

Statements	Reasons
1. $\overline{IA} \cong \overline{IE}$	1. Given
2. $\overline{AG} \perp \overline{IE}, \overline{EK} \perp \overline{IA}$	2. Given
3. $\angle IGA$ and $\angle IKE$ are right angles.	3. Definition of perpendicular lines
4. $\triangle IGA$ and $\triangle IKE$ are right triangles.	4. Definition of right triangle
5. $\overline{AG} \cong \overline{EK}$	5. Isos. Triangle Altitude to Congruent Sides Theorem
6. $\triangle IGA \cong \triangle IKE$	6. HL Congruence Theorem

17. The measure of $\angle GHJ$ is 43°.

19. The measure of $\angle STB$ is 70°.

21. The line of beads represented by $\overline{NU}$ is 12 inches long.

LESSON 6.4

1. The converse of the conditional would be:

If two lines are skew lines, then they do not intersect and are not parallel.

The converse is true.

3. The converse of the conditional would be:

If a triangle is obtuse, then the measure of one of its angles is greater than 90°.

The converse is true.

5. The converse of the conditional would be:

If a triangle is a right triangle, then the lengths of its sides are 5 mm, 12 mm, and 13 mm.

The converse is not true.

7. The converse of the conditional would be:

If two triangles are congruent, then the corresponding sides of the two triangles are congruent.

The converse is true.

9. The inverse of the conditional would be:

If a triangle is not an equilateral triangle, then it is not an isosceles triangle.

The inverse is not true.

11. The inverse of the conditional would be:

If the sum of the internal angles of a polygon is not 180°, then the polygon is not a triangle.

The inverse is true.

13. The inverse of the conditional would be:

If two angles are not the acute angles of a right triangle, then they are not complementary.

The inverse is not true.

15. The inverse of the conditional would be:

If a polygon is not a square, then it is not a rhombus.

The inverse is not true.

17. The contrapositive of the conditional would be:

If a triangle is not an isosceles right triangle, then it is not a right triangle with an acute angle that measures 45°.

The contrapositive is true.

19. The contrapositive of the conditional would be:

If a quadrilateral is not a parallelogram, then it is not a rectangle.

The contrapositive is true.

21. The contrapositive of the conditional would be:

If two angles are not supplementary, then the sum of their measures is not 180°.

The contrapositive is true.

23. The contrapositive of the conditional would be:

If the diameter of a circle is not 16 meters, then the radius of the circle is not 8 meters.

The contrapositive is true.

25.

Statements	Reasons
1. $\overline{XY} \cong \overline{ZY}$	1. Assumption
2. $\overline{WY}$ bisects $\angle XYZ$	2. Given
3. $\angle XYW \cong \angle ZYW$	3. Definition of angle bisector
4. $\overline{YW} \cong \overline{YW}$	4. Reflexive Property of $\cong$
5. $\triangle XYW \cong \triangle ZYW$	5. SAS Congruence Theorem
6. $\overline{XW} \cong \overline{ZW}$	6. CPCTC
7. $\overline{XW} \not\cong \overline{ZW}$	7. Given
8. $\overline{XY} \cong \overline{ZY}$ is false.	8. Step 7 contradicts Step 6. The assumption is false.
9. $\overline{XY} \not\cong \overline{ZY}$ is true.	9. Proof by contradiction

27.

Statements	Reasons
1. $\overline{NM} \cong \overline{NO}$	1. Assumption
2. $\angle OMP \cong \angle MOP$	2. Given
3. $\overline{NP}$ does not bisect $\angle ONM$.	3. Given
4. $\overline{MP} \cong \overline{OP}$	4. Isosceles Triangle Base Angle Converse Theorem
5. $\overline{PN} \cong \overline{PN}$	5. Reflexive Property of $\cong$
6. $\triangle ONP \cong \triangle MNP$	6. SSS Congruence Theorem
7. $\angle ONP \cong \angle MNP$	7. CPCTC
8. $\overline{NP}$ bisects $\angle ONM$.	8. Definition of angle bisector
9. $\overline{NM} \cong \overline{NO}$ is false.	9. Step 8 contradicts Step 3. The assumption is false.
10. $\overline{NM} \not\cong \overline{NO}$ is true.	10. Proof by contradiction

29. $SP > GQ$

31. $m\angle E > m\angle T$

Chapter 7

LESSON 7.1

1. $m \parallel r$

3. $g \parallel p$

5. $n \parallel q$

7. $\overline{GK} \cong \overline{KJ} \cong \overline{JH} \cong \overline{HG}$

9. $\angle GEK$, $\angle KGH$, $\angle GHJ$, $\angle HJK$, $\angle JKG$, $\angle GEH$, $\angle HEG$, and $\angle JEK$ are right angles.

11. $\overline{GE} \cong \overline{JE} \cong \overline{HE} \cong \overline{KE}$

13. $\overline{MN} \cong \overline{TU}$ and $\overline{MT} \cong \overline{NU}$

15. $\angle MTU$, $\angle TUN$, $\angle UNM$, and $\angle NMT$ are right angles.

17. $\overline{MU} \cong \overline{NT}$

19.

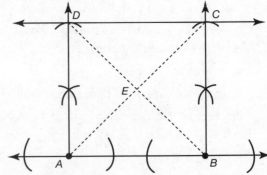

21.

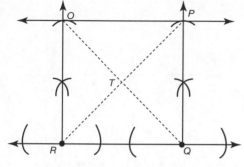

23.

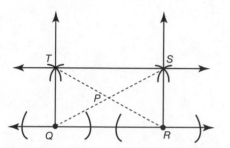

25. You are given square *ABCD* with diagonals $\overline{AC}$ and $\overline{DB}$. By definition of a square, $\angle ADC$ and $\angle BCD$ are right angles. Because all right angles are congruent, you can conclude that $\angle ADC \cong \angle BCD$. Also by definition of a square, $\overline{AD} \cong \overline{BC}$. By the Reflexive Property, $\overline{DC} \cong \overline{DC}$. Therefore, $\triangle ADC \cong \triangle BCD$ by the SAS Congruence Theorem. So, $\overline{AC} \cong \overline{BD}$ by CPCTC.

27.

Statements	Reasons
1. Square *MNLP* with diagonals $\overline{ML}$ and $\overline{NP}$ intersecting at point *Q*	1. Given
2. $\overline{MN} \cong \overline{PM}$	2. Definition of a square
3. $\overline{PQ} \cong \overline{QN}$	3. Diagonals of a square bisect each other
4. $\overline{MQ} \cong \overline{MQ}$	4. Reflexive Property
5. $\triangle PMQ \cong \triangle NMQ$	5. SSS Congruence Theorem
6. $\angle PQM$ and $\angle NQM$ are supplementary.	6. Definition of Linear Pair
7. $\angle PQM \cong \angle MQN$	7. CPCTC
8. $\angle PQM$ and $\angle MQN$ are right angles.	8. If two angles are supplementary and congruent, then they are right angles.
9. $\overline{ML} \perp \overline{NP}$	9. Definition of perpendicular lines

29.

Statements	Reasons
1. Rect *LMNO* with diagonals $\overline{LN}$ and $\overline{OM}$ intersecting at point *K*	1. Given
2. $\overline{LO} \cong \overline{MN}$	2. Opposite sides of a rectangle are congruent.
3. $\angle LKO \cong \angle MKN$	3. Vertical Angle Theorem
4. $\overline{LM}$ perpendicular to $\overline{LO}$ and $\overline{LO}$ perpendicular to $\overline{ON}$	4. Definition of perpendicular lines
5. $\overline{LO}$ parallel to $\overline{MN}$	5. Perpendicular/Parallel Line Theorem
6. $\angle OLN \cong \angle MNL$ $\angle LOM \cong \angle NMO$	6. Alternate Interior Angle Theorem
7. $\triangle OLK \cong \triangle MNK$	7. AAS Congruence Theorem
8. $\overline{LK} \cong \overline{NK}$ $\overline{OK} \cong \overline{MK}$	8. CPCTC

LESSON 7.2

1. $\overline{MN} \cong \overline{LP}$ and $\overline{ML} \cong \overline{NP}$

3. $\overline{MN} \parallel \overline{LP}$ and $\overline{ML} \parallel \overline{NP}$

5. $\overline{UV} \cong \overline{VW} \cong \overline{WX} \cong \overline{XU}$

7. $\overline{UV} \parallel \overline{XW}$ and $\overline{UX} \parallel \overline{VW}$

9.

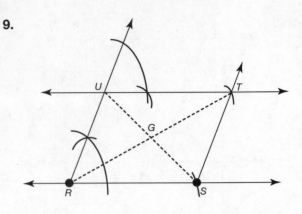

11.

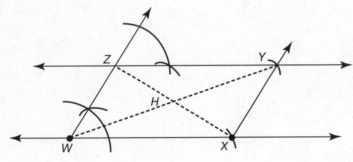

13.

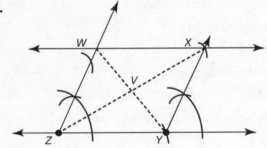

15. $\overline{XY} \cong \overline{ZW}$

17. $\overline{MN} \parallel \overline{PQ}$

19. $\overline{ST} \cong \overline{VU}$

21. We are given parallelogram *ABCD* with diagonals $\overline{AC}$ and $\overline{DB}$. By definition of a parallelogram, $\overline{AB} \parallel \overline{CD}$ and $\overline{AD} \parallel \overline{BC}$. So, $\angle ABD \cong \angle CDB$ and $\angle ADB \cong \angle DBC$ by the Alternate Interior Angle Theorem. By the Reflexive Property, $\overline{DB} \cong \overline{DB}$. Therefore, $\triangle ABD \cong \triangle CDB$ by the ASA Congruence Theorem. So, $\angle BAD \cong \angle DCB$ by CPCTC.

23. We are given parallelogram *HIJK* with diagonals $\overline{HJ}$ and $\overline{KI}$. By definition of a parallelogram, $\overline{HI} \parallel \overline{KJ}$ and $\overline{HK} \parallel \overline{IJ}$.
By the Alternate Interior Angle Theorem, $\angle JHK \cong \angle HJI$ and $\angle IHJ \cong \angle HJK$. By the Reflexive Property, $\overline{HJ} \cong \overline{HJ}$. Therefore, $\triangle KHJ \cong \triangle IJH$ by the Angle Side Angle Congruence Theorem. It follows that $\overline{HI} \cong \overline{KJ}$ and $\overline{HK} \cong \overline{IJ}$ by CPCTC, or opposite sides of the parallelogram are congruent.

25.

Statements	Reasons
1. Rhombus *PQRS* with diagonals $\overline{PR}$ and $\overline{SQ}$ intersecting at point *A*	1. Given
2. $\overline{PQ} \cong \overline{QR} \cong \overline{RS} \cong \overline{SP}$	2. Definition of a rhombus
3. $\overline{PR} \cong \overline{PR}$	3. Reflexive Property
4. $\triangle PQR \cong \triangle PSR$	4. SSS Congruence Theorem
5. $\overline{QS} \cong \overline{QS}$	5. Reflexive Property
6. $\triangle QPS \cong \triangle QRS$	6. SSS Congruence Theorem
7. $\angle QPR \cong \angle SPR$, $\angle QRP \cong \angle SRP$, $\angle PSQ \cong \angle RSQ$, and $\angle PQS \cong \angle RQS$	7. CPCTC

27. Opposite angles are congruent in a parallelogram, so both pairs of opposite angles must be congruent.

29. All rhombi have the properties of a parallelogram, so every rhombus must be a parallelogram. Penny is correct.

31. He could measure the lengths of the four sides of the quadrilateral. If opposite sides are the same length then the quadrilateral is a parallelogram.

LESSON 7.3

1. $\overline{PQ} \cong \overline{QS}$ and $\overline{PR} \cong \overline{SR}$

3. $\overline{PT} \cong \overline{ST}$

5. The bases are $\overline{UV}$ and $\overline{WX}$.

7. The legs are $\overline{UX}$ and $\overline{VW}$.

9.

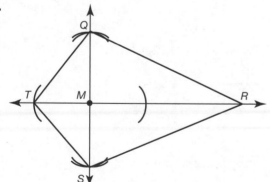

11.

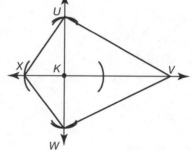

13.

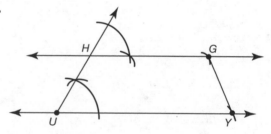

15. $\overline{AB}$ and $\overline{CB}$ are congruent.
$\overline{AD}$ and $\overline{CD}$ are congruent.

17. Triangle *IKL* and triangle *IJL* are both isosceles triangles.

19. $\angle QPS$ and $\angle QRS$ are congruent.
$\angle RQS$ and $\angle PQS$ are congruent.
$\angle RSQ$ and $\angle PSQ$ are congruent.

21. $\overline{AC}$ and $\overline{BD}$ are congruent.

23. The bases are $\overline{IL}$ and $\overline{JK}$.

25. $\overline{PR} \cong \overline{QS}$

27. You are given kite *ABCD* with diagonals $\overline{BD}$ and $\overline{AC}$ intersecting at point *E*. By definition of a kite, we know that $\overline{AB} \cong \overline{AD}$ and $\overline{BC} \cong \overline{CD}$. By the Reflexive Property, you know that $\overline{AC} \cong \overline{AC}$. Therefore, $\triangle ABC \cong \triangle ADC$ by the SSS Congruence Theorem. So, $\angle ABC \cong \angle ADC$ by CPCTC.

29. You are given kite *WYZX* with diagonals $\overline{XY}$ and $\overline{WZ}$ intersecting at point *P*. By definition of a kite, we know that $\overline{WX} \cong \overline{WY}$ and $\overline{XZ} \cong \overline{YZ}$. By the Reflexive Property, you know that $\overline{WZ} \cong \overline{WZ}$. Therefore, $\triangle WXZ \cong \triangle WYZ$ by the SSS Congruence Theorem. So, $\angle XWZ \cong \angle YWZ$ and $\angle XZW \cong \angle YZW$ by CPCTC. By definition of a bisector, $\overline{WZ}$ bisects $\angle XWY$ and $\angle XZY$.

31.

Statements	Reasons
1. Isosceles trapezoid *JKLM* with $\overline{KJ} \cong \overline{LM}$	1. Given
2. $\overline{KL} \parallel \overline{JM}$	2. Definition of a trapezoid
3. $\angle L$ is supplementary to $\angle M$ $\angle K$ is supplementary to $\angle J$	3. Same-side alternate interior angles between parallel lines are supplementary.
4. Construct $\overline{KN} \parallel \overline{LM}$	4. Construction
5. Quadrilateral *KLMN* is a parallelogram.	5. Definition of a parallelogram
6. $\overline{KN} \cong \overline{LM}$	6. Opposite sides of a parallelogram are congruent.
7. $\overline{KJ} \cong \overline{KN}$	7. Transitive Property
8. $\triangle JKN$ is isosceles	8. Definition of an isosceles triangle
9. $\angle J \cong \angle KNJ$	9. Base angles in an isosceles triangle are congruent.
10. $\angle LKN \cong \angle KNJ$	10. Alternate Interior Angles Theorem
11. $\angle J \cong \angle LKN$	11. Transitive Property
12. $\angle LKN \cong \angle M$	12. Opposite angles in a parallelogram are congruent.
13. $\angle J \cong \angle M$	13. Transitive Property
14. $\angle K \cong \angle L$	14. Supplements of congruent angles are congruent.

33.

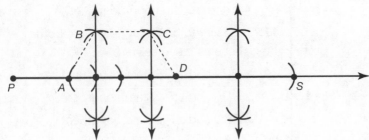

35.

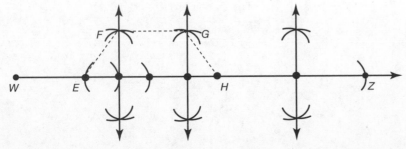

37.

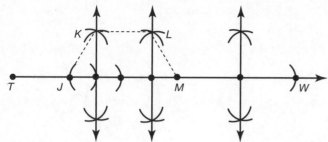

39. The area of the kite is 75 square inches.

41. Magda is incorrect. Parallelograms have two pairs of parallel sides. Trapezoids have exactly one pair of parallel sides. A trapezoid is not a parallelogram.

43. Each of the shorter sides is 14 centimeters.

LESSON 7.4

1.

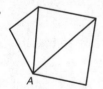

2 triangles

3.

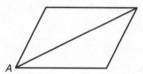

6 triangles

5.

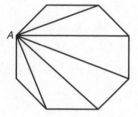

3 triangles

7. The sum of the interior angles is 360°.

9. The sum of the interior angles is 720°.

11. The sum of the interior angles is 1080°.

13. The sum of the interior angles of the polygon is 1080°.

15. The sum of the interior angles of the polygon is 1980°.

17. The sum of the interior angles of the polygon is 3240°.

19. 8 sides

21. 5 sides

23. 23 sides

25. The measure of each interior angle is 135°.

27. The measure of each interior angle is 120°.

29. The measure of each interior angle is 108°.

31. The regular polygon has 5 sides.

33. The regular polygon has 18 sides.

35. The regular polygon has 10 sides.

LESSON 7.5

1.

3.

5.

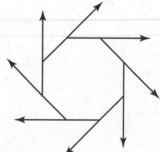

7. 360°

9. 360°

11. 360°

13. 90°

15. 72°

17. 65°

19. 90°

21. 60°

23. 36°

25. 8 sides

27. 10 sides

29. 9 sides

LESSON 7.6

1. square and rhombus

3. kite

5. parallelogram, rectangle, rhombus, and square

7. rhombus, parallelogram, quadrilateral

9. kite, quadrilateral

11. square, rectangle, rhombus, parallelogram, quadrilateral

13. Rectangle.

15. Rhombus.

17. Quadrilateral.

19.
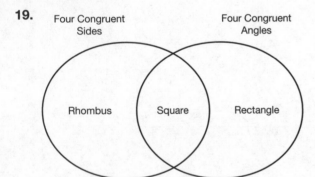

21.
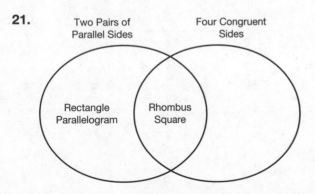

23.
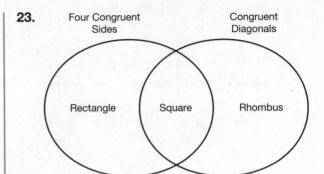

25. False.

27. False.

29. True.

31. 1. Duplicate $\overline{HJ}$ and bisect it to find the midpoint.
  2. Duplicate $\overline{HJ}$ again, labeling it $\overline{IK}$, and bisecting it to find the midpoint.
  3. Draw segments $\overline{HJ}$ and $\overline{IK}$ so that their midpoints intersect.
  4. Connect the endpoints of the segments to form rectangle *HIJK*.

33. 1. Duplicate $\overline{RS}$.
  2. Construct a perpendicular segment to $\overline{RS}$ such that $\overline{RS}$ bisects the perpendicular segment.
  3. Label the perpendicular segment $\overline{TU}$.
  4. Connect the endpoints of the two segments to form kite *RSTU*.

35. 1. Duplicate $\overline{JL}$ and bisect it to find the midpoint.
  2. Draw a segment $\overline{KM}$, and bisect it to find the midpoint.
  3. Draw segments $\overline{JL}$ and $\overline{KM}$ so that their midpoints intersect.
  4. Connect the endpoints of the segments to form parallelogram *JKLM*.

Chapter 8

LESSON 8.1

1. $\dfrac{\text{opposite}}{\text{hypotenuse}} = \dfrac{6}{10} = \dfrac{3}{5}$

3. $\dfrac{\text{opposite}}{\text{hypotenuse}} = \dfrac{15}{17}$

5. $\dfrac{\text{opposite}}{\text{hypotenuse}} = \dfrac{12}{15} = \dfrac{4}{5}$

7. $\dfrac{\text{adjacent}}{\text{hypotenuse}} = \dfrac{20}{25} = \dfrac{4}{5}$

9. $\dfrac{\text{adjacent}}{\text{hypotenuse}} = \dfrac{4.8}{5.0} = \dfrac{24}{25}$

11. $\dfrac{\text{adjacent}}{\text{hypotenuse}} = \dfrac{1.0}{2.6} = \dfrac{5}{13}$

13. $\dfrac{\text{opposite}}{\text{hypotenuse}} = \dfrac{18}{30} = \dfrac{3}{5}$

$\dfrac{\text{adjacent}}{\text{hypotenuse}} = \dfrac{24}{30} = \dfrac{4}{5}$

$\dfrac{\text{opposite}}{\text{adjacent}} = \dfrac{18}{24} = \dfrac{3}{4}$

15. $\dfrac{\text{opposite}}{\text{hypotenuse}} = \dfrac{24}{51} = \dfrac{8}{17}$

$\dfrac{\text{adjacent}}{\text{hypotenuse}} = \dfrac{45}{51} = \dfrac{15}{17}$

$\dfrac{\text{opposite}}{\text{adjacent}} = \dfrac{24}{45} = \dfrac{8}{15}$

17. $\dfrac{\text{opposite}}{\text{hypotenuse}} = \dfrac{5}{\sqrt{2}}$ or $\dfrac{5\sqrt{2}}{2}$

$\dfrac{\text{adjacent}}{\text{hypotenuse}} = \dfrac{5}{\sqrt{2}}$ or $\dfrac{5\sqrt{2}}{2}$

$\dfrac{\text{opposite}}{\text{adjacent}} = \dfrac{5}{5} = 1$

19. In $\triangle ABC$, $\dfrac{\text{opposite}}{\text{hypotenuse}} = \dfrac{3}{5}$.

In $\triangle ADE$, $\dfrac{\text{opposite}}{\text{hypotenuse}} = \dfrac{6}{10} = \dfrac{3}{5}$.

21. In $\triangle ABC$, $\dfrac{\text{opposite}}{\text{hypotenuse}} = \dfrac{10}{10\sqrt{2}} = \dfrac{1}{\sqrt{2}}$ or $\dfrac{\sqrt{2}}{2}$.

In $\triangle ADE$, $\dfrac{\text{opposite}}{\text{hypotenuse}} = \dfrac{25}{25\sqrt{2}} = \dfrac{1}{\sqrt{2}}$ or $\dfrac{\sqrt{2}}{2}$.

23. In $\triangle ABC$, $\dfrac{\text{opposite}}{\text{adjacent}} = \dfrac{8}{15}$.

In $\triangle ADE$, $\dfrac{\text{opposite}}{\text{adjacent}} = \dfrac{24}{45} = \dfrac{8}{15}$.

LESSON 8.2

1. $\tan B = \dfrac{2}{2} = 1$

3. $\tan C = \dfrac{25}{20} = \dfrac{5}{4}$

5. $\tan D = \dfrac{2\sqrt{2}}{15}$

7. $\cot A = \dfrac{4}{3}$

9. $\cot F = \dfrac{7}{15}$

11. $\cot A = \dfrac{4\sqrt{2}}{4\sqrt{2}} = 1$

13. 0.58

15. 1.73

17. 3.73

19. 0.58

21. 1

23. 5.67

25. $x \approx 1.68$ ft

27. $x \approx 41.21$ m

29. $x \approx 1.55$ yd

31. $m\angle X \approx 29.05°$

33. $m\angle X \approx 58.52°$

35. $m\angle X \approx 72.98°$

37. $N \approx 19.10$ mi

39. $h \approx 1715.51$ ft

41. The angle formed by the ramp and the ground is approximately 11.77°.

43. The lifeguard is looking down at an angle of approximately 68.07°.

LESSON 8.3

1. $\sin B = \dfrac{3\sqrt{3}}{6} = \dfrac{\sqrt{3}}{2}$

3. $\sin C = \dfrac{25}{35} = \dfrac{5}{7}$

5. $\sin D = \dfrac{3}{36\sqrt{3}} = \dfrac{\sqrt{3}}{36}$

7. $\csc A = \dfrac{12}{8} = \dfrac{3}{2}$

9. $\csc F = \dfrac{25}{15} = \dfrac{5}{3}$

11. $\csc P = \dfrac{4\sqrt{2}}{3\sqrt{3}} = \dfrac{4\sqrt{6}}{9}$

13. 0.5

15. 0.87

17. 0.97

19. 1.41

21. 1.15

23. 3.86

25. $x \approx 1.29$ ft

27. $x \approx 43.86$ m

29. $x \approx 7.85$ yd

31. $m\angle X \approx 32.23°$

33. $m\angle X \approx 60°$

35. $m\angle X \approx 53.13°$

37. $N \approx 3.71$ mi

39. $l \approx 20.92$ ft

41. The angle formed by the string and the ground is approximately 26.74°.

43. The angle formed by the bleachers and the ground is approximately 19.47°.

LESSON 8.4

1. $\cos B = \dfrac{3\sqrt{3}}{6} = \dfrac{\sqrt{3}}{2}$

3. $\cos C = \dfrac{25}{35} = \dfrac{5}{7}$

5. $\cos D = \dfrac{3}{36\sqrt{3}} = \dfrac{\sqrt{3}}{36}$

7. $\sec A = \dfrac{12}{8} = \dfrac{3}{2}$

9. $\sec F = \dfrac{25}{20} = \dfrac{5}{4}$

11. $\sec P = \dfrac{3\sqrt{5}}{6} = \dfrac{\sqrt{5}}{2}$

13. 0.87

15. 0.5

17. 0.26

19. $\dfrac{1}{\cos(45°)} = 1.41$

21. $\dfrac{1}{\cos(75°)} = 3.86$

23. $\dfrac{1}{\cos(15°)} = 1.04$

25. $x \approx 1.53$ ft

27. $x \approx 15.96$ m

29. $x \approx 3.66$ yd

31. $m\angle X \approx 51.32°$

33. $m\angle X \approx 70.53°$

35. $m\angle X \approx 22.02°$

37. $E \approx 3949.05$ ft

39. $s \approx 124.23$ ft

41. The angle formed by the rope and the dock is approximately 55.15°.

43. The base of the ladder is approximately 5.81 feet from the edge of the house.

LESSON 8.5

1. $\sin \angle A = \dfrac{a}{c}$

$\cos \angle B = \dfrac{a}{c}$

3. $\sec \angle N = \dfrac{p}{m}$

$\csc \angle M = \dfrac{p}{m}$

5. $\sin \angle Y = \dfrac{y}{z}$

$\cos \angle X = \dfrac{y}{z}$

7. I would use the sine ratio because the hypotenuse is given and the length of the side opposite the given angle needs to be determined.

9. I would use the secant ratio because the side adjacent to the given angle is given and the length of the hypotenuse needs to be determined.

11. I would use the tangent ratio because the side adjacent to the given angle is given and the length of the side opposite the given angle needs to be determined.

13. $h \approx 61.59$ ft

15. $d \approx 3865.89$ ft

17. $h = 50$ in.

19. $d \approx 2.34$ ft

21. $d \approx 37.06$ ft

23. $d \approx 15.43$ ft

25. $d \approx 1790.03$ ft

27. $l \approx 32.36$ ft

LESSON 8.6

1. The area of the triangle is approximately 139.9 square centimeters.

3. The area of the triangle is approximately 36.3 square centimeters.

5. The area of the triangle is approximately 379.3 square centimeters.

7. $x \approx 9.2$ cm

9. $x \approx 15.8$ cm

11. $x \approx 20.3$ in.

13. $m\angle B \approx 47.6°$

15. $m\angle B \approx 35.4°$

17. $m\angle B \approx 36.9°$

19. $b \approx 4.7$ in.

21. $a \approx 4.8$ cm

23. $a \approx 25.4$ in.

Chapter 9

LESSON 9.1

1. Point O is the center of the circle.
3. Line AB is a tangent.
5. Segment JH is a chord.
7. Angle SQR is an inscribed angle.
9. Angle URE is an inscribed angle.
11. Angle KOM is a central angle.
13. Angle MOU is a central angle.
15. Arc AC is a minor arc.
17. Arc FHI is a major arc.
19. Arc NPQ is a semicircle.

21.
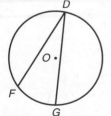

23.
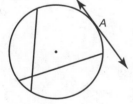

25.
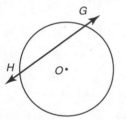

27.
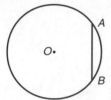

LESSON 9.2

1. The measure of $\overset{\frown}{AB}$ is 90°.
3. The measure of $\overset{\frown}{EF}$ is 45°.
5. The measure of $\overset{\frown}{IJ}$ is 120°.
7. $m\angle XYZ = 80°$
9. $m\angle LKJ = 128°$
11. $m\angle KWS = 70°$
13. $m\angle XYZ = 75°$
15. $m\angle KLS = 56°$
17. $m\angle QBR = 77.5°$
19. $m\overset{\frown}{KM} = 108°$
21. $m\overset{\frown}{QW} = 162°$
23. $m\overset{\frown}{ME} = 104°$
25. $m\angle ACB = 31°$
27. $m\angle EFG = 64°$
29. $m\angle JIK = 84°$
31. $m\overset{\frown}{WY} = 86°$
33. $m\angle WCX = 103°$
35. $m\angle XCZ = 83°$

LESSON 9.3

1. $m\angle RPM = \frac{1}{2}\left(m\overset{\frown}{RM} + m\overset{\frown}{QN}\right)$
3. $m\angle JNK = \frac{1}{2}\left(m\overset{\frown}{LM} + m\overset{\frown}{JK}\right)$
5. $m\angle SWT = \frac{1}{2}\left(m\overset{\frown}{ST} + m\overset{\frown}{VU}\right)$
7. $\overset{\frown}{NP}, \overset{\frown}{QR}$
9. $\overset{\frown}{FIH}, \overset{\frown}{GF}$
11. $\overset{\frown}{BZD}$
13. $m\angle DAC = \frac{1}{2}\left(m\overset{\frown}{DEC} - m\overset{\frown}{BC}\right)$
15. $m\angle SRT = \frac{1}{2}\left(m\overset{\frown}{SVT} - m\overset{\frown}{SU}\right)$
17. $m\angle ECG = \frac{1}{2}\left(m\overset{\frown}{EHG} - m\overset{\frown}{DF}\right)$

19.

Statements	Reasons
1. Chords $\overline{AE}$ and $\overline{BD}$ intersect at point C.	1. Given
2. Draw chord $\overline{AD}$	2. Construction
3. $m\angle ACB = m\angle D + m\angle A$	3. Exterior Angle Theorem
4. $m\angle A = \frac{1}{2} m\widehat{DE}$	4. Inscribed Angle Theorem
5. $m\angle D = \frac{1}{2} m\widehat{AB}$	5. Inscribed Angle Theorem
6. $m\angle ACB = \frac{1}{2} m\widehat{DE} + \frac{1}{2} m\widehat{AB}$	6. Substitution
7. $m\angle ACB = \frac{1}{2}\left(m\widehat{AB} + m\widehat{DE}\right)$	7. Distributive Property

21.

Statements	Reasons
1. Tangents $\overleftrightarrow{VY}$ and tangent $\overleftrightarrow{XY}$ intersect at point Y.	1. Given
2. Draw chord $\overline{VX}$	2. Construction
3. $m\angle VXB = m\angle Y + m\angle YVX$	3. Exterior Angle Theorem
4. $m\angle Y = m\angle VXB - m\angle YVX$	4. Subtraction Property of Equality
5. $m\angle VXB = \frac{1}{2} m\widehat{VWX}$	5. Exterior Angle of a Circle Theorem
6. $m\angle YVX = \frac{1}{2} m\widehat{VX}$	6. Exterior Angle of a Circle Theorem
7. $m\angle Y = \frac{1}{2} m\widehat{VWX} - \frac{1}{2} m\widehat{VX}$	7. Substitution
8. $m\angle Y = \frac{1}{2}\left(m\widehat{VWX} - m\widehat{VX}\right)$	8. Distributive Property

23.

Statements	Reasons
1. Secant $\overleftrightarrow{JL}$ and tangent $\overleftrightarrow{NL}$ intersect at point L.	1. Given
2. Draw chord $\overline{JM}$	2. Construction
3. $m\angle JMN = m\angle MJL + m\angle L$	3. Exterior Angle Theorem
4. $m\angle L = m\angle JMN - m\angle MJL$	4. Subtraction Property of Equality
5. $m\angle JMN = \frac{1}{2} m\widehat{JM}$	5. Exterior Angle of a Circle Theorem
6. $m\angle MJL = \frac{1}{2} m\widehat{KM}$	6. Inscribed Angle Theorem
7. $m\angle L = \frac{1}{2} m\widehat{JM} - \frac{1}{2} m\widehat{KM}$	7. Substitution
8. $m\angle L = \frac{1}{2}\left(m\widehat{JM} - m\widehat{KM}\right)$	8. Distributive Property

25. The measure of arc FI is 120 degrees.

27. The measure of angle X is 17.5 degrees.

29. The measure of arc RS is 130 degrees.

LESSON 9.4

1. The angle of intersection is 90° because diameters that bisect chords are perpendicular bisectors.

3. The measure of $\overset{\frown}{KL}$ is equal to the measure of $\overset{\frown}{LM}$ because a diameter that intersects a chord at a right angle bisects the arc formed by the chord.

5. Chords $\overline{TU}$ and $\overline{XV}$ are congruent because chords that are the same distance from the center of the circle are congruent.

7. $EC = EA = 5$ cm

9. $CD = AB = 24$ cm

11. $m\angle DOC = m\angle AOB = 155°$

13. The measure of $\overset{\frown}{DE}$ is equal to the measure of $\overset{\frown}{FG}$ because the corresponding arcs of congruent chords are congruent.

15. The measure of $\overset{\frown}{QPR}$ is equal to the measure of $\overset{\frown}{PRS}$ because the corresponding arcs of congruent chords are congruent.

17. Segment AB is congruent to segment DC because the corresponding chords of congruent arcs are congruent.

19. $DG \cdot GJ = FG \cdot GH$

21. $TK \cdot KB = AK \cdot KV$

23. $EY \cdot YU = IY \cdot YA$

LESSON 9.5

1. The measure of angle OAB is 90 degrees because a tangent line and the radius that ends at the point of tangency are perpendicular.

3. The measure of angle XYO is 90 degrees because a tangent line and the radius that ends at the point of tangency are perpendicular.

5. The measure of angle TOU is 67 degrees.

7. $\overline{AC} \cong \overline{CB}$

9. $\overline{RS} \cong \overline{RT}$

11. $\overline{DE} \cong \overline{EF}$

13. The measure of angle EGF is 58 degrees.

15. The measure of angle KML is 54 degrees.

17. The measure of angle AVF is 79 degrees.

19. Secant segments: $\overline{PT}$ and $\overline{QT}$
    External secant segments: $\overline{RT}$ and $\overline{ST}$

21. Secant segments: $\overline{WU}$ and $\overline{UY}$
    External secant segments: $\overline{UV}$ and $\overline{UX}$

23. Secant segments: $\overline{FJ}$ and $\overline{GJ}$
    External secant segments: $\overline{HJ}$ and $\overline{IJ}$

25. $RV \cdot TV = SV \cdot UV$

27. $AD \cdot AB = AE \cdot AC$

29. $FA \cdot CA = EA \cdot BA$

31. Tangent segment: $\overline{TU}$
    Secant segment: $\overline{RT}$
    External secant segment: $\overline{ST}$

33. Tangent segment: $\overline{FD}$
    Secant segment: $\overline{FE}$
    External secant segment: $\overline{FG}$

35. Tangent segment: $\overline{EF}$
    Secant segment: $\overline{FH}$
    External secant segment: $\overline{FG}$

37. $(EM)^2 = QM \cdot WM$

39. $(ZG)^2 = ZI \cdot ZX$

41. $(VW)^2 = WU \cdot WE$

Chapter 10

LESSON 10.1

1. No. The triangle is not a right triangle.

3. Yes. The triangle is a right triangle.

5. Yes. The triangle is a right triangle.

7. No. The triangle is not a right triangle.

9. $m\angle B = 35°$

11. $m\angle A = 28°$

13. $m\angle A = 41°$

15. $m\angle D = 99°$

17. $m\angle D = 68°$

19. $m\angle C = 108°$

21.

23.

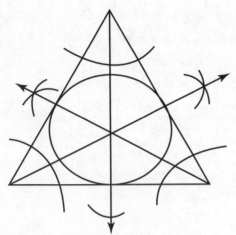

25.

27.

Statements	Reasons
1. $m\widehat{AC} = 40°$, $m\widehat{BC} = 140°$	1. Given
2. $m\widehat{AC} + m\widehat{BC} + m\widehat{AB} = 360°$	2. Arc Addition Postulate
3. $40° + 140° + m\widehat{AB} = 360°$	3. Substitution
4. $m\widehat{AB} = 180°$	4. Subtraction Property of Equality
5. $m\angle C = \frac{1}{2}m\widehat{AB}$	5. Definition of inscribed angle
6. $m\angle C = 90°$	6. Substitution
7. $\triangle ABC$ is a right triangle with right angle C.	7. Definition of right triangle
8. $\overline{AB}$ is the diameter of circle O.	8. Converse of Inscribed Right Triangle-Diameter Theorem

29.

Statements	Reasons
1. Inscribed quad $ABCD$ in circle O, $m\overset{\frown}{AB} = 50°$, $m\overset{\frown}{BC} = 90°$	1. Given
2. $m\overset{\frown}{AB} + m\overset{\frown}{BC} = m\overset{\frown}{ABC}$	2. Angle Addition Postulate
3. $50° + 90° = m\overset{\frown}{ABC}$	3. Substitution
4. $140° = m\overset{\frown}{ABC}$	4. Addition Property of Equality
5. $m\angle D = \frac{1}{2} m\overset{\frown}{ABC}$	5. Inscribed angle
6. $m\angle D = \frac{1}{2}(140°) = 70°$	6. Substitution
7. $\angle D$ and $\angle B$ are supplementary	7. Inscribed Quadrilateral-Opposite Angles Theorem
8. $m\angle D + m\angle B = 180°$	8. Definition of supplementary
9. $70° + m\angle B = 180°$	9. Substitution
10. $m\angle B = 110°$	10. Subtraction Property of Equality

31.

Statements	Reasons
1. $m\overset{\frown}{AB} + m\overset{\frown}{BC} + m\overset{\frown}{CD} + m\overset{\frown}{AD} = 360°$	1. $\overset{\frown}{AB}$, $\overset{\frown}{BC}$, $\overset{\frown}{CD}$, and $\overset{\frown}{AD}$ form the circle
2. $50° + 90° + 90° + m\overset{\frown}{AD} = 360°$	2. Substitution
3. $230° + m\overset{\frown}{AD} = 360°$	3. Addition
4. $m\overset{\frown}{AD} = 130°$	4. Subtraction Property of Equality
5. $m\angle BCD = \frac{1}{2} m\overset{\frown}{BAD}$	5. Definition of measure of inscribed angle
6. $m\angle BCD = \frac{1}{2}(m\overset{\frown}{AB} + m\overset{\frown}{AD})$	6. Substitution Property of Equality
7. $m\angle BCD = \frac{1}{2}(50° + 130°)$	7. Substitution Property of Equality
8. $m\angle BCD = \frac{1}{2}(180°)$	8. Addition
9. $m\angle BCD = 90°$	9. Multiplication

LESSON 10.2

1. The arc is $\frac{1}{9}$ of the circle's circumference.

3. The arc is $\frac{1}{3}$ of the circle's circumference.

5. The arc is $\frac{7}{24}$ of the circle's circumference.

7. $\frac{80}{360} \cdot 2\pi(15)$

9. $\frac{90}{360} \cdot 2\pi(17)$

11. $\frac{180}{360} \cdot 2\pi(31.5)$

13. The arc length of $\overset{\frown}{AB}$ is 3π meters.

15. The arc length of $\overset{\frown}{EF}$ is $\frac{8}{3}\pi$ inches.

17. The arc length of $\overset{\frown}{IJ}$ is $\frac{20\pi}{9}$ cm.

19. The arc length of $\overset{\frown}{MN}$ is $\frac{25}{6}\pi$ mm.

21. The arc length of $\overset{\frown}{AB}$ is 12π cm.

23. The arc length of $\overset{\frown}{EF}$ is 15π in.

25. The arc length of $\overset{\frown}{IJ}$ is $\frac{32}{9}\pi$ cm.

27. The arc length of $\overset{\frown}{MN}$ is $\frac{55}{9}\pi$ cm.

29. 91.4 mm

31. 314.2 ft

33. The radius of the flag pole is about 1 inch.

35. $s = \pi$

37. $s = 4\pi$

39. Arc length $= \frac{160\pi}{9}$ mm

LESSON 10.3

1. The area of sector *AOB* is 27π cm².

3. The area of sector *EOF* is $\frac{75}{4}\pi$ ft².

5. The area of sector *IOJ* is $\frac{256}{5}\pi$ cm².

7. The area of sector *MON* is 216π cm².

9. The area of the shaded segment is approximately 10.3 cm².

11. The area of the shaded segment is approximately 82.4 ft².

13. The area of the shaded segment is approximately 178.1 m².

15. The length of the radius is 8 feet.

17. The length of the radius is 2 meters.

19. The length of the radius is 22 feet.

LESSON 10.4

1. $m\angle EAD = 155°$
   $m\angle CAD = 25°$

3. $m\angle A = 25°$

5. $m\angle C = 75°$

7. $A \approx 3.14$ square centimeters

9. $A \approx 0.35$ square meters

11. $A \approx 25.12$ square centimeters

13. Area of segment $\approx 7.07 - 4.5 \approx 2.57$ square inches

15. Area of segment $\approx 2.09 - 1.73 \approx 0.36$ square centimeters

17. $v = 6$ cm/sec

19. $v = 0.35$ in./sec

21. $v = \frac{5}{24}$ ft/sec

Chapter 11

LESSON 11.1

1. sphere

3. cylinder

5. cone

7. The base of the rectangle is equal to the radius of the cylinder's base.

9. The radius of the circle is equal to the radius of the sphere.

11. Half the width of the square is equal to the radius of the cylinder's base.

LESSON 11.2

1. right triangle; right triangular prism

3. square; square prism

5. rectangle; rectangular prism

7. cylinder

9. triangular prism

11. rectangular prism

13. cone

15. triangular pyramid

17. rectangular pyramid

19. The lengths of the sides of the triangle are the same as the lengths of the sides of the base of the triangular prism. The triangular prism was made by stacking congruent triangles.

21. The radius of the circle is the same as the radius of the base of the cone. The cone was made by stacking similar circles.

23. The lengths of the sides of the rectangle are the same as the lengths of the sides of the base of the rectangular prism. The rectangular prism was made by stacking congruent rectangles.

LESSON 11.3

1. I determined that the area is approximately 300 square yards.

3. volume ≈ 31.4 cubic centimeters

LESSON 11.4

1. volume ≈ 83.73 cubic centimeters

3. volume ≈ 113.04 cubic inches

5. volume ≈ 2355 cubic meters

7. volume ≈ 170.08 cubic centimeters

9. volume ≈ 148.37 cubic feet

11. Volume $= 300$ cubic inches

13. Volume ≈ 179.67 cubic centimeters

15. Volume $= 6600$ cubic feet

17. Volume = 20,286 cubic inches

19. Volume ≈ 416,666.67 cubic yards

LESSON 11.5

1. Volume ≈ 1436.0 cubic meters

3. Volume ≈ 4186.7 cubic inches

5. Volume ≈ 65.4 cubic centimeters

7. Volume ≈ 2143.6 cubic meters

9. Volume ≈ 4186.7 cubic centimeters

LESSON 11.6

1. V = 15 cubic meters

3. V = 40 cubic inches

5. V = 40 cubic feet

7. V ≈ 664.9 cubic meters

9. V ≈ 1570 cubic meters

11. V ≈ 301.4 cubic millimeters

13. V ≈ 763.0 cubic meters

15. V ≈ 157 cubic millimeters

17. V ≈ 512.9 cubic feet

19. V ≈ 100.5 cubic meters

21. V ≈ 75.4 cubic inches

23. V ≈ 3052.08 cubic inches

25. V ≈ 1436.03 cubic millimeters

LESSON 11.7

1. The cross section is a rectangle.

3. The cross section is a rectangle.

5. The cross section is a great circle.

7. The cross section is a rectangle.

9. The cross section is a triangle.

11.

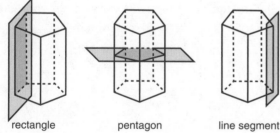

circle   rectangle   ellipse

13.

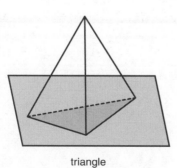

rectangle   pentagon   line segment

15.

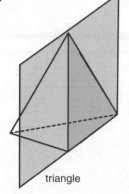

triangle   triangle   triangle

17. A cross section that is parallel to the base is a hexagon congruent to the hexagonal bases. A cross section that is perpendicular to the base is a rectangle.

19. A cross section that is parallel to the base is a triangle similar to the triangle base.
A cross section that is perpendicular to the base, but not parallel to any of the sides of the base is a triangle.
A cross section that is perpendicular to the base and parallel to one of the sides of the base is a trapezoid.

21. A cross section that is parallel to the base is a circle congruent to the circular bases.
A cross section that is perpendicular to the base is a rectangle.

23. A cross section that is parallel to the base is a pentagon congruent to the pentagonal bases.
A cross section that is perpendicular to the base is a rectangle.

25. The solid is a cone. (The solid could also be a cylinder.)

27. The solid is a pentagonal prism. (The solid could also be a pentagonal pyramid.)

29. The solid is a rectangular pyramid. (The solid could also be a cone.)

LESSON 11.8

1.

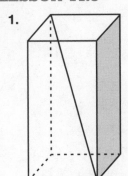

3.

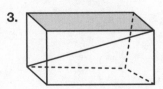

5.

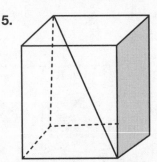

7. The length of the diagonal of the rectangular solid is about 12.33 inches.

9. The length of the diagonal of the rectangular solid is about 19.0 centimeters.

11. The length of the diagonal of the rectangular solid is about 16.83 inches.

13.

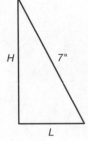
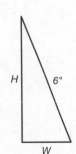

15.

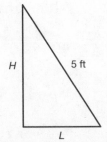
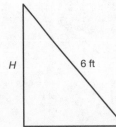
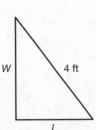

17.

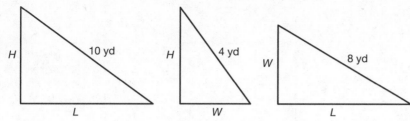

19. The length of the three-dimensional diagonal is $\sqrt{54.5}$ or approximately 7.4 inches.

21. The length of the three-dimensional diagonal is $\sqrt{154}$ or approximately 12.4, feet.

23. The length of the three-dimensional diagonal is $\sqrt{90}$ or approximately 9.5 yards.

25. The diagonal support should be approximately 11.18 feet.

27. The tree will fit in the car. The diagonal length of the car is 85 inches and the height of the tree is 5 feet or 60 inches.

29. A 10-inch stick will not fit inside the box because the diagonal's length is only about 8.8 inches.

Chapter 12

LESSON 12.1

1. $f(x) = x^2 + 3x$

3. $g(s) = s^2 + 4s - 2$

5. $f(n) = 2n^2 - 4n$

7. $-2x^2 + 300x$

9. $-x^2 + 50x$

11. $-2x^2 + 24x$

13. The absolute maximum of the function is at (100, 20,000).

The x-coordinate of 100 represents the width in feet that produces the maximum area.

The y-coordinate of 20,000 represents the maximum area in square feet of the parking lot.

15. The absolute maximum of the function is at about (1.31, 32.56).

The x-coordinate of 1.31 represents the time in seconds after the baseball is thrown that produces the maximum height.

The y-coordinate of 32.56 represents the maximum height in feet of the baseball.

17. The absolute maximum of the function is at (45, 2025).

The x-coordinate of 45 represents the width in feet that produces the maximum area.

The y-coordinate of 2025 represents the maximum area in square feet of the skating rink.

LESSON 12.2

1. The function represented by the graph is a linear function.

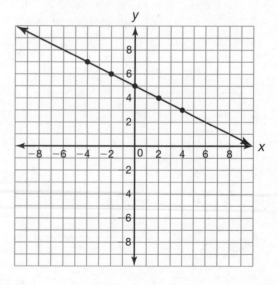

3. The function represented by the graph is a quadratic function.

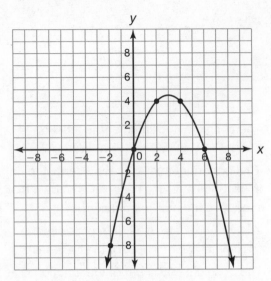

5. The function represented by the graph is a linear function.

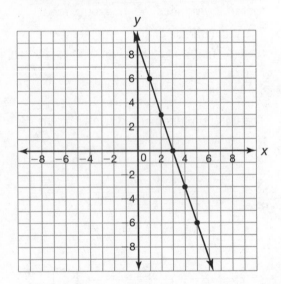

7.

x	y	First Differences	Second Differences
−2	−6		
		3	
−1	−3		0
		3	
0	0		0
		3	
1	3		0
		3	
2	6		

The function represented by the table is a linear function.

9.

x	y	First Differences	Second Differences
−3	3		
		1	
−2	4		0
		1	
−1	5		0
		1	
0	6		0
		1	
1	7		

The function represented by the table is a linear function.

11.

x	y	First Differences	Second Differences
−4	−48		
		21	
−3	−27		−6
		15	
−2	−12		−6
		9	
−1	−3		−6
		3	
0	0		

The function represented by the table is a quadratic function.

1.

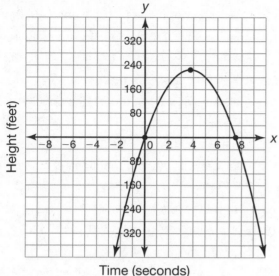

Time (seconds)

Absolute maximum: (3.75, 225)

Zeros: (0, 0), (7.5, 0)

Domain of graph: The domain is all real numbers from negative infinity to positive infinity.

Domain of the problem: The domain is all real numbers greater than or equal to 0 and less than or equal to 7.5.

Range of graph: The range is all real numbers less than or equal to 225.

Range of the problem: The range is all real numbers less than or equal to 225 and greater than or equal to 0.

3.

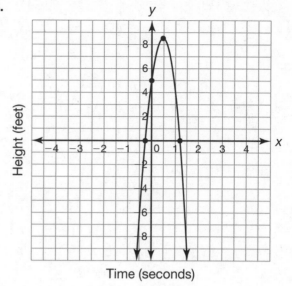

Time (seconds)

Absolute maximum: (0.47, 8.52)

Zeros: (−0.26, 0), (1.20, 0)

Domain of graph: The domain is all real numbers from negative infinity to positive infinity.

Domain of the problem: The domain is all real numbers greater than or equal to 0 and less than or equal to 1.20.

Range of graph: The range is all real numbers less than or equal to 8.52.

Range of the problem: The range is all real numbers less than or equal to 8.52 and greater than or equal to 0.

Answers

5.

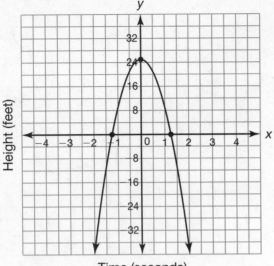

Time (seconds)

Absolute maximum: (0, 25)

Zeros: (−1.25, 0), (1.25, 0)

Domain of graph: The domain is all real numbers from negative infinity to positive infinity.

Domain of the problem: The domain is all real numbers greater than or equal to 0 and less than or equal to 1.25.

Range of graph: The range is all real numbers less than or equal to 25.

Range of the problem: The range is all real numbers less than or equal to 25 and greater than or equal to 0.

7. [−3, 5)

9. (−36, 14]

11. [c, d]

13. Interval of increase: (−3, ∞)

Interval of decrease: (−∞, −3)

15. Interval of increase: (−∞, 1)

Interval of decrease: (1, ∞)

17. Interval of increase: (0, ∞)

Interval of decrease: (−∞, 0)

LESSON 12.4

1. $6(x − 4)$

3. $5(2x + 3)$

5. $−(x + 9)$

7. The x-intercepts are (2, 0) and (8, 0).

9. The x-intercepts are (−4, 0) and (2, 0).

11. The x-intercepts are (−15, 0) and (−5, 0).

13. Answers will vary but functions should be in the form:

$f(x) = a(x + 2)(x − 5)$ for $a < 0$

15. Answers will vary but functions should be in the form:

$f(x) = a(x + 8)(x + 1)$ for $a > 0$

17. Answers will vary but functions should be in the form:

$f(x) = a(x + 5)(x − 2)$ for $a < 0$

19. x-intercepts: (1, 0) and (7, 0)

factored form: $f(x) = (x − 1)(x − 7)$

21. x-intercepts: (−5, 0) and (−15, 0)

factored form: $f(x) = −(x + 5)(x + 15)$

23. x-intercepts: (−4, 0) and (1, 0)

factored form: $f(x) = −3(x + 4)(x − 1)$

25. factored form: $f(x) = 3(x + 6)(x − 2)$

x-intercepts: (−6, 0) and (2, 0)

27. factored form: $f(x) = −2(x − 4)(x − 14)$

x-intercepts: (4, 0) and (14, 0)

29. factored form: $f(x) = (x − 0)(x + 7)$

x-intercepts: (0, 0) and (−7, 0)

LESSON 12.5

1. $h(t) = −16t^2 + 82t + 36$

3. $h(t) = −16t^2 + 110t + 49$

5. $h(t) = −16t^2 + 46t + 25$

7. The vertex of the graph is (2.5, 124).

The axis of symmetry is $x = 2.5$.

9. The vertex of the graph is (2, 104).

The axis of symmetry is $x = 2$.

11. The vertex of the graph is (1.5, 56).

The axis of symmetry is $x = 1.5$.

13. The axis of symmetry is $x = 6$.

15. The axis of symmetry is $x = −7$.

17. The axis of symmetry is $x = −1$.

19. The vertex is (−1, −16).

21. The vertex is (−2, −16).

23. The vertex is (4, 36).

25. Another point on the parabola is (5, 4).

27. Another point on the parabola is (5, 2).

29. Another point on the parabola is (−4, 3).

LESSON 12.6

1. The vertex is (3, 8).

3. The vertex is (1, −8).

5. The vertex is (−9, −1).

7. The vertex is (3, −36).

The function in vertex form is
$f(x) = (x − 3)^2 − 36$.

9. The vertex is (1, −8).

The function in vertex form is
$f(x) = 2(x − 1)^2 − 8$.

11. The vertex is (7.5, 2.25).

The function in vertex form is
$f(x) = −(x − 7.5)^2 + 2.25$.

13. The x-intercepts are (2, 0) and (−4, 0).

The function in factored form is
$f(x) = (x − 2)(x + 4)$.

15. The x-intercepts are (1, 0) and (2, 0).

The function in factored form is
$f(x) = −4(x − 1)(x − 2)$.

17. The x-intercepts are (−2, 0) and (3, 0).

The function in factored form is
$f(x) = \frac{1}{2}(x + 2)(x − 3)$.

19. The function is in vertex form.

The parabola opens up and the vertex is (3, 12).

21. The function is in standard form.

The parabola opens down and the y-intercept is (0, 0).

23. The function is in vertex form.

The parabola opens down and the vertex is (−2, −7).

25. $f(x) = a(x + 1)2 + 4$, for $a < 0$

27. $f(x) = a(x − 3)2 − 2$, for $a > 0$

29. $f(x) = a(x − 5)(x − 12)$, for $a > 0$

LESSON 12.7

1. The graph of $g(x)$ is translated down 5 units.

3. The graph of $g(x)$ is translated up 6 units.

5. The graph of $g(x)$ is translated down 3 units.

7. The graph of $g(x)$ is translated left 4 units.

9. The graph of $g(x)$ is translated left 1 unit.

11. The graph of $g(x)$ is translated left 3 units.

13. The graph of $p(x)$ is a horizontal reflection of the graph of $g(x)$.

15. The graph of $p(x)$ is a horizontal reflection of the graph of $g(x)$.

17. The graph of $p(x)$ is a vertical reflection of the graph of $g(x)$.

19. $(x, y) \rightarrow (x, 4y)$

21. $(x, y) \rightarrow (x, 5y)$

23. $(x, y) \rightarrow (x, 2y)$

25. $g(x) = −(x − 0)^2 + 3$

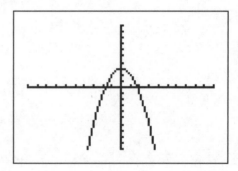

27. $g(x) = 6(x − 4)^2 + 1$

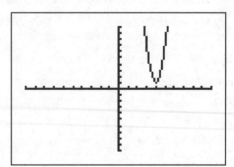

29. $g(x) = -3(x - 4)^2 - 2$

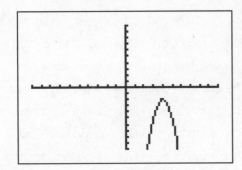

31. The function $g(x)$ is translated 7 units up from $f(x) = x^2$.

33. The function $g(x)$ is translated 8 units up and 2 units right from $f(x) = x^2$.

35. The function $g(x)$ is vertically dilated with a dilation factor of $\frac{2}{3}$ and then translated 9 units down and 4 units left from $f(x) = x^2$.

Chapter 13

LESSON 13.1

1. The terms are $5x$ and 8. The coefficients are 5 and 8.

3. The terms are x^2 and $-4x$. The coefficients are 1 and -4.

5. The term is -18. The coefficient is -18.

7. The expression is a polynomial.

9. The expression is not a polynomial. The first term can be rewritten as $3x^{-1}$ which has an exponent that is not a whole number.

11. The expression is a polynomial.

13. The expression is not a polynomial. The first term can be rewritten as $x^{1/3}$ which has an exponent that is not a whole number.

15. The polynomial is a binomial with a degree of 1.

17. The polynomial is a binomial with a degree of 2.

19. The polynomial is a monomial with a degree of 0.

21. $6x^2 + 2x$

The polynomial is a binomial with a degree of 2.

23. $-5x + 10$

The polynomial is a binomial with a degree of 1.

25. $-w^3 + 4w + 15$

The polynomial is a trinomial with a degree of 3.

27. $-p^4 - 1$

The polynomial is a binomial with a degree of 4.

29. $-18a^3 - 22a^2 + 54a$

The polynomial is a trinomial with a degree of 3.

31. $12x + 2$

33. $x^2 + 5x - 18$

35. $10w^2 - w + 3$

37. $a^2 - 7a + 7$

39. $-6x^5 + 3x^4 + 9x^3 + 3x^2 - 5$

41. $h(2) = (2)^2 + 3(2) - 2$
$\qquad = 4 + 6 - 2$
$\qquad = 8$

43. $h(0) = (0)^2 + 3(0) - 2$
$\qquad = 0 + 0 - 2$
$\qquad = -2$

45. $h(-2) = (-2)^2 + 3(-2) - 2$
$\qquad = 4 - 6 - 2$
$\qquad = -4$

LESSON 13.2

1. $x^2 + 2x + 1$

3. $x^2 + 4x + 4$

5. $2x^2 + 7x + 3$

7. $6x^2 + 14x + 8$

9. $42t^2 + 5t - 25$

11. $90w^2 + 71w - 8$

13. $2x^2 + 12x$

15. $7x^2 - 35x$

17. $x^3 + 3x^2 - x - 3$

19. $3x^3 + 15x^2 - 3x$

21. $x^3 + 8x^2 + 11x - 2$

LESSON 13.3

1. $x(x + 9)$

3. $5(x^2 + 4x - 3)$

5. $y(y^2 - 7)$

7. There is no greatest common factor.

9. $7(m^3 - 3)$

11. $x^2 + 4x + 3 = (x + 1)(x + 3)$

13. $x^2 - x - 6 = (x + 2)(x - 3)$

15. $x^2 + 7x + 10 = (x + 2)(x + 5)$

17. $x^2 - 2x - 8 = (x - 4)(x + 2)$

19. $m^2 + 6m - 7 = (m + 7)(m - 1)$

21. $4w^2 + 12w - 40 = 4(w + 5)(w - 2)$

23. $3m^3 + 36m^2 + 60m = 3m(m + 10)(m + 2)$

25. $x^2 + 11x + 10 = (x + 1)(x + 10)$

27. $m^2 + 2m - 35 = (m + 7)(m - 5)$

29. $3n^2 - 27n + 60 = 3(n - 5)(n - 4)$

31. $x^2 + 11x + 28 = \underline{(x + 4)(x + 7)}$

$x^2 - 11x + 28 = \underline{(x - 4)(x - 7)}$

$x^2 + 3x - 28 = \underline{(x - 4)(x + 7)}$

$x^2 - 3x + 28 = \underline{(x + 4)(x - 7)}$

33. $x^2 + 12x + 27 = \underline{(x + 3)(x + 9)}$

$x^2 - 12x + 27 = \underline{(x - 3)(x - 9)}$

$x^2 + 6x - 27 = \underline{(x - 3)(x + 9)}$

$x^2 - 6x - 27 = \underline{(x + 3)(x - 9)}$

35. $x^2 + 12x + 11 = \underline{(x + 1)(x + 11)}$

$x^2 - 12x + 11 = \underline{(x - 1)(x - 11)}$

$x^2 + 10x - 11 = \underline{(x - 1)(x + 11)}$

$x^2 - 10x - 11 = \underline{(x + 1)(x - 11)}$

37. $x^2 + 4x + 4 = (x + 2)(x + 2)$

39. $-32 - 12m - m^2 = -(m + 4)(m + 8)$

41. $5x^2 + 10x - 15 = 5(x + 3)(x - 1)$

LESSON 13.4

1. The roots are -3 and -2.

3. The roots are -7 and 5.

5. The roots are 0 and -8.

7. The roots are 4 and 8.

9. The roots are $-\frac{3}{2}$ and 1.

11. The zeros are 0 and 5.

13. The zeros are -6 and -5.

15. The zeros are $-\frac{5}{2}$ and -2.

17. The zeros are -2 and 1.

LESSON 13.5

1. $x^2 - 25 = (x + 5)(x - 5)$

3. $x^3 + 27 = (x + 3)(x^2 - 3x + 9)$

5. $5(x + 2)(x^2 - 2x + 4)$

7. $(2a - 3)(4a^2 + 6a + 9)$

9. $x^2 + 16x + 64 = (x + 8)(x + 8)$

11. $2(x - 7)(x - 7)$

13. $z(z + 9)(z + 9)$

15. The roots are -10 and 10.

17. The root is -2.

19. The root is -11.

21. The zeros are -15 and 15.

23. The zeros are $-\frac{1}{3}$ and $\frac{1}{3}$.

25. The zeros are $-\frac{5}{2}$ and $\frac{5}{2}$.

LESSON 13.6

1. $\sqrt{25} = \pm 5$

3. $\sqrt{400} = \pm 20$

5. $\pm 4\sqrt{2}$

7. $\pm 10\sqrt{3}$

9. $\sqrt{7} \approx 2.6$

11. $\sqrt{96} \approx 9.8$

13. $\sqrt{109} \approx 10.4$

15. The roots are approximately 6.3 and -6.3.

17. The roots are approximately 3.9 and -3.9.

19. The roots are approximately 0.3 and 9.7.

21. The roots are $4\sqrt{3}$ and $-4\sqrt{3}$.

23. The roots are $3\sqrt{3}$ and $-3\sqrt{3}$.

25. The roots are $12 + 2\sqrt{2}$ and $12 - 2\sqrt{2}$.

LESSON 13.7

1. $x^2 + 2x + 1 = (x + 1)^2$

3. $x^2 + 12x + 36 = (x + 6)^2$

5. $x^2 + 11x + \frac{121}{4} = \left(x + \frac{11}{2}\right)^2$

7. $\dfrac{25}{}$

9. $\dfrac{6}{}$

11. $\dfrac{49}{4}$

13. $\dfrac{26}{}$

15. The roots are approximately 1.16 and −5.16.

17. The roots are approximately −0.20 and −9.80.

19. The roots are approximately 0.30 and −3.30.

Chapter 14

LESSON 14.1

1. $x \approx 1.193$ or $x \approx -4.193$

3. $x \approx 1.098$ or $x \approx -4.098$

5. $x = -0.25$ or $x = 0.5$

7. $x = -2 - \dfrac{3}{2}\sqrt{2}$ or $x = -2 + \dfrac{3}{2}\sqrt{2}$

9. $x = 1 - \dfrac{\sqrt{30}}{3}$ or $x = 1 + \dfrac{\sqrt{30}}{3}$

11. $x = \dfrac{-5 + \sqrt{17}}{-4}$ or $x = \dfrac{-5 - \sqrt{17}}{-4}$

13. Because $b^2 - 4ac > 0$ the function has two zeros.

$x = -1$ or $x = 7$

15. Because $b^2 - 4ac < 0$ the function has no zeros.

17. Because $b^2 - 4ac = 0$ the function has one zero.

$x = -1$

LESSON 14.2

1. $y = -0.97x^2 + 4.84x + 0.03$

$r^2 \approx 0.99$

Because the r^2 value is close to 1, the quadratic regression equation is a good fit for the data.

3. $y = -0.73x^2 - 2.93x + 3.84$

$r^2 \approx 0.55$

Because the r^2 value is not close to 1, the quadratic regression equation is not a good fit for the data.

5. $y = 0.71x^2 - 4.10x + 6.77$

$r^2 \approx 0.86$

Because the r^2 value is close to 1, the quadratic regression equation is a good fit for the data.

LESSON 14.3

1. $x = 6$ or $x = 1$

Solution: $x \in (-\infty, 1]$ or $x \in [6, \infty)$

3. $x \approx 3.887$ or $x \approx -4.887$

Solution: $x \in (-4.887, 3.887)$

5. $x = 1$ or $x = 3$

Solution: $x \in (-\infty, 1]$ or $x \in [3, \infty)$

7. It will take just over 2.3 seconds for the balloon to reach the ground.

9. The balloon is more than 10 feet above the ground between 0.1536 seconds and 2.034 seconds.

11. The balloon is more than 20 feet above the ground between 0.5850 seconds and 1.602 seconds.

LESSON 14.4

1. The system has two solutions: (7, 14) and (1, 2).

3. The system has two solutions:

$\left(-6\dfrac{1}{2}, 4\dfrac{1}{2}\right)$ and (−2, 0).

5. The system has one solution: $\left(-\dfrac{3}{2}, 3\right)$.

7. The system has two solutions: $\left(-\dfrac{1}{2}, 2\dfrac{1}{4}\right)$ and (3, 4).

9. The system has no real solutions.

11. The system has no real solutions.

Chapter 15

LESSON 15.1

1. The numbers 10, 31, and 1970 are in the set of natural numbers.

3. The numbers 54, 216, and 2594 are in the set of integers.

5. The numbers $\sqrt{2}$ and π are in the set of irrational numbers.

7. The set of natural numbers is closed under addition and multiplication because when you add or multiply any two natural numbers, the sum or product is always a natural number.

The set of natural numbers is not closed under subtraction because when you subtract a natural number from a natural number, the difference can be 0 or a negative integer.

The set of natural numbers is not closed under division because when you divide a natural number by a natural number, the quotient can be a fraction.

9. The set of rational numbers is closed under each of the four operations because when you add, subtract, multiply, or divide two rational numbers, the result is always a rational number. Note that division by zero is not defined to allow division to be closed for the set of rational numbers.

11. The set of whole numbers is closed under addition and multiplication because when you add or multiply any whole numbers, the result is always a whole number.

The set of whole numbers is not closed under subtraction because when you subtract a whole number from a whole number, the difference can be a negative number.

The set of whole numbers is not closed under division because when you divide a whole number by a whole number, the quotient can be a fraction.

13. I could solve equations A, B, C, and J.

15. I could solve equations A, B, C, D, E, F, and J.

17. I could solve equation H.

19. The decimal 0.4444 . . . is equal to $\frac{4}{9}$.

21. The decimal 0.8181 . . . is equal to $\frac{9}{11}$.

23. The decimal 0.3939 . . . is equal to $\frac{13}{33}$.

25. The decimal 0.1212 . . . is equal to $\frac{4}{33}$.

27. The decimal 0.4848 . . . is equal to $\frac{16}{33}$.

LESSON 15.2

1. Associative Property of Multiplication

3. Additive Identity

5. Multiplicative Inverse

7. Multiplicative Identity

9. Distributive Property of Multiplication over Addition

11. $8x + (12x + 28)$ — Distributive Property of Multiplication over Addition

$(8x + 12x) + 28$ — Associative Property of Addition

$20x + 28$ — Combine like terms

13. $11(0 + x - 9)$ — Subtract

$11(x - 9)$ — Additive Identity

$11x - 99$ — Distributive Property of Multiplication over Subtraction

15. $3(7x + 5 - 5)$ — Commutative Property of Addition

$3(7x + 0)$ — Combine like terms

$3(7x)$ — Additive Identity

$21x$ — Multiply

17. $x + 19 + (-19) = 23 + (-19)$ — Addition Property of Equality

$x + 0 = 23 + (-19)$ — Combine like terms

$x = 23 + (-19)$ — Additive Identity

$x = 4$ — Combine like terms

19. $13x \cdot \dfrac{1}{13} = 52 \cdot \dfrac{1}{13}$ — Multiplication Property of Equality

$x(13) \cdot \dfrac{1}{13} = 52 \cdot \dfrac{1}{13}$ — Commutative Property of Multiplication

$x(1) = 52 \cdot \dfrac{1}{13}$ — Multiply

$x = 52 \cdot \dfrac{1}{13}$ — Multiplicative Identity

$x = 4$ — Multiply

21. $9x - 24 + 2 = 32$ — Distributive Property of Multiplication over Subtraction

$9x - 22 = 32$ — Combine like terms

$9x - 22 + 22 = 32 + 22$ — Addition Property of Equality

$9x + 0 = 32 + 22$ — Combine like terms

$9x = 32 + 22$ — Additive Identity

$9x = 54$ — Combine like terms

$9x \cdot \dfrac{1}{9} = 54 \cdot \dfrac{1}{9}$ — Multiplication Property of Equality

$x(9) \cdot \dfrac{1}{9} = 54 \cdot \dfrac{1}{9}$ — Commutative Property of Multiplication

$x(1) = 54 \cdot \dfrac{1}{9}$ — Multiply

$x = 54 \cdot \dfrac{1}{9}$ — Multiplicative Identity

$x = 6$ — Multiply

23. $7x + 1 = \dfrac{12x}{2} + \dfrac{6}{2}$ — Distributive Property of Division over Addition

$7x + 1 = 6x + 3$ — Simplify

$7x + 1 - 1 = 6x + 3 - 1$ — Addition Property of Equality

$7x = 6x + 2$ — Combine like terms

$7x - 6x = 6x + 2 - 6x$ — Addition Property of Equality

$7x - 6x = 2 + 6x - 6x$ — Commutative Property of Addition

$x = 2$ — Combine like terms

25. $3\left(\dfrac{2x - 5}{3}\right) = 3(-2x + 17)$ Multiplication Property of Equality

$2x - 5 = 3(-2x + 17)$ Simplify

$2x - 5 = -6x + 51$ Distributive Property of Multiplication over Addition

$2x - 5 + 5 = -6x + 51 + 5$ Addition Property of Equality

$2x = -6x + 56$ Combine like terms

$2x + 6x = -6x + 56 + 6x$ Addition Property of Equality

$2x + 6x = -6x + 6x + 56$ Commutative Property of Addition

$8x = 56$ Combine like terms

$\dfrac{1}{8} \cdot 8x = \dfrac{1}{8} \cdot 56$ Multiplication Property of Equality

$x = 7$ Multiply

LESSON 15.3

1. 1

3. $-i$

5. -1

7. 1

9. 1

11. $3i$

13. $2\sqrt{5}i$

15. $9 - 8i$

17. $2 - \sqrt{2}i$

19. $3xi$

21. $8x + 8i - 9$

23. $x^2 + 2xi + 3$

25. The real part is 24. The imaginary part is $0i$.

27. The real part is 7. The imaginary part is $3i$.

29. The real part is 0. The imaginary part is $-35i$.

31. The real part is 52. The imaginary part is $0i$.

33. integer, rational number, real number, complex number .

35. natural number, whole number, integer, rational number, real number, complex number

37. rational number, real number, complex number

39. rational number, real number, complex number

LESSON 15.4

1. 1

3. $-i$

5. -1

7. $6\sqrt{2}i$

9. $49 - 10\sqrt{2}i$

11. $\sqrt{3}i - 3$

13. $-2\sqrt{7}i + \dfrac{(\sqrt{21} - \sqrt{3})}{3}$

15. $-5 + 14i$

17. $-i + 8$

19. $15 + 21i$

21. $-10i - 9$

23. 10

25. 54

27. 0.37

29. monomial

31. monomial

33. binomial

35. $x^2 - 12xi - 36$

37. This expression cannot be simplified.

39. $x^3 + 4x^2i + 16x + 64i$

41. $7 - 2i$

43. $-8i$

45. $2 + 11i$

47. $-13 + 6i$

49. $\frac{39}{61} + \frac{2}{61}i$

51. $-\frac{18}{13} - \frac{14}{13}i$

53. $\frac{21}{5} + \frac{12}{5}i$

1. The equation has two imaginary roots.

3. The equation has a one real root.

5. The equation has two imaginary roots.

7. The zeros are $\frac{1}{2}i$ and $-\frac{1}{2}i$.

9. The zeros are $-1 + 2i$ and $-1 - 2i$.

11. The zeros are $-1 + i$ and $-1 - i$.

13. The zeros are $2 + \sqrt{5}i$ and $2 - \sqrt{5}i$.

Chapter 16

LESSON 16.1

1.

Time (days)	Savings (dollars)
0	100
1	80
2	60
3	40
4	40
5	40
6	30
7	20
8	10
9	0

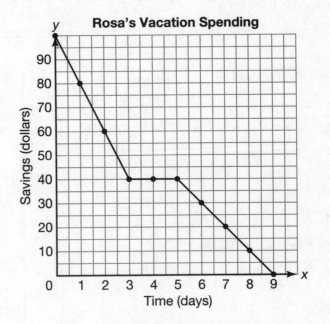

3.

Time (weeks)	Weight (pounds)
0	146
1	144
2	142
3	140
4	138
5	137
6	136
7	134
8	132

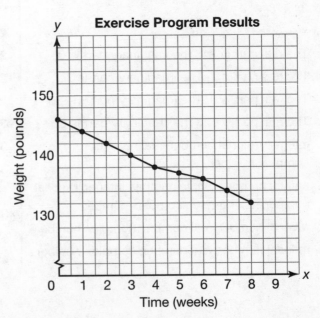

5.

Time (days)	Earnings (dollars)
0	0
1	18
2	36
3	54
4	90
5	126
6	144
7	162

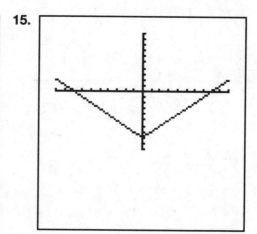

Maria's Paper Route

7. $f(x) = \begin{cases} -5x + 60, & 0 \leq x \leq 3 \\ 45, & 3 < x \leq 6 \\ -2x + 57, & 6 < x \leq 9 \end{cases}$

9. $f(x) = \begin{cases} -5x + 80, & 0 \leq x \leq 3 \\ -x + 68, & 3 < x \leq 8 \\ -2x + 76, & 8 < x \leq 9 \end{cases}$

11. $f(x) = \begin{cases} -10x + 100, & 0 \leq x \leq 4 \\ 60, & 4 < x \leq 10 \\ -3x + 90, & 10 < x \leq 18 \end{cases}$

13.

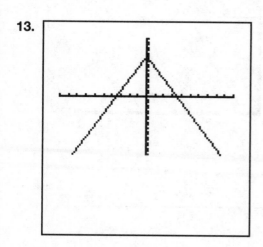

$f(x) = -|4x| + 14$

15.

$f(x) = |x| - 8$

17.

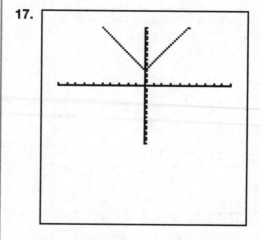

$f(x) = |3x| + 5$

LESSON 16.2

1. $f(x) = \begin{cases} 0.18x, & 0 < x \le 50 \\ 0.16x, & 50 < x \le 100 \\ 0.14x, & 100 < x \le 150 \\ 0.12x, & 150 < x \le 200 \\ 0.10x, & 200 < x \end{cases}$

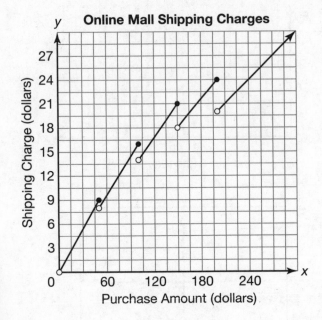

Online Mall Shipping Charges

y-axis: Shipping Charge (dollars)
x-axis: Purchase Amount (dollars)

3. $f(x) = \begin{cases} 0.05x, & 0 < x \le 20 \\ 0.10x, & 20 < x \le 40 \\ 0.15x, & 40 < x \le 60 \\ 0.20x, & 60 < x \end{cases}$

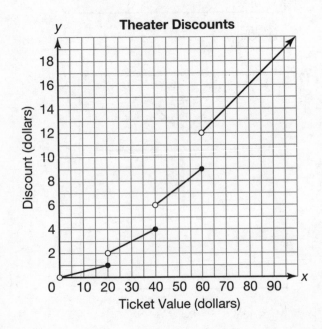

Theater Discounts

y-axis: Discount (dollars)
x-axis: Ticket Value (dollars)

5. $f(x) = \begin{cases} 0.09x, & 0 < x \le 100 \\ 0.08x, & 100 < x \le 200 \\ 0.07x, & 200 < x \le 300 \\ 0.06x, & 300 < x \end{cases}$

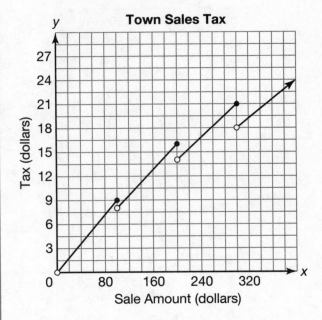

Town Sales Tax

y-axis: Tax (dollars)
x-axis: Sale Amount (dollars)

7. $f(x) = \begin{cases} 50, & 0 < x \le 100 \\ 30, & 100 < x \le 200 \\ 10, & 200 < x \le 300 \\ 0, & 300 < x \end{cases}$

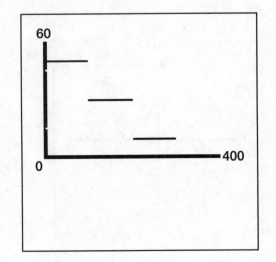

9. $f(x) = \begin{cases} 8, & 0 < x \le 1 \\ 10, & 1 < x \le 2 \\ 12, & 2 < x \le 3 \\ 14, & 3 < x \le 4 \\ 16, & 4 < x \le 5 \end{cases}$

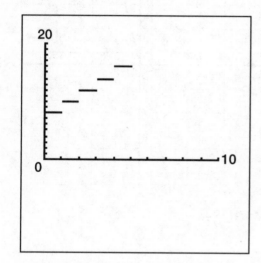

11. $f(x) = \begin{cases} 10, & 0 < x \le 1 \\ 22, & 1 < x \le 2 \\ 34, & 2 < x \le 3 \\ 46, & 3 < x \le 4 \\ 58, & 4 < x \le 5 \end{cases}$

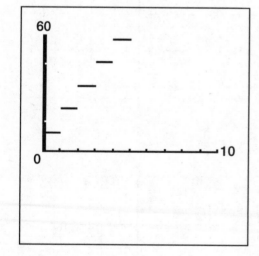

13. $\lfloor 4.5 \rfloor = 4$

15. $\lceil -8.3 \rceil = -8$

17. $\lfloor 7.3 \rfloor = 7$

19. $\lceil 7.9 \rceil = 8$

LESSON 16.3

1. Relationship domain: students in your school

Relationship range: all of the sports chosen

The relationship is a function because for each student there is exactly one favorite sport.

Reverse relationship domain: all of the sports chosen

Reverse range: students in your school

The reverse relationship is not a function because for each sport there may be more than one student who chose it as their favorite.

3. Relationship domain: students in your class

Relationship range: red, blue, orange, green, and yellow marbles

The relationship is a function because for each student there is exactly one marble chosen.

Reverse relationship domain: red, blue, orange, green, and yellow marbles

Reverse range: students in your class

The relationship is not a function because for each color of marble there may be more than one student who chose it.

5. Relationship domain: members of your family

Relationship range: all of the games chosen

The relationship is a function because for each member of your family there is exactly one favorite game.

Reverse relationship domain: all of the games chosen

Reverse range: members of your family

The reverse relationship is not a function because for each game there may be more than one family member who chose it as their favorite.

7. Open the dresser drawer.

9. Jog 5 blocks west and 3 blocks south.

11. Subtract 7 then multiply by 2.

13.

Feet	Inches
1	12
2	24
3	36
4	48
5	60

Let i = the number of inches.

Let f = the number of feet.

$i = 12f$

Inverse: $f = \dfrac{i}{12}$

15.

Pints	Cups
2	4
4	8
6	12
8	16
10	20

Let p = the number of pints.

Let c = the number of cups.

$c = 2p$

Inverse: $p = \dfrac{c}{2}$

17.

Feet	Yards
3	1
9	3
12	4
18	6
24	8

Let f = the number of feet.

Let y = the number of yards.

$y = \dfrac{f}{3}$

Inverse: $f = 3y$

19. $f^{-1}(x) = \dfrac{x}{4}$

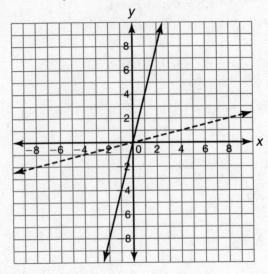

21. $f^{-1}(x) = \dfrac{1}{2}x - \dfrac{1}{2}$

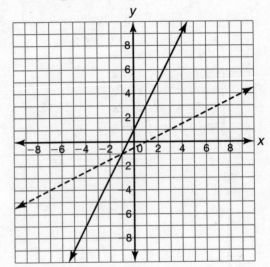

23. $f^{-1}(x) = \dfrac{3}{2}x + 12$

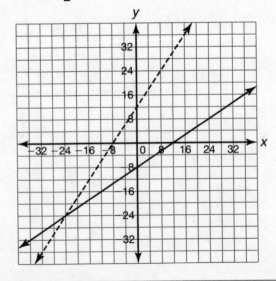

Answers

25. The corresponding point on the graph of $f^{-1}(x)$ is (5, 2).

27. The corresponding point on the graph of $f^{-1}(x)$ is (−1, −4).

29. The corresponding point on the graph of $f^{-1}(x)$ is (−7, 1).

31. The functions are inverses because $f(g(x)) = g(f(x)) = x$.

33. The functions are inverses because $f(g(x)) = g(f(x)) = x$.

35. The functions are inverses because $f(g(x)) = g(f(x)) = x$.

LESSON 16.4

1.

x	f(x)
−2	1
−1	3
0	5
1	7
2	9

x	f⁻¹(x)
1	−2
3	−1
5	0
7	1
9	2

The function is one-to-one because both the original function and its inverse are functions.

3.

x	f(x)
−2	12
−1	−3
0	−8
1	−3
2	12

x	f⁻¹(x)
12	−2
−3	−1
−8	0
−3	1
12	2

The function is not one-to-one because its inverse is not a function.

5.

x	f(x)
−2	−3
−1	−3
0	−3
1	−3
2	−3

x	f⁻¹(x)
−3	−2
−3	−1
−3	0
−3	1
−3	2

The function is not one-to-one because its inverse is not a function.

7. The function is one-to-one because both the original function and its inverse are functions.

9. The inverse function does not pass the Vertical Line Test. So, the function is not one-to-one because its inverse is not a function.

11. The function is one-to-one because both the original function and its inverse are functions.

13. The function is a linear function. A linear function that is not a constant function is a one-to-one function. So, the function is one-to-one.

15. The function is a linear function. A linear function that is not a constant function is a one-to-one function. So, the function is one-to-one.

17. The function is a linear absolute value function. A linear absolute value function is never a one-to-one function. So, the function is not one-to-one.

19. $f^{-1}(x) = \pm\sqrt{\dfrac{x}{7}}$

21. $f^{-1}(x) = \pm\sqrt{\dfrac{x - 11}{6}}$

23. $f^{-1}(x) = \pm\sqrt{\dfrac{x + 6}{-4}}$

25. $f^{-1}(x) = \pm\sqrt{\dfrac{x}{2}}$

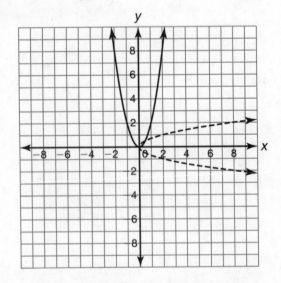

For the function $y = 2x^2$ with $x \geq 0$, the inverse is $y = \sqrt{\dfrac{x}{2}}$.

For the function $y = 2x^2$ with $x \leq 0$, the inverse is $y = -\sqrt{\dfrac{x}{2}}$.

27. $f^{-1}(x) = \pm\sqrt{\dfrac{x + 2}{-4}}$

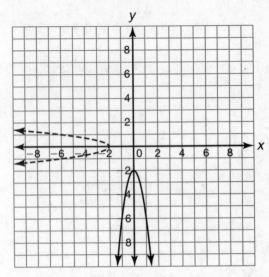

For the function $y = -4x^2 - 2$ with $x \geq 0$, the inverse is $y = \sqrt{\dfrac{x + 2}{-4}}$.

For the function $y = -4x^2 - 2$ with $x \leq 0$, the inverse is $y = -\sqrt{\dfrac{x + 2}{-4}}$.

29. $x = y \qquad x = -y$
$\qquad\qquad -x = y$

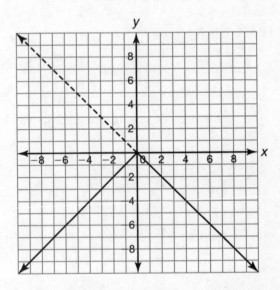

For the function $y = x$ with $x \leq 0$, the inverse is $y = x$.

For the function $y = -x$ with $x \geq 0$, the inverse is $y = -x$.

Chapter 17

LESSON 17.1

1. Parallel.
3. Perpendicular.
5. Neither.
7. perpendicular
9. neither
11. neither
13. $y = \frac{4}{5}x + \frac{6}{5}$
15. $y = 7x - 37$
17. $y = \frac{1}{3}x + 5$
19. $y = -\frac{1}{2}x + \frac{13}{2}$
21. $y = \frac{5}{2}x - 13$
23. $y = -\frac{1}{6}x - 2$
25. $x = -2$
27. $x = 9$
29. $x = -5$
31. $y = 7$
33. $y = -3$
35. $y = 8$
37. The distance from the point (0, 4) to the line $f(x) = 2x - 3$ is approximately 3.13 units.
39. The distance from the point (−2, 5) to the line $f(x) = \frac{2}{3}x - \frac{1}{6}$ is approximately 5.41 units.
41. The distance from the point (3, −1) to the line $f(x) = \frac{1}{3}x - 6$ is approximately 3.79 units.

LESSON 17.2

1. Point C can have an infinite number of locations as long as the location satisfies one of the following conditions:
   - Point C could be located anywhere on line $y = 3$ except where $x = 2$.
   - Point C could be located anywhere on line $y = -3$ except where $x = 2$.
3. Point C can have an infinite number of locations as long as the location satisfies one of the following conditions:
   - Point C could be located anywhere on circle A between the y-values of 3 and 9 except where $x = 2$.
   - Point C could be located anywhere on circle B between the y-values of −3 and −9 except where $x = 2$.
5. Point C can have an infinite number of locations as long as the location satisfies one of the following conditions:
   - Point C could be located anywhere on line $y = 0$ except where $x = 2$.
   - Point C could be located anywhere on circle A except where $x = 2$.
   - Point C could be located anywhere on circle B except where $x = 2$.
7. Triangle ABC is scalene because all of the side lengths are different.
9. Triangle ABC is isosceles because segments AC and BC are congruent.
11. Triangle ABC is scalene because all of the side lengths are different.
13. Triangle ABC is a right triangle because segments AB and AC have negative reciprocal slopes.
15. Triangle ABC is an obtuse triangle.
17. Triangle ABC is a right triangle because segments AB and BC have negative reciprocal slopes.

LESSON 17.3

1. $AB = \sqrt{34}$
3. $RS = \sqrt{130}$
5. $MN = \sqrt{26}$
7. The slopes of the segments are the same. The segments are parallel.
9. The slopes of the segments are negative reciprocals. The segments are perpendicular.
11. The slopes of the segments are the same. The segments are parallel.
13. $y = \frac{2}{3}x - 5$
15. $y = 5$
17. $y = -5x + 27$
19. The coordinates of point D are (−4, 14).

21. The coordinates of point D are (1, 2).

23. The coordinates of point D are (−9, −13).

25. Quadrilateral $ABCD$ can best be described as a rectangle.

27. Quadrilateral $ABCD$ can best be described as a trapezoid.

29. Quadrilateral $ABCD$ can best be described as a square.

Chapter 18

LESSON 18.1

1. $\triangle ABC$ is an inscribed triangle in circle O with the hypotenuse as the diameter of the circle, therefore the triangle is a right triangle by the Right Triangle Diameter Theorem.

3. Because the slopes of $\overleftrightarrow{AB}$ and $\overline{CA}$ are opposite reciprocals, $\overleftrightarrow{AB}$ is perpendicular to $\overline{CA}$.

5. $AD^2 \overset{?}{=} AB \cdot AC$

$\quad 5^2 \overset{?}{=} (\sqrt{5})(\sqrt{125})$

$\quad 5^2 \overset{?}{=} \sqrt{625}$

$\quad 25 = 25 \qquad \checkmark$

7. Opposite sides are parallel and all sides are congruent, so the quadrilateral formed by connecting the midpoints of the rectangle is a rhombus.

9. Opposite sides are parallel and opposite sides are congruent, so the quadrilateral formed by the midpoints of the parallelogram is a parallelogram.

11. Opposite sides are parallel, consecutive sides are perpendicular, and all four sides are congruent, so the quadrilateral formed by the midpoints of the square is a square.

LESSON 18.2

1. $x^2 + y^2 = 16$

3. $(x - 6)^2 + (y - 5)^2 = 1$

5. $(x - 4)^2 + y^2 = 16$

7. $(x + 3)^2 + (y - 1)^2 = 9$

center: (−3, 1), radius: 3

9. $(x - 1)^2 + (y - 1)^2 = 1$

center: (1, 1), radius: 1

11. $(x + 4)^2 + \left(y - \dfrac{2}{3}\right)^2 = \dfrac{1}{9}$

center: $\left(-4, \dfrac{2}{3}\right)$, radius: $\dfrac{1}{3}$

13. center: (−2, −2), radius: 5

15. This equation does not represent a circle because $A \neq C$, or $1 \neq 4$.

17. $(x + 3)^2 + (y + 5)^2 = 62$, or

$\quad (x + 3)^2 + (y + 5)^2 = 36$.

LESSON 18.3

1. point P does not lie on circle A.

3. point P must lie on circle A.

5. point P must lie on circle A.

7.

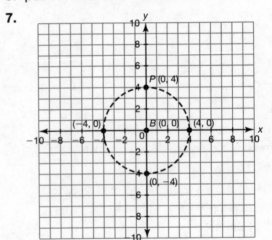

9.

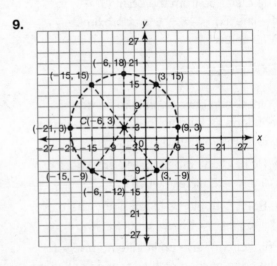

11.

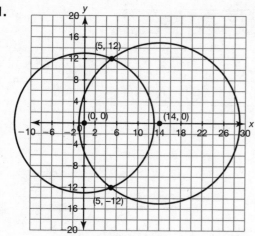

11.

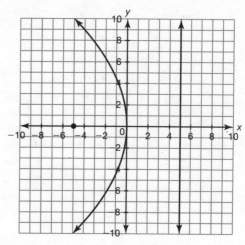

LESSON 18.4

1. $x^2 = 4y$

3. $8x = y^2$

5. Vertex: (0, 0)
   Axis of symmetry: $x = 0$
   Value of p: -0.75
   Focus: (0, -0.75)
   Directrix: $y = 0.75$

7. Vertex: (0, 0)
   Axis of symmetry: $x = 0$
   Value of p: 1
   Focus: (0, 1)
   Directrix: $y = -1$

9.

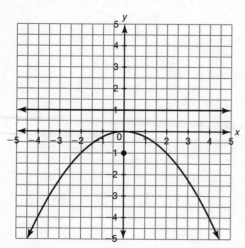

LESSON 18.5

1. $y^2 - 4x + 4y = 0$

3. $x^2 - 10x - 12y + 1 = 0$

5. Vertex: (3, 4)
   Axis of symmetry: $x = 3$
   Value of p: 2
   Focus: (3, 6)
   Directrix: $y = 2$

7. Vertex: (-2, 0)
   Axis of symmetry: $x = -2$
   Value of p: 2
   Focus: (-2, 2)
   Directrix: $y = -2$

9.

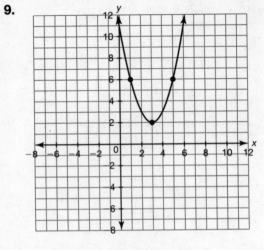

x	y
1	6
3	2
5	6

11.

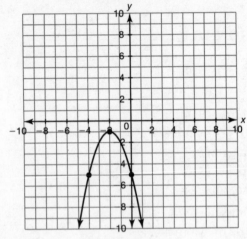

x	y
−4	−5
−2	−1
0	−5

13. $(x - 2)^2 = -3(y + 2)$

15. $(x + 1)^2 = -2y$

Chapter 19

LESSON 19.1

1. The sample space is 1, 2, 3, 4, 5, 6.

3. The sample space is W, W, X, X, X, Y, Y, Y, Y, Y, Z, Z.

5. The sample space is 2, 4, 6, 8, 10, 12, 14.

7.

Outcomes	Plain Bagel	Blueberry Bagel	Sesame Seed Bagel	Cheese Bagel
Probability	$\frac{1}{3}$, or 0.33	$\frac{1}{6}$, or 0.17	$\frac{1}{12}$, or 0.08	$\frac{5}{12}$, or 0.42

This is a non-uniform probability model.

9.

Outcomes	Cube	Cylinder	Pyramid
Probability	$\frac{1}{3}$, or 0.33	$\frac{1}{3}$, or 0.33	$\frac{1}{3}$, or 0.33

This is a uniform probability model.

11.

Outcomes	A Block	B Block	C Block	D Block
Probability	$\frac{1}{4}$, or 0.25	$\frac{1}{4}$, or 0.25	$\frac{1}{4}$, or 0.25	$\frac{1}{4}$, or 0.25

This is a uniform probability model.

13. $P(\text{greater than } 7) = \dfrac{5}{12}$

$P(\text{not greater than } 7) = \dfrac{7}{12}$

15. $P(5) = \dfrac{2}{12}$, or $\dfrac{1}{6}$

$P(\text{not a } 5) = \dfrac{10}{12}$, or $\dfrac{5}{6}$

17. $P(\text{shaded}) = \dfrac{15}{31}$

$P(\text{not shaded}) = \dfrac{16}{31}$

LESSON 19.2

1. • The actions are choosing a shaded block from the first set and choosing an unshaded block from the second set.
- The outcomes of choosing a shaded block are cylinder, pyramid, and cube. The outcomes of choosing an unshaded block are cylinder, pyramid, and cube.
- The outcomes of each action form disjoint sets because one set had shaded blocks and the other has unshaded blocks.
- The events are choosing a shaded block and choosing an unshaded block.
- The events are independent because the outcome of the first event does not affect the outcome of the second event.

3. • The actions are spinning the spinner and flipping the coin.
- The outcomes of spinning the spinner are 1, 2, 3, 4, 5, 6, 7, 8, 9, 10, 11, and 12. The outcomes of flipping a coin are heads up and tails up.
- The outcomes of each action form disjoint sets because the sets do not have any common elements.
- The events are spinning a 3 and a flipping a coin that results in tails up.
- The events are independent because the outcome of the first event does not affect the outcome of the second event.

5. • The actions are you choosing a number cube and your friend choosing a number cube.
- The outcomes of your choice are all the number cubes in the bowl. The outcomes of your friend's choice are all the number cubes in the bowl, except for the number cube you choose.
- The outcomes of each action form intersecting sets because the sets have common elements.
- The events are you choosing a number cube with a 3 and your friend choosing a number cube with a 5.
- The events are dependent because the outcome of the first event does affect the outcome of the second event.

7. • The actions are you choosing one numbered ping pong ball and then choosing another numbered ping pong ball.
- The outcomes of your first choice are all of the numbered ping pong balls. The outcomes of your second choice are all of the numbered ping pong balls, except for the one chosen first.
- The outcomes of each action form intersecting sets because the sets have common elements.
- The events are you choosing an even-numbered ping pong ball first and an odd-numbered ping pong ball second.
- The events are dependent because the outcome of the first event does affect the outcome of the second event.

9. Tree Diagram:

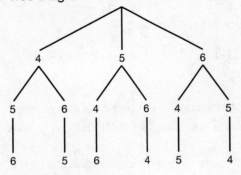

Organized List:

456	546	645
465	564	654

11. Tree Diagram:

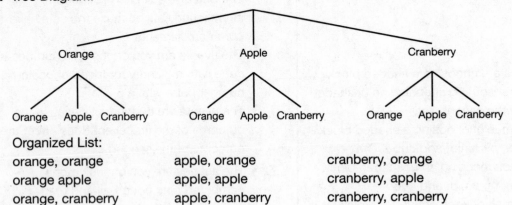

Organized List:

orange, orange	apple, orange	cranberry, orange
orange apple	apple, apple	cranberry, apple
orange, cranberry	apple, cranberry	cranberry, cranberry

13. Tree Diagram:

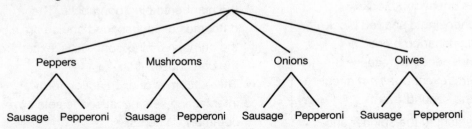

Organized List:

peppers, sausage	mushrooms, sausage
peppers, pepperoni	mushrooms, pepperoni
onions, sausage	olives, sausage
onions, pepperoni	olives, pepperoni

15. There are 120 different orders of the students possible.

17. There are 11,232,000 different passwords possible.

19. There are 248,832 different ways for Gina to listen to 5 of her 12 favorite songs.

21. There are 479,001,600 ways to arrange the team members in a row.

LESSON 19.3

1. The probability that a player wins 5 times in a row is $\frac{1}{243}$.

3. The probability that the first two spinners land on 1 is $\frac{1}{24}$.

5. The probability of choosing two marbles with stripes is $\frac{7}{34}$.

7. The probability of choosing all 4 aces is $\frac{1}{270,725}$.

9. The probability of choosing 4 discs in alphabetical order is $\frac{9}{1820}$.

11. The probability of choosing 4 students with birthdays in June, July, or August is $\frac{2}{325}$.

LESSON 19.4

1. The probability of choosing a block labeled with a T or a block labeled with a 6 is $\frac{11}{32}$.

3. The probability of a one on the 1st roll or a one on the 2nd roll is $\frac{11}{36}$

5. The probability that the student chosen from the math class or the student chosen from the history class is in the band is $\frac{15}{32}$.

7. The probability of choosing Monday or Tuesday is $\frac{11}{42}$.

9. The probability of choosing a cube with a 2 first or a cube with a 3 second is $\frac{32}{105}$.

11. The probability that the first ball has stars or the second ball has stripes is $\frac{9}{190}$.

13. The probability of shaded box first or an shaded box second is $\frac{2}{5}$.

LESSON 19.5

1. The probability of choosing a 2 first and a 3 second is $\frac{1}{9}$.

3. The probability of choosing a triangle first or a square second is $\frac{4}{9}$.

5. The probability of choosing a quarter first or a dime second is $\frac{49}{121}$.

7. The probability of choosing a triangle first, a cube second, and a cylinder third is $\frac{9}{220}$.

9. The probability of choosing a white ball first or a shaded ball second is $\frac{11}{15}$.

11. The probability of choosing a black sock first and a black sock second is $\frac{14}{95}$.

13. The probability of choosing a numbered card first or a King second is $\frac{158}{221}$.

LESSON 19.6

1. The probability of a spin resulting in a number less than 7 and an A or B is $\frac{1}{6}$.

3. The probability all three friends will be assigned the same type of job is $\frac{64}{165}$.

5. The probability of choosing a red ball from Group 1 and a red ball from Group 2 is $\frac{1}{18}$.

7. experimental probability $= \frac{12}{200} = \frac{3}{50}$

9. experimental probability $= \frac{15}{175} = \frac{3}{35}$

11. experimental probability $= \frac{12}{250} = \frac{6}{125}$

13. The theoretical probability is greater.

15. The experimental probability is greater.

17. The experimental probability is greater.

Chapter 20

LESSON 20.1

1. $\frac{11}{30} \approx 0.367$

3. $\frac{5}{30} \approx 0.167$

5. $\frac{3}{30} = 0.1$

7. $\frac{8}{30} \approx 0.267$

9. $\frac{31}{174} \approx 17.8\%$

11. $\frac{25}{174} \approx 14.4\%$

13. $\frac{17}{174} \approx 9.8\%$

15. $\frac{11}{174} \approx 6.3\%$

17. $\frac{48}{174} \approx 27.6\%$

19. $\frac{36}{174} \approx 20.7\%$

21. $\frac{116}{174} \approx 66.7\%$

23. $\frac{62}{210} \approx 0.295 = 29.5\%$

25. $\frac{78}{210} \approx 0.371 = 37.1\%$

27. $\frac{58}{210} \approx 0.276 = 27.6\%$

29. $\frac{56}{210} \approx 0.267 = 26.7\%$

31. $\frac{20}{210} \approx 0.095 = 9.5\%$

33. $\frac{104}{210} \approx 0.495 = 49.5\%$

35. 0.42

37. 0.14

39. 0.42

41. 0.22

43. 0.03

45. 0.61

47. 0.67

LESSON 20.2

1. $P(B \text{ on the first roll}) = \frac{1}{5}$

3. $P(\text{consonant on the second roll}) = \frac{3}{5}$

5. $P(A$ on the first roll and consonant on the second roll$) = \frac{3}{25}$

7. $P(B$ or D on the second roll, given that the first roll is a consonant$) = \frac{2}{5}$

9. $P(A$ on the second roll, given that the first roll was a vowel$) = \frac{1}{5}$

11. $P(B \mid A) = 0.4$

13. $P(B \mid A) = \frac{1}{10}$

15. The probability of choosing two red paper clips is approximately 15.7%.

17. The probability of choosing a green paper clip second, given that a black paper clip was chosen first is approximately 27.0%.

19. The probability of choosing a green paper clip second, given that a non-green paper clip was chosen first is approximately 27.0%.

21. a. $P(\text{significant improvement} \mid \text{medicine cream}) = 60\%$

b. Significant improvement, S, and medicine cream treatment, M, are dependent events because the value of $P(S \mid T)$ is not equal to the value of $P(S)$.

23. a. $P(\text{medicine cream} \mid \text{moderate improvement}) \approx 41.7\%$

b. Medicine cream treatment, MT, and moderate improvement, MI, are dependent events because the value of $P(MT \mid MI)$ is not equal to the value of $P(MT)$.

LESSON 20.3

1. $_8P_3 = 336$

3. $_{10}P_4 = 5040$

5. $_6P_6 = 720$

7. There are 358,800 possible codes.

9. There are 132 different ways for Caleb to select 2 activities.

11. $_{11}C_4 = 330$

13. $_5C_3 = 10$

15. $_8C_4 = 70$

17. $_{25}C_4 = 12,650$

19. $_7C_5 = 24$

21. The probability of guessing correctly is $\frac{1}{720}$.

23. The probability of selecting a PIN that begins with 3 even digits and ends with 3 odd digits is $\frac{1}{20}$.

25. The probability of choosing 2 seniors, 2 juniors, and 2 sophomores is $\frac{180}{1001}$.

27. The probability of choosing 3 seniors, 2 juniors, and 1 sophomore is $\frac{160}{1001}$.

29. The letters in the word SUNNY can be arranged 60 different ways.

31. The letters in the word ARRANGE can be arranged 1260 different ways.

33. The letters in the word PARALLEL can be arranged 3360 different ways.

35. The flowers can be arranged around the base of the tree in 39,916,800 different ways.

37. The candles can be arranged around the birthday cake in 362,880 different ways.

39. The teachers can be arranged around the table in 120 different ways.

LESSON 20.4

1. The probability that Malcolm makes a par on the next 2 holes is $\frac{4}{9}$.

3. The probability that Missy will make the next two penalty kicks is $\frac{9}{25}$.

5. The probability of a red result on the next two spins is $\frac{9}{64}$.

7. 30.2%

9. 20.1%

11. 26.8%

13. 8.7%

15. 20.8%

17. 26.7%

LESSON 20.5

1. The probability of a dart landing in the shaded area is approximately 78.5%.

3. The probability of a dart landing in the shaded area is approximately 63.7%.

5. The probability of a dart landing in the shaded area is approximately 69.8%.

7. The probability of a dart landing in the shaded area is approximately 47.7%.

9. I would expect 2 out of the 12 outcomes to result in a 1.

11. I would expect 8 out of the 12 outcomes to result in a number greater than 2.

13. 6

15. 4.5

17. 12.67